ELEMENTARY ANATOMY

AND

PHYSIOLOGY

ELEMENTARY ANATOMY
AND
PHYSIOLOGY

BY

JAMES WHILLIS
M.D., M.S., F.R.C.S.

University Reader in Anatomy, Guy's Hospital
Medical School ; late Lecturer in Anatomy in
the University of Durham

FOREWORD BY

T. B. JOHNSTON, M.D., Ch.B.
Professor of Anatomy, University of London

With 87 ILLUSTRATIONS prepared from
original drawings by Pauline Lariviére

LONDON
J. & A. CHURCHILL Ltd.
104 GLOUCESTER PLACE
PORTMAN SQUARE
Reprinted
1940

To My Father

First Edition   .   .   . 1938
„   „   Reprinted . 1940

Printed in Great Britain

FOREWORD

MOST teachers of experience will agree that the instruction of senior and advanced students calls for much less effort and discrimination than does the instruction of junior students. This applies particularly to Human Anatomy, a subject which has no natural starting point. The interest which any student takes in a compulsory part of his curriculum depends, to some extent at least, on the kind of introduction with which he is provided. For many years past I have had the opportunity of observing that the intimate relationship existing between structure and function, properly stressed and adequately presented, is capable of arousing real interest in the mind of the average medical student, especially in his first term in the Dissecting Room. On this account, it has been my practice to substitute for the customary series of detailed lectures a short course of introductory lectures of a very elementary and general character. There has hitherto been one great drawback to this plan, namely that there was no text-book of reasonable size which dealt with the subject in a similar way; consequently, much of the value of the spoken word was lost for lack of its reiteration in print. This drawback has now been eliminated and Dr. Whillis is to be congratulated, very warmly, on the way in which he has succeeded in correlating structure and function, and in emphasising, in an unobtrusive manner, the essential inter-dependence of Anatomy and Physiology. His book provides the right approach to the study of Human Anatomy, and on that account it is equally suitable for medical students, nurses, and any others who propose to study the subject, no matter how deeply they may intend to delve into it subsequently.

T. B. JOHNSTON

GUY'S HOSPITAL,
  LONDON.

AUTHOR'S PREFACE

THE fuller text-books of Anatomy, although excellent for the senior student, leave the elementary student a little bewildered as to what must be selected from them to amplify instruction received in lectures.

It is hoped that this book will fill the gap, and that the combination of Anatomy with some simple Physiology will make the study of the structure of the body more interesting and profitable to the student during his first year of Medicine. The physiological matter included is not intended to trespass in any way on the function of the existing elementary text-books of Physiology, but is limited to the essentials of function. No attempt has been made to cover the subject in its wider aspects.

The rigid selection exercised in the writing of the text makes the book suitable also for nurses and others who need an elementary treatment of the subjects during their period of training, and a book to which they can refer in their subsequent professional work. Much of the material which is, perhaps, too detailed for the preliminary period, but which may be useful later, has been printed in small type, so that the selection of the essentials should be relatively easy. Many instances of the practical application of Anatomy and Physiology are included, and should materially increase the interest of the subjects.

The illustrations, which have been prepared from original drawings executed with great care and patience by Miss Pauline Lariviére, are of semi-diagrammatic type. Their simplicity should make the text easy to read and understand.

The British Revised Terminology has been used in the anatomical description, but the older names are included both in the text and in the index, so that no difficulty should arise in this respect.

In conclusion, I must express my cordial thanks to many of my colleagues for their help in the preparation of the book. In particular I am indebted to Professor T. B. Johnston for his constructive criticism and encouragement; to Mr. W. R. Spurrell, whom I have consulted on several points in Physiology; to Miss Larivíere for her patience in the production of the drawings for the figures; and to Mr. S. H. Wass, who has assisted me throughout in the revision of the subject-matter and the proofs.

JAMES WHILLIS.

Guy's Hospital
  Medical School.

CONTENTS

ANATOMY

CHAPTER I

THE HUMAN BODY

CELLS, TISSUES, ORGANS. THE BODY AS A WHOLE

CELLS

ANIMAL cells are the units of which the body is built.

Cells (Fig. 1, F) are composed of a jelly-like substance called **protoplasm,** and, although varying considerably in size, are all so

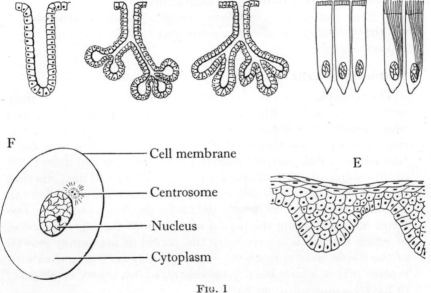

FIG. 1

A. Simple tubular gland.
B. Racemose glands.
C. Columnar epithelium.

D. Ciliated columnar epithelium.
E. Stratified squamous epithelium.
F. Animal cell.

minute that the microscope is needed to see them. In the human body the cells (with the exception of the red corpuscles of the blood in post-natal life) all contain a **nucleus,** or central portion, which is highly specialised in structure and function. Inside the nucleus is a network of a material called **chromatin**. Near the nucleus, in the surrounding protoplasm, which is termed **cytoplasm,** is the **centrosome,** a structure concerned with the changes which take place when the cell divides. The outermost part of the cytoplasm differs in some way from the remainder. Sometimes this difference is shown by the presence of an outer condensed film, very thin, and called the **cell membrane.** More frequently, however, the difference is recognisable only by the fact that certain substances can and others can not pass in or out of the cell through this peripheral layer of protoplasm. The remainder of the cytoplasm may present granules or other modifications. Such granules may be the precursors of substances produced by the cell when it is in a state of increased activity.

Living cells all have the following characteristics :—

1. They can grow and so become mature.

2. They can be stimulated into some form of activity. This property is called **irritability** or **excitability.**

3. They can divide to produce two cells, each of which exhibits all the propensities of the parent cell. This phenomenon is reproduction.

1. Growth of Cells

The protoplasm is a compound of chemical substances, mainly proteins and salts with water, and, in order to grow, the cell must have these substances exhibited to it in such a way that it can absorb and use them. Cells are therefore bathed in a fluid, termed **tissue fluid,** derived mainly from the blood, and if deprived of this source of nutrition they fail to grow and will die. Having reached maturity each cell can either remain for an indefinite period in that state, or it may divide to produce two cells. The latter happens during the period of growth of the organ or tissue of which the cell is a part, until the period of maximum growth of the whole body is reached. Subsequently cells may divide to replace others which have been destroyed by injury or disease, or have become worn out by work.

2. Irritability of Cells

The stimuli to which cells may respond are mechanical, chemical, and nervous forms of stimulation, and the action of light and heat, etc. The result may show itself as movement or alteration of the shape of the cell, as the liberation of substances produced by the cell (secretion), or in various other ways. The usual stimuli which excite the cells in the body are impulses brought to the cell along nerves, or the action of chemical substances reaching the cell from the blood *viâ* the tissue fluid.

3. Reproduction

Cells multiply by a parent cell dividing into two similar cells, each containing half the nuclear material and cytoplasm of the original cell. The change begins in the nucleus, and it is probable that through the chromatin in the nucleus the new cells inherit the characteristics of the parent. This form of division, involving extensive preliminary nuclear changes, is called **mitotic division.** A simpler type of division is seen more rarely, and is called **amitotic division,** or simple fission. The latter occurs in the multiplication of bacteria.

All the activities of cells involve a series of changes known collectively as **metabolism.** During active periods certain parts of the cellular substance become broken down ; this is termed **katabolism.** To repair this breakdown nutrient material is taken up by the cell and built up to form new protoplasm, these processes being termed respectively **assimilation** and **anabolism.**

TISSUES

Cells may work as isolated individual units, as, for example, the corpuscles of the blood, or they may be joined together by intercellular substance to form a tissue. The following are the varieties of tissues occurring in the body :—

1. Connective Tissues

(*a*) **Areolar Tissue.** This consists of cells entangled in a loose network of very delicate white fibres with a small admixture of yellow elastic fibres (Fig. 2).

(*b*) **Adipose Tissue (Fat).** This is similar to areolar tissue except that some of the cells are distended with fat which pushes the nucleus away to the periphery and replaces most of the cytoplasm (Fig. 2).

(*c*) **Reticular Tissue.** Here the cells are entangled in a very loose net of white fibres which are very fine. Most of the intercellular substance is fluid. The special variety called **lymphoid tissue** has masses of small round cells, the lymphocytes, grouped in the meshwork.

1—2

4

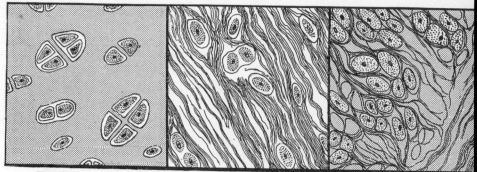

Hyaline cartilage.   White fibrocartilage.   Elastic cartilage.

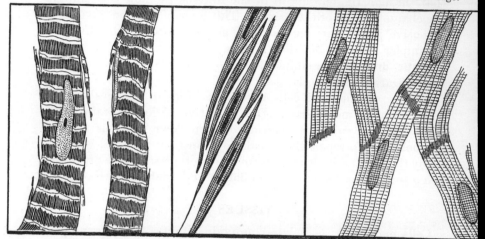

Striped muscle.   Plain muscle.   Cardiac muscle.

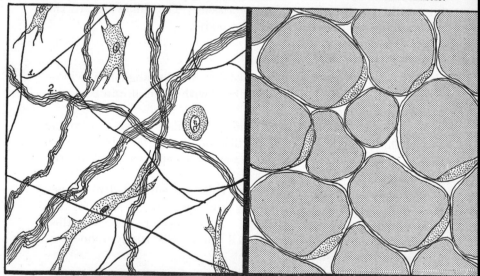

Areolar tissue.   Adipose tissue.
1. Elastic fibre   (Fat distending the cells is shaded.)
2. White fibre.   Fig. 2.

(*d*) **Elastic Tissue.** This tissue is found in small amounts all over the body, but especially in the windpipe, in the walls of arteries, and in certain of the ligaments. The fibres forming the intercellular substance are branched and unite with one another, a phenomenon never seen in white fibres.

(*e*) **Fibrous Tissue.** The intercellular substance of this tissue is formed of parallel white fibres closely packed into bundles which are firmly bound together. In the interstices between the bundles areolar tissue is found. White fibrous tissue is found especially in tendons, ligaments, and the deep fascia (p. 60).

(*f*) **Cartilage.** Three types of cartilage are seen, differing from one another in that the cells are embedded in various ground substances (Fig. 2).

Hyaline cartilage has a translucent homogeneous intercellular substance or matrix, and the cells are few in number. *White fibrocartilage* has a matrix of white fibrous tissue. *Yellow elastic cartilage* has an admixture of elastic fibres in the matrix.

(*g*) **Bone.** Osseous tissue is characterised by the fact that the intercellular substance is laid down in layers, and has deposited in it calcium and other mineral salts which make it very hard. A more detailed account of its structure will be found in the section on osteology (p. 9).

2. Muscular Tissue (Fig. 2)

The units of muscular tissue are cells which have been modified and elongated to form **muscle fibres.** These are grouped into bundles, and these in turn into fasciculi or sheets. There are three types of muscle :—

(*a*) **Striped, skeletal or voluntary muscle.** Here the fibres are long and transversely striated. This type is under the control of the will.

(*b*) **Unstriped, plain or involuntary muscle.** This type cannot be controlled by the will. It is found especially in the organs such as the bowel, and in the walls of blood-vessels. The cells which form it are long and flattened, and without striations.

(*c*) **Cardiac muscle.** This is found in the heart, is involuntary, but is striped. The fibres differ from those of skeletal muscle in that they are shorter, and branched to form a network with adjacent fibres.

3. Nervous Tissue

This consists of nerve cells and their processes with a varying amount of intercellular connective tissue called neuroglia. A fuller account will be found in the section on the nervous system (p. 235).

4. Fluid Tissues

Some authorities regard the blood and lymph as tissues in which the intercellular substance is entirely fluid. Accounts will be found in the appropriate chapters.

5. Epithelial Tissues (Fig. 1)

Epithelium consists of cells which are specialised to form coverings for body surfaces and linings for tubes such as the bowel. The special variety forming the linings of blood- and lymph-vessels and lining the serous cavities of the body is called endothelium. There is no intercellular substance in epithelial tissues, the cells being cemented together by inspissated lymph. The cells may be arranged in a single layer, when the epithelium is termed **simple,** or there may be many layers superimposed, in which case it is termed a **stratified** epithelium. Epithelial tissues do not contain blood-vessels and the cells receive their nutrition from the fluid exuded into the adjacent tissues.

According to the variety of cells present, epithelia may be classified as :—

(*a*) Flattened.   (*d*) **Columnar.**
(*b*) **Polygonal or spheroidal celled.**   (*e*) **Ciliated.**
(*c*) **Cubical.**

The last-named variety is composed of cells, usually columnar in shape, possessing along their free edge hairs which vibrate during life. This movement of the cilia is capable of moving particulate matter along the surface of the mucous membrane of which the cell is a part.

Epithelium may be arranged in sheets spread out over a surface or lining a cavity. On the other hand, it may form closed or open sacs such as in glands. The latter present a variety of forms some of which are shown in Fig. 1. In some situations especially in the lining of the alimentary and respiratory tracts, certain of the epithelial cells are capable of producing the substance called **mucus**; the term '' **mucous membrane** '' is therefore applied to the tissue.

ORGANS

It has been shown that cells become aggregated to form tissues ; similarly tissues become grouped together to form organs, each of which, by virtue of the types of tissues which make it up, can perform certain functions. A group of organs acting together forms a system.

THE BODY AS A WHOLE

Man belongs to the group of animals known as vertebrates, *i.e.*, possessing a backbone which is made up of a number of small sections called **vertebræ.** Inside this backbone or **spinal column** is contained the spinal cord from which arise most of the nerves of the body. Surrounding the spinal column are groups of muscles, and in the region of the chest the **ribs** pass forwards from the column to reach the breast-bone in front. The spaces between the ribs are filled by sheets of muscle, and running round in each space amongst this muscle is one of the nerves which has come off the spinal cord. The ribs and breast-bone at the sides and in front and the spinal column behind, together with their associated muscles, thus enclose a space called the **thoracic cavity** which contains the lungs and heart, etc. Below this cavity, and separated from it by the midriff or diaphragm, is the **abdomen** containing the organs of digestion. The walls of this cavity are formed in a way similar to those of the thorax. The spine and the muscles surrounding it are found behind. At the sides and in front, except in the extreme upper part, there are no bones like the ribs, and the wall of the abdominal cavity is quite soft and composed of muscles. As the diaphragm is at a higher level than the lowest of the ribs, the cavity of the abdomen encroaches somewhat on the bony thorax, and here ribs are present in the abdominal wall. Below, the abdomen is continuous with the **pelvic cavity**, which is enclosed by the lowest part of the vertebral column and the two hip bones. The thorax and the abdomen together make up the trunk. The continuation of the vertebral column above the trunk is the foundation of the neck. **The skull,** in the interior of which is found the brain, is joined to its upper end. At this point the brain is continuous with the spinal cord inside the vertebral column. Appended to the trunk are the **upper and lower limbs.** Each consists of a part buried in the trunk (the limb girdle), and a free part. For example, the shoulder blade and collar bone and the muscles associated with them form the buried part of the upper limb.

ANATOMICAL TERMS

In order to facilitate the description of structures in the body an exact terminology has been evolved by anatomists. The body is always described as if standing upright on the feet with the palms of the hands turned forwards. A plane passing through the middle of the body from front to back (Fig. 3, A), is termed the **median plane.** Planes (B) parallel to the median plane are termed **sagittal planes.** Planes at right angles to the median plane are called **coronal planes** (C). The term **horizontal plane** needs no elaboration. Structures nearer to the head end of the

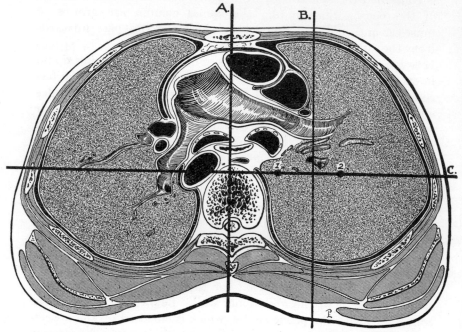

Fig. 3. A horizontal section through the thorax to illustrate the planes used in anatomical description.

body are said to be **above** or **superior,** and structures nearer the tail end **below** or **inferior.** The point 1 (Fig. 3) is described as being **medial** to the point 2, *i.e.*, nearer the median plane. The point 2 being farther away from the median plane than B, is described as more **lateral.** The terms **ventral** (towards the belly) and **anterior** denote nearer the front of the body, and **dorsal** or **posterior** nearer the back.

In the limbs **proximal** means nearer the trunk, **distal** means farther away from the trunk.

CHAPTER II

OSTEOLOGY

INTRODUCTORY

THE bony skeleton forms the rigid framework of the body. The bones of which it is composed serve, in the trunk, to protect the organs of the thorax and abdomen and make the movements of respiration possible. In the limbs they form a system of jointed levers by which co-ordinated movements of these parts are brought about.

Structure of Bone (Fig. 4)

It has been stated above (p. 5) that bone is one of the connective tissues. It owes its hardness to the mineral salts which are incorporated in it. Calcium carbonate and calcium phosphate form the large proportion of this **inorganic** matter which, in all, makes up about two-thirds of the weight of the bone. If this inorganic matter be dissolved out of the bone by steeping it in dilute acid the **organic** portion only will be left, and it is found that the bone can be bent and twisted in all directions. The bones of young children contain relatively less inorganic salts than those of adults and they are therefore less hard and brittle.

Two kinds of bone are found in the skeleton—**compact** substance and **spongy or cancellous** substance. Compact substance is found on the outside of bones, forming a hard layer on the surface. Spongy substance is found inside the compact tissue and is relatively large in amount in flat bones and in the expanded ends of long bones where the increase in size necessary to form good joint surfaces would, if the end consisted of compact bone, result in great increase of weight.

If a section of a long bone be examined it will be seen that the shaft or central portion consists almost entirely of compact substance and is tubular in form, the hollow in the interior being the **marrow cavity**. The extremities of a long bone consist of spongy substance covered by a thin layer of compact substance. There is here no true marrow cavity, but the marrow is found in the interstices of the spongy bone. The marrow found in the marrow cavity of a long bone is yellow and contains a large amount of fat. That entangled in the interstices of the spongy substance in the extremities of long bones, in the ribs and vertebræ, and in flat bones generally, is red in colour. This red

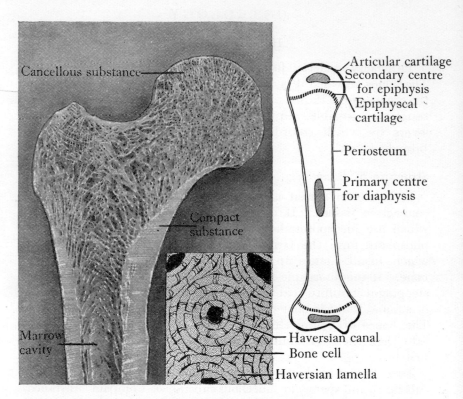

Cancellous substance

Compact substance

Marrow cavity

Articular cartilage
Secondary centre for epiphysis
Epiphyscal cartilage

Periosteum

Primary centre for diaphysis

Haversian canal
Bone cell
Haversian lamella

FIG. 4. The structure and development of bone. The section on the left is through the upper end of the femur.

marrow is the site of formation of the cells of the blood (see Chapter VII, p. 127).

If a section of compact bone be examined with the microscope it will be found to be traversed by channels called **Haversian canals.** These canals contain blood-vessels and nerves. Surrounding these canals are concentric lamellæ or plates of bone termed **Haversian lamellæ,** and between adjacent Haversian systems are the **interstitial lamellæ.** On the surface of the bone are the **circumferential lamellæ,** which lie parallel with one another. The **bone cells** or corpuscles lie in minute spaces between the bone lamellæ.

The articular ends of bones are covered with a special variety of hyaline cartilage termed **articular cartilage.**

The **periosteum** is the membrane which surrounds the bone. It is composed of fibrous tissue and some of the fibres perforate the circumferential lamellæ of the compact substance beneath, binding these together and increasing the security of attachment of the periosteum. Where the bone is covered by articular cartilage the periosteum gives place to and is continuous with the membrane called **perichondrium** which covers the cartilage. The periosteum is of great importance as it carries blood-vessels to the bone, particularly to the compact substance of the shaft. If it become detached the underlying bone will die. In addition to the periosteal vessels, larger arteries called nutrient vessels enter the marrow cavity and divide to supply the interior of the bone.

Development of Bone

The bones of the skeleton are developed in two ways. The flat bones develop in membrane and the long bones develop in bars of cartilage which are formed by alteration of the more primitive embryonic tissue. In both cases, however, the processes are essentially similar in that cells called **osteoblasts** invade the area of ossification and calcium salts are deposited so as to give the necessary hardness. The process, which in most bones commences before birth, is not uniform throughout the bone, but begins in one or more **centres of ossification.** Some bones have only one such centre, but all the long bones of the limbs and many others have more than one. The first, which appears before birth, is called the **primary centre,** and from it the shaft and sometimes other parts of the bone are formed. (At birth many of the bones are still cartilaginous, and even the long bones are cartilaginous at their extremities.) After birth **secondary centres** appear for the ends of the bone, and later for some of the more prominent projections. During the period of growth the bone thus consists of a central part (formed from the primary centre) called the **diaphysis,** and two ends called **epiphyses,** joined to the diaphysis by thin plates of growing cartilage into which ossification has not yet spread. By the age of twenty-five years even these epiphyseal plates become converted into bone, and the epiphyses and the diaphysis form a complete whole of continuous bone. The bones grow in thickness mainly by deposition just under the periosteum, and in length by progressive ossification in the region of the epiphyses.

Physiology of Bone Formation

In order that the above changes may take place it is necessary that the blood contain *calcium* and *phosphorus* in a certain proportion relative to one another. These substances must be taken in the diet, which must also contain a sufficiency of *vitamin D.* (See p. 113.) During pregnancy the same requirements must be taken by the mother. Adequate sunshine is a factor which co-operates in bone formation, and it is possible that the actual deposit of calcium is due to an enzyme (p. 114) present in the cartilage which is to be ossified. Milk is the most important source of calcium in the diet, especially in children. Where the diet is deficient in vitamin D, and children live in slums where sunshine rarely is adequate, diseases of the bones such as rickets are prevalent.

CLASSIFICATION OF BONES

Bones are classified according to their shape into :—

Long Bones

These consist of a shaft or central portion with two ends or extremities. Their structure has been described above.

Flat Bones

These have two tables of compact substance enclosing a layer of spongy substance between them. Examples are the shoulder-blade and many of the skull bones.

Irregular Bones and Short Bones

These consist mainly of spongy substance covered with a thin layer of compact substance on the surface. The vertebræ and bones of the wrist and ankle are examples. Sesamoid bones (see patella) are of this type.

THE SKELETON

The student must realise that in studying the bones it is essential to have access to the dried specimens themselves. The text-book description is intended as a guide in looking at the bone and will lose most of its value if not used in this way.

The skeleton is made up of the bones and cartilages of the body. It has two main parts, axial and appendicular. The axial skeleton comprises the vertebral column, the skull, the ribs and sternum, and the hyoid bone.

The appendicular skeleton is made up of the bones of the limbs and of the limb girdles (p. 7) connecting them with the trunk.

THE AXIAL SKELETON

THE VERTEBRAL COLUMN

This consists of **twenty-four** separate and **movable vertebræ,** and of the **sacrum** and **coccyx.**

The separate vertebræ are arranged in groups ; **seven** in the **cervical** or neck region, **twelve** in the **thoracic** or chest region, and **five** in the **lumbar** or loin region. Each of these bones presents certain characteristics which are common to all vertebræ.

Characters of a Vertebra (Fig. 5)

Each vertebra, except the first cervical, consists of a **body** and a **neural arch**, which together enclose the large **vertebral foramen** for the spinal cord in the centre.

The body is placed anteriorly and is joined to the bodies of the vertebræ above and below it by discs of fibrocartilage, the **intervertebral discs.**

The neural arch consists of the **pedicles** or roots attached to the body on each side, and the **laminæ**, flattened plates of bone which complete the arch posteriorly.

Projecting laterally on each side from the junction of the pedicle with the lamina is the **transverse process.** On the upper and lower surfaces of the neural arch are the **articular processes**. The pair on the upper surface articulate with the inferior articular processes of the vertebra above, and those on the inferior surface with the superior articular processes of the vertebra below. Projecting backwards and downwards in the median plane posteriorly is the **spinous process** (spine) of the vertebra. This is the process which can be felt just under the skin of the back.

Cervical vertebræ are recognised by their relatively small size, and by the foramen which is present in the transverse process. The spinous process is short and bifid at its extremity (Fig. 6).

Thoracic vertebræ are larger than the cervical. The bodies and transverse processes present facets for articulation with the ribs. The spinous process is very long, and directed obliquely downwards (Fig. 5).

Lumbar vertebræ are the largest of all. The transverse processes are very slender and the spinous process is a square piece of bone directed straight backwards (Fig. 6).

Atypical Vertebræ. There are atypical vertebræ in the cervical, thoracic, and lumbar regions, but for the present purpose only the first and second cervical will be considered (Fig. 6). *The first cervical,* termed the *atlas,* has no body. The latter has become fused with the *second cervical* or *axis* to form the tooth-like projection called the odontoid process (dens) around which the ring-like atlas rotates in turning movements of the head.   The odontoid process is held in place

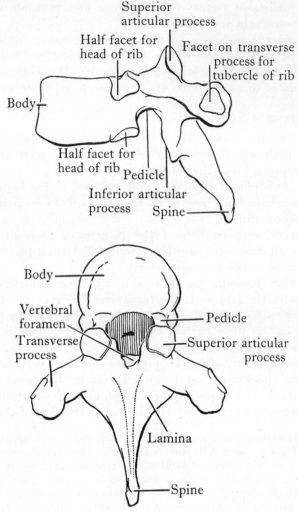

Fig. 5. *A typical vertebra* (thoracic). The upper diagram viewed from the left side and the lower diagram viewed from above and behind.

in the anterior part of the ring of the atlas by a strong ligament. The posterior part of the ring of the atlas is occupied by the spinal cord. The other atypical vertebræ are found where very freely movable parts of the column join less movable parts. They are the seventh cervical and first thoracic, the lower three thoracic, and the last lumbar vertebræ.

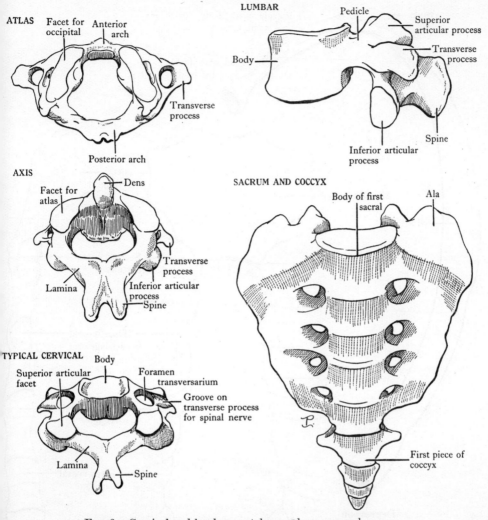

FIG. 6. Cervical and lumbar vertebræ and sacrum and coccyx.

The Sacrum (Fig. 6)

The sacrum is a wedge-shaped bone, concave anteriorly. Above, it is joined to the lower end of the last lumbar vertebra, and on each side it articulates with the hip-bone. The two hip-bones and the sacrum and coccyx together form the bony basin termed the **pelvis**.

The sacrum is really five fused vertebræ, and traversing it is a canal which represents the superimposed vertebral foramina. Anteriorly

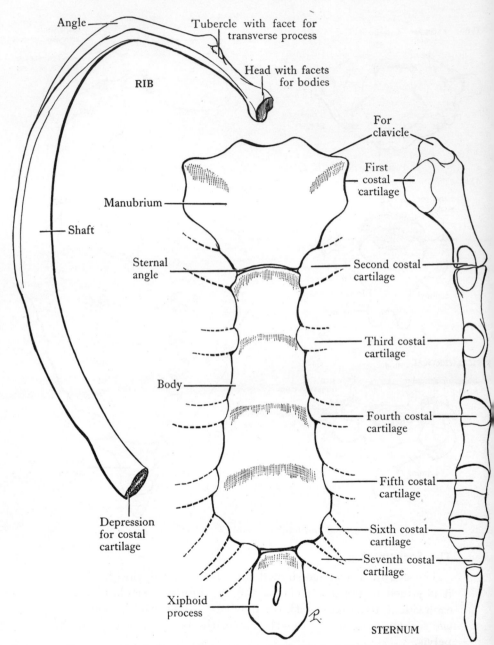

FIG. 7.   Typical rib viewed from below and behind, and sternum, anterior and right lateral views.

and posteriorly foramina open out of the sacral canal and transmit the rami of the sacral nerves out of the bone.

The **coccyx** is the rudimentary tail in man. It consists of three or four fused vertebral bodies. There is no vertebral canal. Above, it articulates with the apex of the sacrum.

The Spine as a Whole

The spine as a whole presents the following curvatures :—

Two primary curves, present at birth, and both concave forwards ; these are in the **thoracic** and **sacral** regions.

Two secondary curves are present, both convex forwards ; they are :—

The **cervical** curvature, which appears when the child begins to hold up its head at the age of about six months, and the **lumbar** curve, which appears when the child begins to sit upright, and becomes more marked when it begins to walk, between the ages of twelve months and two years.

Function of Vertebræ

The bodies of the vertebræ are for the transmission of the body weight. They are larger in the lower part of the column because the weight to be borne gradually increases from above downwards. The column is made up of sections so as to allow a certain amount of movement. Undue mobility, which might result in injury of the spinal cord, is prevented by the articular processes. The intervertebral discs act as shock absorbers, and permit movement between the sections. The neural arch serves to protect the spinal cord, whilst the spinous and the transverse processes form a series of levers for attachment of muscles and ligaments. In the thoracic region the transverse processes are specially large for articulation with the ribs.

THE STERNUM (Fig. 7)

The sternum or breast-bone can be felt beneath the skin in the median plane on the front of the chest. It consists of three parts, namely, the **manubrium,** the **body** and the **xiphoid process,** named from above downwards. In early life the parts are connected by joints, but after middle age the joints become calcified. Laterally, the sternum is joined to the ribs by **costal cartilages.** The upper and lateral angles of the manubrium, together with the adjacent areas of the first costal cartilages, form the sockets for the clavicles.

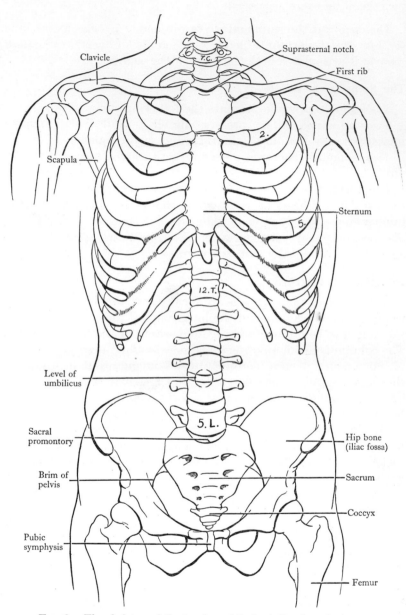

FIG. 8.   The skeleton of the trunk and limb girdles from in front.

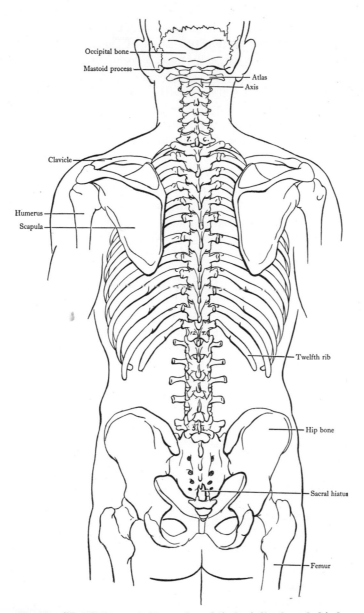

Fig. 9. The skeleton of the trunk and limb girdles from behind.

THE RIBS (Figs. 7, 8 and 9)

There are twelve ribs on each side. Each is a curved flat bone, consisting from behind forwards of a **head,** a **neck,** a **tubercle,** a **shaft,** and an **anterior extremity.** Most of the ribs present, on the deep surface near the lower border, a *costal groove* which lodges the intercostal vessels.

All ribs articulate posteriorly with the vertebral column.

The **first seven pairs** are connected to the sternum by costal cartilages and are called **true ribs.**

The remaining **five pairs** are **false ribs.** The eighth, ninth and tenth costal cartilages are joined each to the cartilage immediately above.

The **eleventh and twelfth** ribs end freely among the muscles of the back ; they are termed **floating ribs.**

Occasionally extra ribs are present. These occur in the lower cervical and upper lumbar regions. A cervical rib may press on the *brachial plexus* (p. 262), causing serious interference with the nerves of the arm.

THE THORAX (Fig. 8)

The bony thorax is bounded behind by the **vertebral column,** in front by the **sternum,** and between these by the **ribs** and **costal cartilages.** It has an oblique superior aperture or **inlet,** and a larger **inferior aperture.** As stated above (p. 7), the part below the diaphragm is really a part of the abdomen.

The movements of the thorax are described on p. 66.

THE SKULL

The skull consists of a number of bones immovably fixed together, and one movable bone, the lower jaw or mandible. The part formed of fixed bones presents an upper portion containing the brain and a lower smaller part forming the skeleton of the face. The joints between the bones are called sutures.

The Part Containing the Brain

The part containing the brain is ovoid in form, with the smaller end anteriorly. The following bones enter into its formation :—

Parietal	. . .	2 ⎫ One on each side.
Temporal	. . .	2 ⎭
Occipital	. . .	1
Sphenoid	. . .	1
Ethmoid	. . .	1
Frontal	. . .	1

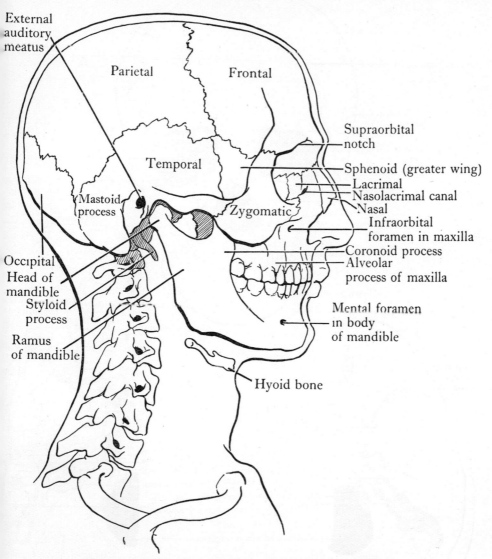

External auditory meatus

Parietal

Frontal

Temporal

Supraorbital notch

Sphenoid (greater wing)

Lacrimal

Nasolacrimal canal

Nasal

Infraorbital foramen in maxilla

Mastoid process

Zygomatic

Coronoid process

Alveolar process of maxilla

Occipital

Head of mandible

Styloid process

Mental foramen in body of mandible

Ramus of mandible

Hyoid bone

FIG. 10.   The skeleton of the head and neck from the right side.

The position of the bones can be seen in Figs. 10 and 11.

This part of the skull comprises a convex upper part, or vault, and a base.

The Vault

The bones of the vault can be felt beneath the scalp.

The **occipital bone** is placed posteriorly and the prominence

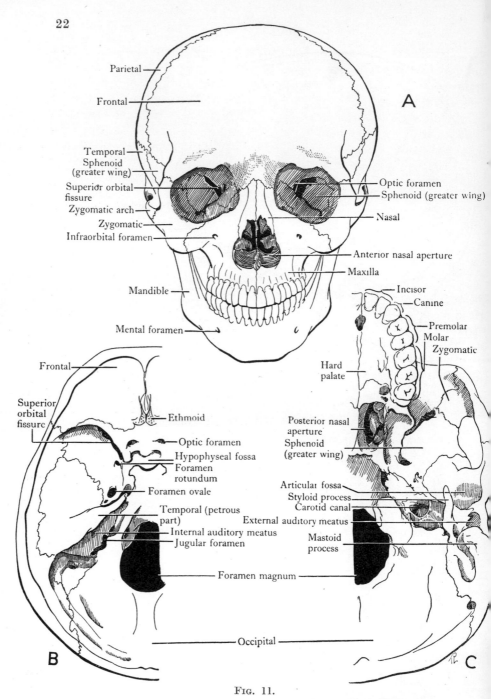

FIG. 11.

A. The skull from in front.   B. Internal surface of the base of the skull.
C. External surface of the base of the skull.

termed the external occipital protuberance or inion can be felt on it in the living just above the nape of the neck. The occipital bone articulates in front with both temporal bones and both parietal bones. (The joint with the parietal bones is called the lambdoid suture because of its resemblance to the Greek letter λ.)

Each **parietal bone** articulates below with the temporal and sphenoid bones, and, above, meets its fellow of the opposite side in the median plane to form the sagittal suture on the top of the skull.

The **frontal bone** forms the skeleton of the forehead and meets both parietal bones in the coronal suture which crosses the top of the skull from side to side.

The frontal bone is separated from the two **temporal bones** by the greater wings of the **sphenoid bone.**

The Base

The anterior part of the base is hidden on the outside (Fig. 11, C) by the skeleton of the face. It can be seen in its entirety from the inside if the skull-cap be sawn off (Fig. 11, B).

The **internal surface** of the base is related to the brain and presents three main parts, viz. :—the **anterior, middle and posterior cranial fossæ.**

The **anterior fossa** is, near the median plane, above the nasal cavity ; here it is formed by the ethmoid bone. More laterally, its floor is formed on each side by the frontal bone and the lesser wing of the sphenoid bone which separate the anterior fossa from the orbit.

The **middle fossa** has two lateral parts containing the temporal lobes of the brain (p. 252) and occupying a position just behind the orbits, and a median part, the hypophyseal fossa for the hypophysis cerebri (p. 315). The hypophyseal fossa occupies a position just above and behind the posterior part of the roof of the nose. The floor of the middle fossa is made up of parts of the sphenoid and temporal bones.

The **posterior fossa** lodges the hind-brain and, in the median plane, presents the foramen magnum through which the brainstem is continuous with the spinal cord. The posterior fossa is formed mainly by the occipital bone, but also by the temporal bones, the postero-inferior angles of the two parietal bones, and the posterior part of the body of the sphenoid bone. The latter is joined by bone to the occipital a little in front of the foramen magnum.

The wedge-shaped part of the temporal bone which enters into the formation of the lateral parts of the middle and posterior cranial fossæ is called, because of its hardness, the petrous part. It contains in its interior the cavities of the ear (p. 288).

The **external surface** of the base (Fig. 11, C) is hidden anteriorly by the facial skeleton which, on this view, presents the **hard**

palate, and just above this the two **posterior nasal apertures**
separated from each other by the nasal septum. The palate is
formed mainly by the maxillæ or upper jawbones, but partly
also by the palatine bones. Each maxilla presents peripherally
the raised alveolar process in which the roots of the upper teeth
are embedded.

The posterior nasal apertures are the openings through which
the nose communicates with the nasopharynx (p. 94), the roof
of which is formed by the parts of the sphenoid and occipital
bones between the foramen magnum behind and the posterior
nasal apertures in front.

Lateral to the pharyngeal region of the external surface of the
base of the skull is the region occupied by the joint with the lower
jaw and the muscles which move it. This neighbourhood is
limited laterally by the **zygomatic arch** which is formed partly by
the zygomatic bone and partly by the temporal bone. On the
latter at the posterior end of the zygomatic arch is the **articular
fossa** for the head of the mandible, and just above and behind this
the **external auditory meatus** can be seen if the skull be viewed
from the lateral side.

The posterior part of the external surface of the base of the
skull is associated with the vertebral column and the muscles
which surround it. Lateral to the **foramen magnum** are the
occipital condyles for articulation with the superior facets on the
atlas. Behind the external auditory meatus the **mastoid process**
of the temporal bone forms a prominent feature of this part of the
skull, and anteromedial to this the pointed **styloid process** of the
temporal bone projects downwards and forwards from the base.
Medial to the styloid process the **jugular foramen** (Fig. 11, B),
opening into the posterior fossa between the occipital and
temporal bones, and the **carotid canal** (Fig. 11, C) in the temporal
bone transmit the vessels of the same names.

Practical Considerations. Fractures of the skull may follow
blows on the head. If the damage be inflicted by a sharp
instrument or over a very limited surface the fragments of bone
may be depressed. In these injuries the inner table (p. 12) of
compact substance is often more extensively damaged than the
outer table, and fragments of bone may be driven into the underlying brain-tissue. Fissured fractures or cracks of the skull bones
follow violence of a more general kind, such as falling on the head.
Such cracks may extend into parts of the skull which are accessible
to the outside air, for example, the ear or the roof of the nose

and pharynx, and be evidenced by the escape of blood and cerebrospinal fluid from these cavities. Since the nose, throat, and external ear contain many micro-organisms, infection of the membranes of the brain is liable to follow. Hence the necessity for scrupulous care of the ears, etc., in the nursing of such cases.

The Skeleton of the Face

The skeleton of the face is best seen from in front. In the upper part the forehead is formed by the **frontal bone,** and on this may be noted the superciliary ridges and the upper margins of the orbital cavities. At the root of the nose the frontal bone articulates with the two **nasal bones** and with the **frontal processes of the maxillæ** or upper jaw-bones. Below this the **anterior nasal aperture** is bounded at the sides and below by the maxillæ. It should be noted that the nasal skeleton is completed in front by the cartilages of the nose.

At the sides of the root of the nose are the **orbital cavities** for the eyes.

The aperture of each orbit is bounded above by the frontal bone, medially by the frontal process of the maxilla and the maxillary process of the frontal, below by the body of the maxilla and by the zygomatic bone, and laterally by the zygomatic bone and the zygomatic process of the frontal. The cavity has superior, medial, inferior, and lateral walls. The lateral wall is, in part, separated from the roof by a cleft termed the **superior orbital fissure,** and from the floor by the **inferior orbital fissure.** At the apex of the orbit, near the medial end of the superior orbital fissure, is the **optic foramen.** The anterior part of the medial wall presents the **lacrimal groove** leading into the **nasolacrimal canal** which runs down to the lower part of the lateral wall of the nose.

The facial skeleton below the orbits is formed by the two **maxillæ** (upper jaw-bones) and lateral to the orbit on each side by the **zygomatic bone,** which makes the prominence of the " cheek-bone."

The Mandible

The lower jaw consists of a curved **body,** the upper part of which is called the **alveolar process,** and bears the lower teeth, and of the **rami,** which project upwards from the posterior ends of the body on the two sides. The junction of the body with the ramus is called the **angle.** Each ramus bears at its upper end the pointed **coronoid process** and the **head,** the latter attached to the ramus by the **neck,** and articulating with the fossa, already described, on the temporal bone (p. 24).

On the facial surface of the body is seen the **mental foramen,** which transmits a part of the inferior dental branch of the trigeminal nerve on to the face. The inferior dental nerve enters the jaw on the deep surface of the ramus about its middle and runs in a canal in the bone, supplying the lower teeth on its way.

The Nasal Cavity (Fig. 28)

The nasal cavity opens on to the face at the **anterior nasal aperture,** and into the nasopharynx at the **posterior nasal apertures.** It is divided into two halves by the **nasal septum** formed in the median plane by the *vomer* and part of the *ethmoid bone.* The skeleton of the external nose and the anterior part of the septum are completed by the *nasal and septal cartilages.*

The *lateral wall* of each half of the cavity is subdivided into channels called **meatuses** by projecting bones called **conchæ** (turbinate bones), of which there are three. The air sinuses round the nose and the nasolacrimal canal from the orbit open into the meatuses.

The *roof* of the nose slopes anteriorly where it is formed by the **nasal bones** and posteriorly where it is formed by the **sphenoid.** In the middle it is formed by the part of the **ethmoid** bone which separates the nose from the anterior cranial fossa. This plate of bone is pierced by the filaments of the olfactory nerves.

Air Sinuses. The air sinuses communicating with the nose are spaces found in the maxillary, frontal, ethmoid, sphenoid and palate bones. They are lined by mucous membrane continuous with that of the nose. They contain air, and serve to lighten the skull and to give extra resonance to the voice. (In a common cold the alteration in the character of the voice is due partly to blockage of their openings.) Being continuous with the nose, they are liable to be involved in infections of that cavity. Secretion is drained from them into the nose partly by gravity and partly by the movement of the cilia of the epithelium with which they are lined (p. 6). When these cilia are destroyed by chronic inflammation the sinus may fail to drain, although its opening may be quite patent. This is especially so in the maxillary sinus, whose opening into the nose is higher than its floor.

The Fœtal Skull

The skull of the newly born infant presents several points of difference from that of the adult. In the first place the face is much smaller relative to the brain-case than it is in the adult. This is only partly due to the fact that the teeth have not erupted. Secondly, ossification has not extended completely throughout the various bones. Because of this there are gaps, filled only by membrane, at the two ends of the sagittal suture. The gap between the frontal and the parietal bones is termed the **anterior fontanelle,** and that between the occipital and parietal bones the **posterior fontanelle.** Over these areas pulsation of the underlying brain can be observed in a baby's head. The fontanelles close when ossification extends to the limits of the bones bounding them, generally by the age of two years.

During the passage of the child's head through the pelvic canal in parturition, pressure on the skull alters its shape considerably. This process is termed "moulding." The adjacent bones may even overlap one another, but will always recover their position a few days after birth. If the fontanelles can be felt with the examining finger, this may give some indication of the position of the child's head during parturition.

The Hyoid Bone (Fig. 10)

The hyoid is a U-shaped bone situated in the root of the tongue and connected with the jaw by the muscles of the floor of the mouth. Below, it is joined to the thyroid cartilage of the larynx by a membrane (thyrohyoid membrane), whilst behind, it gives attachment to part of the wall of the pharynx and to the root of the tongue. The bone can be felt in the living by grasping the anterior part of the neck just below the level of the jaw.

THE TEETH

Each tooth consists of a **crown,** *i.e.,* that part which projects above the gum, a **root** embedded in the jaw, and a **neck** just where the tooth enters the jaw, and at the point where the crown joins the root. The tooth is hollow, the cavity in the interior being the **pulp cavity.** Through tiny canals at the apex of the root vessels and nerves enter the pulp cavity from the jaw to supply the tooth. The body of the tooth is composed of a substance called **dentine.** Over the crown the dentine is covered by a harder substance called **enamel,** whilst the root is covered by the **cement** which meets the enamel at the neck. The socket in the jaw is lined by the **periodontal membrane,** which is continuous outside with the periosteum, which covers the alveolar process of the jaw. The alveolar process is also covered by mucous membrane which constitutes the soft part of the gum.

Practical Considerations

Erosion of the enamel allows micro-organisms present in the mouth to affect the tooth and destroy the dentine. Such decay exposes delicate nerve-endings in the tooth and gives rise to *toothache*. The infection may extend into the pulp cavity and thence to the bone surrounding the root. From here the process may spread to the gum, either alongside the root or through the bone and give rise to a *gumboil*.

Diseases such as rickets, where the calcium metabolism is interfered with, give rise to marked delay in the eruption of the teeth, and render them less resistant to decay later.

Man is provided with two sets of teeth during his life, the deciduous and the permanent.

The deciduous or milk teeth commence to erupt during the first year of life, and begin to be shed at about the age of six years. There are **twenty** of them in all. In each jaw on each side of the median plane are two **incisors**, one **canine**, and two **molars** in that order from front to back.

The permanent teeth (Figs. 10 and 11) are **thirty-two** in number. In each jaw on each side of the median plane are two **incisors**, one **canine**, two **premolars** (or bicuspids) and three **molars**. The canine teeth are popularly known as the " eye teeth," and the third molars as the " wisdom teeth."

Eruption of Teeth

The **deciduous teeth** usually erupt in the following order at the ages given [1]:—

Lower central incisors . . .	Six to nine months.
Lower lateral incisors and first molars	Ten months.
Canines	Sixteen to twenty months.
Second molars	Twenty to twenty-four months.

The **permanent teeth** push from below and cut off the blood supply to the milk teeth so that the latter become loose and drop out. They erupt as follows :—

First molars (six-year molars) .	Sixth year.
Central incisors	Seventh year.
Lateral incisors	Eighth year.
First premolars	Ninth year.
Second premolars . . .	Tenth year.
Canines	By the twelfth year.
Second molars	By the thirteenth year.
Third molars (wisdom) . . .	By the twenty-fifth year.

It should be noted that the above dates are liable to enormous variation without the teeth being in any way abnormal. If, however,

[1] C. S. Tomes.

the first dentition be delayed markedly in its onset it is probable that some disease such as rickets is present.

THE APPENDICULAR SKELETON

It has been stated above (p. 7) that the skeleton of each limb consists of a buried part, the limb girdle, and a free part. In the **upper limb,** which is adapted for **mobility,** the attachment of the limb girdle to the trunk is mainly muscular, the only actual joints being those between the medial end of the clavicle and the sternum, and between the lateral end of the clavicle and the scapula. This arrangement allows the scapula to move fairly freely on the posterior wall of the thorax. In the case of the **lower limb,** however, the two hip bones articulate firmly behind with the sacrum and in front with one another. This gives a firm structure, the pelvis, through which the body weight is transmitted from the vertebral column to the lower limbs. It is an arrangement adapted especially for **stability.**

The mobility of the upper limb is further increased by the relative shallowness of the glenoid fossa (see scapula) for the humerus, and also by the clavicle acting as a prop carrying the scapula laterally into a position where it can move freely on the trunk. The depth of the acetabulum (see hip-bone) in which the head of the femur is sunk increases the stability of the lower limb at the sacrifice of some mobility.

THE SKELETON OF THE UPPER LIMB

The Limb Girdle (Figs. 8, 9, 12 and 13)

The Clavicle

The clavicle, or collar bone, is a long bone which is slightly curved, with a convexity forwards in its medial two-thirds, and a concavity forwards in its somewhat flattened lateral one-third. Medially it articulates with the sternum and the first costal cartilage, and laterally with the acromion process of the scapula. Behind the middle of the clavicle the large bundle of vessels and nerves enters the axilla (armpit) from the neck. It should be noted that the clavicle with its joints forms the only bony support for the scapula and the arm, and that if the bone be broken the arm tends to drop for a considerable distance, being then supported by muscles only. The clavicle can be felt beneath the skin along its whole length.

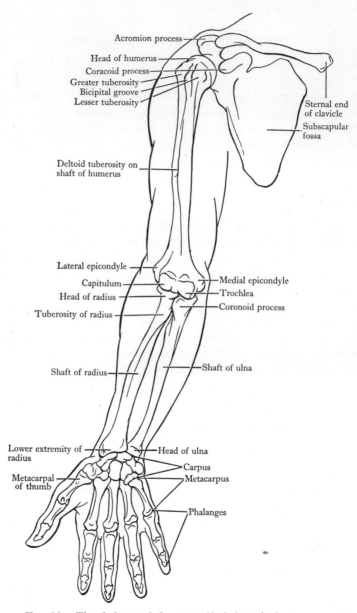

Acromion process

Head of humerus
Coracoid process
Greater tuberosity
Bicipital groove
Lesser tuberosity

Sternal end
of clavicle

Subscapular
fossa

Deltoid tuberosity on
shaft of humerus

Lateral epicondyle
Capitulum
Head of radius
Tuberosity of radius

Medial epicondyle
Trochlea
Coronoid process

Shaft of radius

Shaft of ulna

Lower extremity of
radius

Head of ulna

Carpus

Metacarpal
of thumb

Metacarpus

Phalanges

FIG. 12. The skeleton of the upper limb from in front.

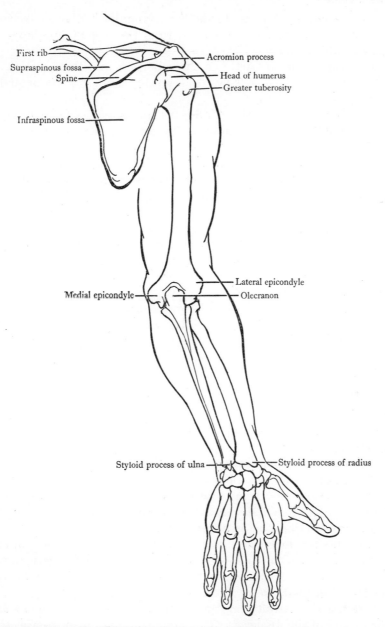

First rib

Supraspinous fossa

Spine

Infraspinous fossa

Acromion process

Head of humerus

Greater tuberosity

Lateral epicondyle

Medial epicondyle

Olecranon

Styloid process of ulna

Styloid process of radius

FIG. 13. The skeleton of the upper limb from behind.

The Scapula

The scapula, or shoulder blade, is a triangular flat bone covering the posterior surface of the thorax from the second rib above to the seventh rib below (Fig. 9).

The body, or main part, has three borders and three angles.

The borders are—axillary, or lateral ; vertebral, or medial ; and superior.

The angles are—superior ; inferior ; and lateral, which presents the **glenoid fossa,** forming the socket for the head of the humerus.

Projecting from the posterior surface is the **spine** of the scapula, which bears at its lateral end the **acromion process.** Both the spine and the acromion can be felt beneath the skin. From the upper border of the scapula near the lateral angle projects the **coracoid process.** The clavicle articulates with the acromion process, and this joint is rendered more stable by the conoid and trapezoid ligaments which pass from the inferior surface of the lateral third of the clavicle to the coracoid process.

The anterior surface of the scapula forms the posterior wall of the axilla or armpit, and is called the subscapular fossa.

The posterior surface is subdivided by the spine into two fossæ ; the supraspinous fossa above, and the larger infraspinous fossa below.

The Free Part of the Upper Limb (Figs. 12 and 13)

The Humerus

The humerus is the bone of the upper arm. It is a long bone and has a shaft and two extremities.

The upper extremity consists of the following parts :—

The head, rather less than a hemisphere, covered by articular cartilage, and articulating with the glenoid cavity of the scapula in the shoulder-joint. It is separated from the rest of the bone by a slight constriction, the **anatomical neck.**

The greater tuberosity is at the lateral part of the upper extremity. Prolonged down from it on to the upper part of the front of the shaft is the crest of the great tubercle, or the **lateral lip of the bicipital groove** (intertubercular sulcus).

The lesser tuberosity projects from the anterior surface of the upper end of the humerus. The ridge running down from it, the crest of the lesser tubercle, forms the **medial lip of the bicipital groove.**

The bicipital groove lodges the tendon of the long head of the biceps muscle as it passes out of the shoulder-joint down into the arm.

The **lower extremity** of the humerus takes part in the formation of the elbow joint. This articular portion consists of two parts, the **trochlea** or pulley surface **for the ulna,** and the **capitulum for the radius.** The axis of the trochlea is so directed that the ulna, when articulated with it, forms an angle with the humerus called the **carrying angle.** This will be evident at once if the student place the elbow close in to the side and extend the forearm with the palm of the hand pointing forwards ; the hand will then be some inches away from the thigh.

The lower end of the humerus is not entirely occupied by the trochlea and capitulum. Projecting on the medial side is the **medial epicondyle,** and on the lateral side is the **lateral epicondyle.** Both of these can be felt beneath the skin in the living.

The **shaft** of the humerus is cylindrical in form and somewhat flattened towards the lower end. Running on to it from the tuberosities are the **lips of the bicipital groove.** Passing upwards from each epicondyle is a sharp ridge. These ridges are termed the **medial and lateral supracondylar ridges,** and give attachment to the medial and lateral intermuscular septa which separate the extensor muscles behind the humerus from the flexor muscles in front. On the middle of the lateral surface of the shaft is a rough V-shaped marking, the **deltoid tuberosity.** The part of the shaft immediately below the upper extremity is called the **surgical neck,** as fractures of the bone sometimes occur in this situation.

The following nerves are in immediate contact with the humerus and may be injured in fractures of the bone :—
The axillary or circumflex at the surgical neck.
The radial or musculospiral, winding spirally round the back of the bone is in contact with the middle one-third of the shaft.
The ulnar behind the medial epicondyle. The nerve is sometimes stimulated by blows in this situation, giving rise to the peculiar sensation in the ulnar part of the hand, which justifies the name " funny bone " given to this bony projection.

The Bones of the Forearm

The radius and the ulna are the two bones of the forearm. With the hand in the supine position, *i.e.,* with the palm directed forwards, the bones are parallel. When the hand is pronated (*i.e.,* turned over so that the palm is directed backwards) the radius rotates so as to cross the ulna, pivoting round an axis passing through the upper end of the radius above and the lower end of the ulna below. The two bones are connected by the **interosseous membrane,** which, in addition to binding them together, increases materially the area for attachment of muscles.

The Ulna

The ulna takes a large share in the formation of the elbow joint and enters very little into the formation of the wrist. Being a long bone, it has a shaft and two extremities.

The **upper extremity** consists of two processes, **the olecranon** projecting upwards, and **the coronoid** projecting forwards. The deep hollow enclosed by the two processes articulates with the trochlea of the humerus and is called the **trochlear notch.** On the lateral side of the coronoid is the articular surface for the head of the radius called the **radial notch.** The olecranon can be felt just beneath the skin. When the elbow joint is extended, the two epicondyles of the humerus and the upper border of the olecranon are in a straight line ; when the elbow is fully flexed the three points form an equilateral triangle.

The **shaft** of the ulna is triangular on section. The posterior border can be felt in its entire length beneath the skin of the forearm.

The **lower extremity** of the ulna comprises the **head,** which articulates with the radius, and the **styloid process** projecting downwards from the back of the head.

The Radius

The radius is placed on the lateral side of the ulna. It also has a shaft and two extremities.

The **upper extremity** consists of the head, neck, and tuberosity.

The **head** has the form of a thick disc. The upper surface is cupped for articulation with the capitulum, whilst the edge of the disc articulates with the coronoid process of the ulna and the annular ligament (p. 52).

The **neck** is the constricted part below the head.

The **tuberosity** is the projection on the medial side just below the neck.

The head of the radius can be felt to rotate during the movements of pronation and supination. It lies almost immediately beneath the skin on the posterior surface of the limb about an inch distal to the lateral epicondyle of the humerus.

The **shaft** is triangular on section, and attached to the ulna by the interosseous membrane.

The **lower extremity** is large, and takes a great part in the formation of the wrist joint, articulating with the scaphoid and semilunar bones. The pointed projection from its lateral part is called the **styloid process.** It can be felt in the depression between the tendons at the base of the thumb (the "anatomical snuff-box").

The Skeleton of the Wrist and Hand

In the region of the wrist are eight irregular bones constituting the **carpus.** Distal to these are the bones of the palm, **the metacarpus.** The bones of the fingers and thumb are called **phalanges.**

The Carpus

The bones making up this region are arranged in two rows, proximal and distal.

The four bones of the *first row*, from the lateral to the medial side, are : the **scaphoid**, the **semilunar**, the **triquetral** and the **pisiform.**

The bones of the *distal row*, from the lateral to the medial side, are : the **trapezium**, the **trapezoid**, the **capitate** and the **hamate.** Projecting from the front of the carpus are four eminences, viz. :—The tuberosity of the scaphoid and the ridge on the trapezium on the lateral side, and the pisiform bone and the hook of the hamate on the medial. The presence of these eminences makes a groove on the anterior surface of the wrist ; this groove is converted into a tunnel for the flexor tendons by the **flexor retinaculum** (p. 78).

The Metacarpus

There are five metacarpal bones, one for each digit. That for the thumb is much more movable than the others and is set in a plane at right angles to them. This allows the movement of the thumb across the fingers (opposition) which makes the hand so suitable for prehension. The remaining four form the skeleton of the palm of the hand. The muscles surrounding the metacarpal of the thumb constitute the **thenar eminence**, those round the metacarpal of the little finger the **hypothenar eminence.**

The Phalanges

Each of the four fingers has three phalanges. The thumb has only two. The terminal phalanges, because they bear the nails, are called the ungual phalanges.

THE SKELETON OF THE LOWER LIMB (Figs. 8, 9, 14 and 15)

The Limb Girdle

The lower limb girdle is in the form of a complete ring, the pelvis, made up of the two hip bones and the sacrum and coccyx. The latter have been described with the vertebral column (p. 15).

The Hip Bone

The hip bone consists of three parts, the ilium, the ischium, and the pubis, which join together in the cup-shaped depression, the **acetabulum,** on the lateral surface. The acetabulum receives the head of the femur in the formation of the hip joint. In children the three parts of the hip bone are separated by a strip of cartilage.

The upper portion of the hip bone, which is expanded into a curved plate, is called the **ilium.** The upper edge of this part is called the *iliac crest,* and it ends anteriorly at the *anterior superior iliac spine,* and posteriorly at the *posterior superior spine.* On the anterior margin of the ilium, just above the acetabulum, is the *anterior inferior spine,* while just below the posterior superior spine is the *posterior inferior spine.* Below the latter the posterior margin turns sharply in to form part of the boundary of the *great sciatic notch.* The deep surface of the posterior part of the ilium articulates with the sacrum.

Below and behind the ilium is the **ischium,** the upper end of which forms part of the acetabulum. The posterior edge of the ischium forms part of the boundary of the great sciatic notch, which is bounded below by a sharp spike, the *ischial spine.* Below this is the shallower *lesser sciatic notch.*

On the lower end and the lower portion of the posterior surface of the ischium is the rough part termed the *tuberosity.* The *ramus* of the ischium is a bar of bone passing forwards from the lower end to meet the pubis in front, and forming, with part of the pubis, the lower boundary of the **obturator foramen,** the large hole just below the acetabulum.

Below and in front of the ilium is the **pubis.** This consists of a *body* which joins its fellow of the opposite side in the *pubic symphysis,* and two *rami,* one passing above the obturator foramen to the acetabulum, and the other below the obturator foramen to join the ramus of the ischium. Projecting from the lateral end of the upper border of the body of the pubis, which is called the *pubic crest,* is the *pubic tubercle.*

The Pelvis (Figs. 8 and 9)

The pelvis, formed by the two hip bones and the sacrum, consists of two parts, the **false pelvis** and the **true pelvis.** The false pelvis is the part above the **brim** and between the alæ or wings of the iliac parts of the hip bones. The **pelvic brim** is formed posteriorly by the upper margin (promontory) of the sacrum ; laterally by a curved line on the ilium and on the superior ramus of the pubis, and in front by the pubic crests and the symphysis. It separates the false pelvis above from the true pelvis below.

The **true pelvis** has a **superior aperture or inlet** bounded by the pelvic brim, and an **inferior aperture or outlet,** the boundary of which is completed on each side by the **sacrotuberous ligament** between the tuberosity of the ischium and the lateral edge of the sacrum. The **pelvic canal** between the inlet and the outlet has to transmit the fœtal head during parturition, and, as the measurements of the inlet give an indication of those of the whole cavity, it is important to know the normal average **diameters** in the female. They are as follows :—

The **antero-posterior** or **conjugate** diameter (from the symphysis pubis to the promontory), about 11 centimetres.

The **transverse** diameter (from the middle of the brim on one side to the same point on the other side), $13\frac{1}{2}$ centimetres.

The **oblique** diameter (from the junction of the ilium and pubis on one side to the sacroiliac joint of the opposite side), $12\frac{1}{2}$ centimetres.

The measurements of the pelvic outlet are :—

Antero-posterior (symphysis to tip of coccyx), 9 to $11\frac{1}{2}$ centimetres.

Transverse (between the two ischial tuberosities in their posterior parts), $11\frac{1}{2}$ centimetres.

In addition to forming the girdle for the two lower limbs, the pelvis forms part of the wall of the abdominal cavity, giving extensive attachments to abdominal muscles and protecting the pelvic viscera. The bone is in close relationship with some of the latter, and they are liable to severe injuries in fractures of this part.

The Free Part of the Lower Limb (Figs. 14 and 15)

The Femur

The femur or thigh-bone consists of a shaft and two extremities.

The **upper extremity** presents the head, the neck, and the greater and lesser trochanters.

The **head** articulates with the acetabulum to form the hip joint. A deep pit is present about its middle for an intra-articular ligament of the joint.

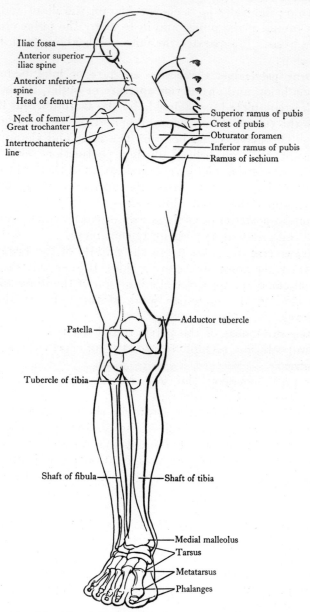

Iliac fossa

Anterior superior
iliac spine

Anterior inferior
spine

Head of femur

Neck of femur
Great trochanter

Intertrochanteric
line

Superior ramus of pubis
Crest of pubis
Obturator foramen
Inferior ramus of pubis
Ramus of ischium

Adductor tubercle

Patella

Tubercle of tibia

Shaft of fibula

Shaft of tibia

Medial malleolus
Tarsus
Metatarsus
Phalanges

FIG. 14.   The skeleton of the lower limb from in front.
Right side.

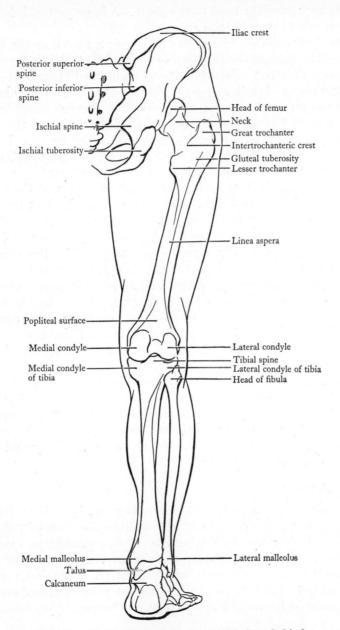

FIG. 15. The skeleton of the lower limb from behind.
Right side.

The neck joins the head to the shaft. A large part of it is inside the capsule of the hip joint.

The Trochanters. The great trochanter is placed on the lateral part of the bone at the junction of the neck and the shaft. There is a deep pit (the trochanteric fossa) on its medial surface. Most of the muscles of the buttock are attached to the great trochanter.

The lesser trochanter is the conical projection found on the posteromedial surface at the junction of the neck and the shaft. It gives attachment to the psoas muscle. The two trochanters are connected on the back of the bone by the **intertrochanteric crest.** The **intertrochanteric line** on the anterior surface actually does not reach the lesser trochanter, but winds round the medial side of the shaft to reach the linea aspera on the back of the bone.

The shaft of the femur is of cylindrical form and gets gradually larger towards the lower end. On its posterior surface in the middle one-third is the rough ridge termed the **linea aspera.** Prolonged upwards from this to the base of the great trochanter is the **gluteal tuberosity,** whilst prolonged downwards are lines running to the condyles at the lower end. These are the supra-condylar ridges, and they enclose between them the **popliteal surface.** The shaft is curved anteriorly and the linea aspera forms a buttress on the concavity, as well as giving attachment to muscles.

The lower end of the femur presents the two **condyles** for articulation with the tibia. The condyles are separated from one another posteriorly by a deep notch, but are joined to one another anteriorly by the **patellar articular surface.** Where the medial supracondylar ridge meets the medial condyle is the prominence called the **adductor tubercle.**

The Patella

The patella, or kneecap, is a sesamoid bone, *i.e.,* a bone formed in a tendon for the purpose of altering the direction of pull of a muscle. It is found in the tendon of the quadriceps extensor muscle of the thigh, and takes part in the formation of the knee joint, articulating posteriorly with the femur. The patella can be felt readily beneath the skin, and with the knee extended and the leg supported it can be moved about on the underlying femur.

The Bones of the Leg

The tibia on the medial side and the fibula on the lateral side form the skeleton of the leg below the knee. The tibia is much the larger, and takes the greater share in the formation of the knee and ankle joints. The fibula takes a small part in the formation of the ankle joint, but does not enter into the knee joint at all, articulating above with the tibia only. Very little movement takes place between the two bones, and in this respect they differ strikingly from the bones of the forearm. The tibia and fibula are connected by the interosseous membrane which increases the area for the attachment of muscles.

The Tibia

The tibia is a long bone with a shaft and two extremities.

The **upper extremity** consists of two condyles and the tubercle.

The **condyles** are for articulation with the corresponding condyles of the femur. The upper surface of the tibia between the condyles presents the **tibial spine** (intercondyloid eminence) which, together with the rough areas in front of and behind it, gives attachment to important structures inside the knee joint.

The **tubercle** of the tibia is the eminence on the anterior surface of the upper extremity. It is the insertion of the great extensor muscles of the thigh through the ligamentum patellæ.

The **shaft** is triangular on section. The prominent anterior border, beginning above at the tuberosity, is called the **shin.** The whole of the medial surface of the tibia is subcutaneous.

The **lower extremity** is slightly expanded. It articulates below with the talus in the ankle joint. Laterally it is joined to the fibula by ligaments. On its medial side is the projection called the **medial malleolus,** which can be felt beneath the skin on the medial side of the ankle.

The Fibula

The fibula forms a slender bony bar alongside the tibia and serves to increase the area available for attachment of muscles.

The **upper extremity or head** articulates with the lateral condyle of the tibia. It has a pointed projection from its upper part called the **styloid process.**

The **shaft** is connected to the tibia by the interosseous membrane.

The **lower extremity** is called the **lateral malleolus,** and can be felt beneath the skin on the lateral side of the ankle. With the tibia it completes the socket for the talus. The tip of the lateral malleolus is a little lower than the tip of the medial malleolus.

The Skeleton of the Foot

The skeleton of the foot comprises the bones of the **tarsus** and **metatarsus** and the **phalanges.** The elements are arranged in a way similar to those of the hand, but in the foot their disposition is modified so that the weight of the body, reaching the foot *viâ* the bones of the leg, is transmitted to the ground through a series of **arches** formed by the foot-bones. The arches are supported by muscles and ligaments and serve two purposes : Firstly, they absorb shocks, their supports being elastic, and, secondly, they leave room for vessels and nerves in the sole and relieve them from the effects of the pressure of the body weight.

The Tarsus. These irregular bones, seven in number, are arranged, like those of the carpus, in two rows, proximal and distal. The bones of the **proximal row** are the **calcaneum** and, resting on the upper surface of this, the **talus.** The talus is directed medially in its anterior part, and its head lies medial to the anterior end of the calcaneum but on a higher level. The **navicular** bone is interposed between this part of the talus and the bones of the **distal row** (**cuneiforms**) on the medial side of the foot, whereas the calcaneum articulates directly with the **cuboid** of the distal row on the lateral side. The talus being above the calcaneum, this makes the inner border of the foot considerably higher than the outer border.

Proximal Row

The calcaneum is the largest of the tarsal bones. It is below the talus and its posterior part (the " heel-bone "), which projects backwards beyond the plane of the ankle joint, forms the posterior pillar of the longitudinal arch of the foot and transmits the body weight to the ground.

The talus has a body which enters into the ankle joint, fitting into the socket formed by the tibia and the two malleoli. Anterior to the body are the neck and head. Inferiorly the talus articulates with the calcaneum, whilst the head articulates anteriorly with the navicular bone.

Intermediate

The *navicular* articulates posteriorly with the talus and anteriorly with the three cuneiforms. The *tuberosity* of the navicular projects on the medial side of the foot and can be felt just beneath the upper border of the ordinary shoe.

The Distal Row

The *cuneiform bones* are wedge-shaped and join the navicular behind to the three medial metatarsals in front. They are named the *medial* (first), the *intermediate* (second), and the *lateral* (third).

The cuboid articulates behind with the calcaneum and in front with the two lateral metatarsal bones.

Fractures

A fracture is the solution of continuity of a bone. The bone may be healthy at the time, or may be the seat of some disease which predisposes to fracture (pathological fracture). If the bone be near the skin one or other fragment may perforate to the surface (compound fracture). The risk lies here in infection, which may follow. Compound fracture may be caused also by violence from outside, such as occurs in gunshot wounds, etc. It is especially dangerous in the skull, where infection of the brain may follow. Other complications of fracture include damage to nearby vessels, nerves, and viscera, the latter being fairly common in the thorax and pelvis.

Union of fractures takes place in a time which varies according to the size and type of the bone broken. In all cases the blood poured out at the original injury clots, and the clot later becomes infiltrated with calcium salts and finally converted into true bone by the osteoblasts (see p. 11) in the vicinity. The preliminary scaffolding formed by organisation of the blood clot is called " callus." It is not capable of bearing weight or other strain, so that until the final bone has formed and consolidated the part must be supported by splints or other means. Splints and extension are used in the early stages to prevent deformity resulting from the pull of muscles or the action of gravity on the broken bone. During the treatment of a fracture the muscles of the part must receive careful attention, otherwise the prolonged immobilisation may result in permanent impairment of function.

CHAPTER III

THE JOINTS OR ARTICULATIONS

JOINTS are found in the body in the situations where bones come together. Long bones usually articulate with one another at their expanded extremities, flat bones, such as those of the skull, by their edges.

Where no movement is required bones are united by fibrous tissue. Where slight movement is required pads of fibrocartilage are generally found uniting the bones. Where free movement is necessary the connection between the bones must be looser, and provision must be made for the bones to glide on one another. Such joints possess in the synovial membrane a mechanism for lubrication and have a definite joint cavity.

Joints can accordingly be classified as fibrous joints, cartilaginous joints, and synovial joints.

Fibrous Joints

These are seen where movement of the bones on one another is not wanted. A scheme is shown in Fig. 16. It will be noted that the bones are connected by fibrous tissue which blends with the periosteum. There are three varieties of fibrous joints : **sutures,** seen only in the skull where the bones meet at their edges ; peg-joints (gomphoses), as seen in the **tooth-sockets** ; and the type seen only in the inferior joint between the tibia and fibula, where the bones are connected by an **interosseous ligament.**

Cartilaginous Joints

These are of two types, primary and secondary.

Primary cartilaginous joints are found in young people between the diaphyses and epiphyses of bones (p. 11). They are temporary in character, the intervening hyaline cartilage undergoing ossification as age advances.

Secondary Cartilaginous Joints (Fig. 16 C). Here the bones, the **ends** of which are **covered by articular cartilage,** are **connected by** an intervening **pad of fibrocartilage** and by **ligaments** on the surface. The joints between the vertebral bodies, and that between the

44

two pubic bones, are examples. Slight movement is permitted in secondary cartilaginous joints.

Synovial Joints

These joints (Figs. 16, D and E) are modified so as to allow a considerable degree of movement. The **ends** of the bones, which have to glide on one another, are **covered with articular cartilage.** The bones are **connected by** a sleeve of fibrous tissue called the **capsular ligament,** which must be sufficiently lax to allow the degree of movement necessary at the joint. To prevent friction due to the rubbing together of the surfaces a fluid, called synovial fluid, is secreted into the joint by the **synovial membrane.** The latter covers everything in the joint not covered by articular cartilage. It lines the deep surface of the capsular ligament and is reflected from this on to the non-articular bone. It will cover also any intra-articular structures such as tendons, pads of fat, ligaments, or fibrocartilaginous discs. The joint cavity contains the fluid poured out by the synovial membrane. Synovial joints, whilst allowing considerable movement, must be sufficiently stable to prevent dislocation of the two bones during movements. Such **stability** may depend on a variety of factors :—

Adaption of Bony Surfaces. The hip is a good example of such a joint. It is of the type known as ball-and-socket, the rounded head of the femur fitting so accurately into the cup-shaped acetabulum that, so long as the capsule be intact, it is impossible for the bones to separate.

Strength of the Capsular Ligament. Many joints have very strong capsules which permit of movement within safe limits.

Strengthening Bands (Ligaments) in the Capsular Ligament or in Association with it. Such bands are so placed as to prevent displacement whilst allowing the necessary movement to take place freely. For example, they are found at the sides of a hinge type of joint.

Muscles Surrounding the Joint. Most freely movable joints are surrounded by the muscles which produce the movements. These, being in immediate contact or blended with the capsule, materially strengthen the joint. The patellar ligament of the knee joint and the muscles round the shoulder are examples.

Intra-articular Ligaments. When strengthening bands in the capsule at the periphery of the joint would limit or prevent movement, dislocation is prevented by ligaments near the centre of the joint. The cruciate ligaments of the knee are examples.

Intra-articular Tendons. By their disposition, tendons which traverse the joint may contribute to stability. The long head of the biceps in the shoulder acts in this way.

Fibrocartilages. Intra-articular fibrocartilage may be found forming the rim of joint sockets so as to make them deeper, as, for instance, the glenoid labra of the hip and shoulder, or they may be in the form of **intra-articular discs.** Such discs may divide the joint cavity completely, as in the sternoclavicular and temporomandibular joints. They may, on the other hand, be incomplete, as, for example, the semilunar cartilages of the knee joint. Discs coapt bony surfaces which would not otherwise fit well, for instance, the flat upper surfaces of the tibial condyles and the rounded condyles of the femur in the knee joint. They also act as shock absorbers, and minimise the amount of synovial fluid necessary for lubrication.

Intra-articular Structures. In addition to ligaments, tendons and fibrocartilages described above, pads of fat may be found in joints. They fill up space and so economise synovial fluid. The pads in the elbow joint and the infrapatellar pad in the knee joint are examples.

As a general rule all these intra-articular structures are covered with synovial membrane, which excludes them from the joint cavity proper.

Classification of Synovial Joints. Synovial joints may be classified according to the movement which takes place in them :—

Gliding Joints. In these the movement takes place in one plane. Examples are found in the joints of the carpus, tarsus, and of the articular processes of the vertebræ.

Hinge Joints. In these the movement takes place round one axis. The elbow and ankle are examples.

Pivot Joints. Here again the movement is round one axis. The radio-ulnar joints are examples.

Condyloid and Saddle Joints. In these, movement takes place round two axes.

Ball-and-socket Joints. Here the movement is round three axes. The hip and shoulder are examples. The movement in these joints is greater than in any other type.

Movements

The following terms used in connection with movements may need some explanation :—

Flexion. In the head, vertebral column, hip, shoulder, elbow, wrist and fingers this implies a bending of the part towards the front of the body. In the knee it means bending the limb. In the ankle " plantar flexion " means movement towards the sole ; "dorsiflexion" means bending the foot towards the front of the leg. In the toes flexion implies bending towards the sole of the foot.

Extension. This is the opposite movement to flexion.

Abduction. Abduction is movement away from the median plane except in the case of the digits of the hand and foot where it implies movement away from the middle finger or second toe.

Adduction. Adduction is the opposite to abduction.

Rotation. Rotation is movement round the long axis of the part concerned, and the term is applied to the humerus and femur at the shoulder and hip and to the vertebral column.

Circumduction. This is a combination of all the above movements.

Inversion. This movement occurs in the foot. The sole is turned inwards and at the same time the anterior part of the foot is bent medially.

Eversion. This is the opposite movement to inversion.

The Joints Classified According to Type

Fibrous Joints
Sutures of the skull.
Sockets of teeth.
Inferior tibiofibular joint.

Secondary Cartilaginous Joints
Bodies of the vertebræ.
Symphysis pubis.
Manubrium and body of the sternum (usually).

Primary Cartilaginous Joints
Costal cartilages with the ribs.
First costal cartilage with the sternum.

Synovial Joints
Gliding
Articular processes of the vertebræ.
Carpus, tarsus, metacarpus and metatarsus.

Acromioclavicular.
Upper end of fibula with the tibia.
Sternoclavicular.
Heads and tubercles of the ribs with the vertebræ.
Costal cartilages (except first) with the sternum.
Sacroiliac joint.

Hinge
Elbow.
Knee.
Ankle.
Interphalangeal joints of fingers and toes.

Pivot
Atlas and dens of the axis.
Joints between the radius and the ulna.

Condyloid
Temporomandibular.
Atlas and the base of the skull.
Wrist.
Metacarpophalangeal and metatarsophalangeal.

Ball-and-socket
Hip.
Shoulder.

Ligaments
Ligaments are generally composed of inelastic white fibrous tissue arranged in parallel bundles. A few contain a proportion of elastic tissue.

Bursæ
Where muscles surround joints, or where bony points are subjected to pressure, sacs, of a structure similar to that of synovial membrane, are provided to prevent friction between the parts. In many cases the bursæ communicate with the synovial cavity of the neighbouring joint, but in others they are entirely separate. Synovial sheaths of tendons are similar structures (p. 78).

THE MAIN JOINTS IN THE UPPER AND LOWER LIMBS
THE UPPER LIMB
The Shoulder Joint
This is a synovial joint of the ball-and-socket type.

The Bones

The bones are the **glenoid cavity** of the scapula and the **head of the humerus.** The former is deepened slightly by the **glenoid labrum** attached round its rim.

The Capsular Ligament

The capsular ligament is fairly lax to allow of the free movement which takes place and the joint depends for its stability largely on the muscles which cross and are attached to the capsular ligament.

Intra-articular Structure

The tendon of origin of the long head of the biceps muscle of the arm arises within the joint and, traversing its cavity, leaves through an opening in the capsule to pass into the bicipital groove between the tuberosities of the humerus. It steadies the head of the humerus against the glenoid fossa.

The Synovial Membrane

The synovial membrane covers the glenoid labrum, the deep surface of the capsular ligament, and is reflected as a tubular sheath along the tendon of the biceps.

Movements

Being a ball-and-socket joint, movement is very free. The following are possible : Flexion and extension ; abduction and adduction ; medial and lateral rotation of the humerus ; and circumduction. These movements take place relative to the plane of the scapula and not the trunk. As the scapula lies against the ribs so that the glenoid cavity faces forwards as well as laterally, abduction is a movement of the arm forwards and laterally ; flexion brings the arm forwards and across the trunk. Movement of the arm above the head is a combination of movement at the shoulder joint and rotation of the scapula on the chest wall.

The Elbow Joint (Fig. 17, A)

This joint is really two joints enclosed in the same capsule and having a common joint cavity. They are the superior radio-ulnar joint at which rotation of the radius takes place in the movements of pronation and supination, and the joint between the humerus on the one hand and the radius and the ulna on the other. At this latter joint the movements of flexion and extension of the forearm take place.

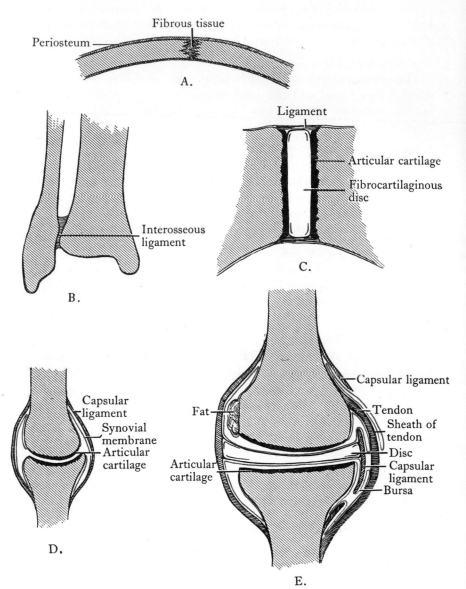

Fig. 16.   Scheme of the types of joints.   Fibrous joints : A, suture ;
B, inferior tibio fibular ; C, secondary cartilaginous joint (symphysis
pubis) ; D and E, synovial joints.

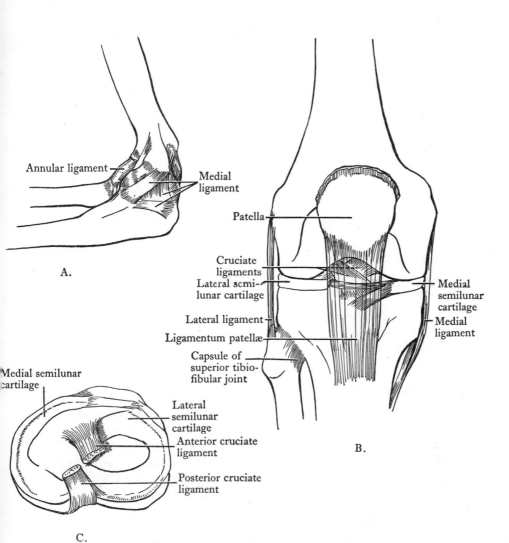

Annular ligament

Medial ligament

A.

Patella

Cruciate ligaments

Lateral semi-lunar cartilage

Lateral ligament

Ligamentum patellæ

Capsule of superior tibio-fibular joint

Medial semilunar cartilage

Medial ligament

B.

Medial semilunar cartilage

Lateral semilunar cartilage

Anterior cruciate ligament

Posterior cruciate ligament

C.

FIG. 17.   A, Right elbow joint (medial side); B, right knee joint; C, intra-articular structures of right knee viewed from above.

4*

The Superior Radio-ulnar Joint

The margin of the head of the **radius** articulates **with the radial notch** on the lateral side of the coronoid process of the ulna. It is held in position by the **annular or ring-like ligament.**

The Humero-radio-ulnar Joint

The Bones

The bones are the **trochlea** of the humerus with the **trochlear notch** formed by the coronoid and olecranon processes of the ulna, and the upper cupped surface of the **head of the radius** with the **capitulum** of the humerus.

The Capsular Ligament

The capsular ligament is strengthened by anterior, posterior medial and lateral bands. The **medial band** (ulnar collateral) is triangular, while the **lateral band** (radial collateral) is a flattened ligament attached below to the annular ligament.

Intra-articular Structures

Pads of fat are present in the radial, coronoid and olecranon fossæ of the humerus.

Synovial Membrane

The membrane covers the non-articular bone in the joint, the deep surface of the capsular ligament, and the intra-articular pads of fat.

The Inferior Radio-ulnar Joint

The two bones are connected by a **triangular fibrocartilaginous disc,** attached to the root of the styloid process of the ulna on the one hand, and to the lower end of the radius on the other. This disc separates the ulna from the wrist joint. The capsular ligament of the inferior radio-ulnar joint is deficient above and the synovial membrane bulges a little here.

The Interosseous Membrane

This connects the shafts of the radius and ulna. Its fibres are directed upwards and laterally to the radius, and they are put into tension when force is transmitted to the radius from the hand.

Pronation and Supination

In the position of supination, *i.e.,* with the palm of the hand directed forwards, the radius and ulna are parallel. In pronation of the hand, the radius rotates round an axis passing through its own head above and through the head of the ulna below. This rotation of the radius brings it across the ulna. Further rotation of the whole arm at the shoulder joint will bring the limb into a position with the back of the hand pointing towards the thigh.

THE LOWER LIMB

The Hip Joint

This is a synovial joint of the ball-and-socket type.

Bones

The **head of the femur** and the **acetabulum** of the hip-bone form the joint. The acetabular surface is horse-shoe shaped and encloses the non-articular part of the acetabulum, the acetabular fossa. The acetabulum is deepened by a glenoid labrum.

Capsular Ligament

The ligament is attached to the hip-bone just beyond the rim of the acetabulum. Distally it includes the whole of the femoral neck in front, but behind only the proximal part of the neck is included, about half an inch being extracapsular.

Thickenings in the Capsule (ligaments)

There are several of these, but only one is of great importance, the **iliofemoral or Y-shaped ligament.** This is found in front of the joint, and is extremely strong. When standing upright, the body weight falls along a line behind the hip joint so that there is a tendency for this to become over-extended. This is prevented by the strong ligament in front, which helps the muscles to maintain the erect posture without undue fatigue.

Intra-articular Structures

The **ligament of the head of the femur** (ligamentum teres) extends from the extremities of the acetabular notch and from the transverse ligament which bridges the notch to the fovea or pit on the head of the femur. Its function is not known. In the acetabular fossa is a **pad of fat.**

The Synovial Membrane

The synovial membrane covers the deep surface of the capsular ligament, from which it is reflected to cover the neck of the femur.

4**

It also covers the fat in the acetabular fossa and forms a sheath for the ligament of the head of the femur.

Movements

Being a ball-and-socket joint, the hip joint is capable of flexion, extension, abduction, adduction, circumduction and rotation.

The Knee Joint (Figs. 17, B and C)

This is a synovial joint of a condyloid type.

The Bones

The bones are the **condyles of the femur,** the **condyles of the tibia,** and the **patella.**

The Capsular Ligament

The capsular ligament is formed largely by expansions from the surrounding muscles.

Structures Strengthening the Capsule

In front of the joint, attached above to the patella and below to the tuberosity of the tibia, is the **patellar ligament.** This is really the tendon of insertion of the great quadriceps muscle of the thigh. At the sides the capsular ligament is strengthened by the **medial and lateral ligaments,** these prevent displacement of the bones from side to side.

Intra-articular Structures

To prevent the femur from sliding forwards or backwards off the upper surface of the tibia the **cruciate ligaments,** so named because they cross one another, bind the two bones together inside the joint. The stability of the knee depends very largely on these ligaments. To give better adaption of the joint surfaces, and to absorb shocks, partial intra-articular discs are found separating the femur and tibia. They are called, on account of their shape, the **semilunar cartilages.** Occupying a large part of the space in the anterior part of the joint is a **pad of fat** situated just behind the patellar ligament.

The Synovial Membrane

The deep surface of most of the capsule, both upper and lower surfaces of the menisci, and the infrapatellar pad of fat are covered by the membrane. The cruciate ligaments are covered in front and at the sides.

Bursæ Round the Knee

Several of these structures are found in this locality. Those of most importance are :—

1. Communicating with the joint. Under the quadriceps extensor muscle and under the semimembranosus muscle, the former in front of, and the latter behind, the joint.

2. Not communicating with the joint. The prepatellar bursa. This is between the skin and the front of the patella. When inflamed it forms an obvious swelling in this region, the condition being termed " housemaid's knee."

Movements

Flexion and extension of the leg take place at the joint.

Ankle Joint

This is a synovial joint of the hinge type.

Bones

The body of the **talus** fits into a socket formed by the inferior surface of the **tibia and the two malleoli.** It will be remembered that the medial malleolus is part of the tibia and the lateral malleolus is formed by the fibula.

The Capsular Ligament

The capsular ligament is somewhat thin, but is strengthened by strong **medial and lateral ligaments.** The medial is called the deltoid ligament on account of its triangular form. The lateral ligament has three bands. The anterior and posterior bands pass from the lateral malleolus to the talus, the intermediate band is attached to the malleolus above and to the lateral surface of the calcaneum below.

The Synovial Membrane

The synovial membrane covers the deep surface of the capsular ligament.

Movements

Movements of the ankle are " plantar flexion " or bending towards the sole of the foot, and " dorsiflexion " or bending towards the front of the leg.

Joints of the Axial Skeleton

The Vertebral Column. The bodies of the vertebræ are attached to one another by the **intervertebral discs** of fibrocartilage. These act also as shock absorbers. Ligaments running down the anterior and posterior surfaces of the bodies strengthen the union. The **articular processes** are united by synovial joints.

The **atlas and axis.** The atlas is held in place on the dens of the axis by the **transverse ligament.** Rotation of the head can take place here.

The Ribs. The ribs form synovial joints with the bodies and transverse processes of the vertebræ at their heads and tubercles respectively. Anteriorly, the ribs blend with the costal cartilages, which, in the case of the true ribs, form synovial joints with the margin of the sternum, except in the case of the first rib, where the union is cartilaginous.

The Skull with the Vertebral Column

There are synovial joints between the atlas and the condyles of the occipital bone. Here nodding movements of the head take place.

The Lower Jaw with the Skull

The head of the mandible forms a synovial joint with the articular fossa on the temporal bone. An articular disc divides the joint completely.

In opening the mouth the condyle passes forwards on to the anterior margin of the articular surface and may slip over in excessive yawning, etc. (Reduction is effected by pressing downwards and backwards against the molar teeth.) In chewing, the heads of the two sides move forwards alternately.

Dislocations. Occasionally bones become displaced on one another and a dislocation results.

In traumatic dislocation the capsule is torn and the dislocated bone passes through the rent into the tissues round the joint. This condition is particularly likely to occur with sudden movements when the surrounding muscles are taken " off their guard."

Reduction of the dislocation is usually procured by reversing the movement which caused it, thus making the displaced bone pass back through the rent in the capsule.

Pathological dislocation is due to destruction of the bony surfaces or of the ligaments by disease.

CHAPTER IV

MUSCLES AND FASCIÆ

It has been stated in an earlier chapter (p. 5) that muscular tissue is of three kinds, namely, striped or voluntary ; unstriped or plain, which is involuntary ; and cardiac, which is striped, but at the same time involuntary. In the present section it is proposed to deal with the voluntary muscles and further reference to the other types will be made in the appropriate chapters.

The skeletal muscles are all of the voluntary type, although some of them, such as those used in breathing, are used automatically without an effort of will. Even the latter type are, however, under the control of the will, as we can breathe in or out, or hold our breath if we wish, although we do not ordinarily think at all in the acts of breathing. The muscles make up a considerable part of the body weight and, as will be seen later, the tissue is of great importance in many of the metabolic processes of the body.

Structure, Form and Attachments of Muscles

A muscle consists of bundles of muscle **fibres,** which are elongated cells, each capable, when the appropriate stimulus is applied, of shortening or contracting. Each individual fibre is surrounded by a connective tissue sheath called the **sarcolemma,** whilst fibres are bound together into bundles or fasciculi by fibrous tissue called the **perimysium.** Finally the bundles are bound together to form the whole muscle by the fibrous tissue sheath termed the **epimysium.** At the extremities of the muscle the fibrous tissue of the epi- and perimysium blends with the parallel bundles of white fibres which form the **tendons** by which the muscle is attached to the bones. The amount of tendon may be extremely small, when the attachment is termed " fleshy," but it is always present between the muscle fibres and the actual bone. At the attachment of the tendon the fibrous tissue of its bundles blends with that of the periosteum, the latter being bound down firmly by the perforating fibres which penetrate the superficial lamellæ of the bone.

The muscles vary greatly in form according to the function which they have to perform. In many the fleshy part formed by the fibres is fusiform in shape and is called the **belly** of the muscle. In some situations, such as the abdominal and thoracic walls, the fibres are arranged in flat sheets, and in such cases the tendons are flattened also and are called **aponeuroses.**

Tendons

These are formed of closely packed bundles of white fibres running parallel with one another and with a very small amount of areolar tissue separating them. They vary greatly in form in various muscles, some being rounded and thick, others flat and thin.

As stated above, tendons are present to increase the security of attachment of muscles to bones. The attachments are always tendinous, although this may not be obvious to the unaided eye. Tendons are also found where a muscle changes its direction and where muscles cross joints. If tendons were not formed in the neighbourhood of joints the latter would be very much hampered in their movements by bulky masses of muscle round about them.

Origin and Insertion of Muscles

The attachment of a muscle which is usually stationary during the action of the muscle is called the origin. The attachment which moves is the insertion. Where the amount of movement of the insertion towards the origin is small relative to the total length of the muscle, the muscle belly is short and the tendon is long. Where the movement is very great relative to the length of the muscle very little tendon is present and the muscle consists almost entirely of fibres.

Grouping of Muscles

Muscles are usually found acting together in groups for the production of certain movements. To retain them in position and prevent them getting out of place by their movement during active contraction, they are held together by fascia.

Fasciæ

The fasciæ are membranous sheets which, throughout the body, invest the more delicate and specialised structures such as organs, muscles and blood-vessels. They vary in thickness, density and structure, and in many situations form considerable

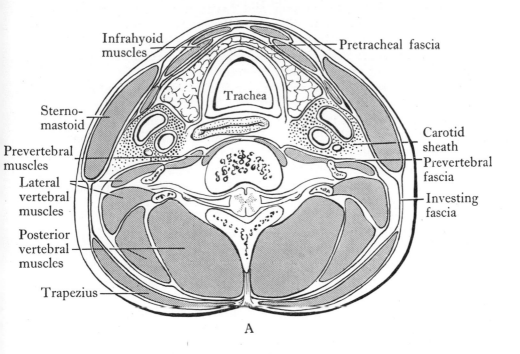

Infrahyoid muscles

Pretracheal fascia

Trachea

Sterno-mastoid

Carotid sheath

Prevertebral muscles

Prevertebral fascia

Lateral vertebral muscles

Investing fascia

Posterior vertebral muscles

Trapezius

A

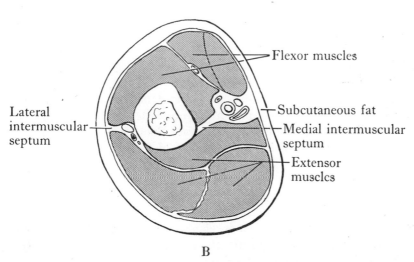

Flexor muscles

Lateral intermuscular septum

Subcutaneous fat

Medial intermuscular septum

Extensor muscles

B

FIG. 18. Section of Neck and Arm.

masses filling spaces round and between muscles and organs. The fasciæ render it possible for adjacent structures in the body to move freely relative to one another, with a minimum of friction, and, in some situations, are specially adapted to prevent displacement of muscles and the like.

There are two main varieties of fascia, the superficial and the deep.

The superficial fascia is found over the entire surface of the body immediately beneath the skin. In most situations it contains a considerable quantity of fat, varying in amount with the nutrition of the individual. In it are found the blood-vessels, lymphatics, and nerves of the skin, and in the face, neck, and perineum it contains muscles which are attached to the skin.

The subcutaneous tissue forms one of the main " fat depots " of the body, and, by virtue of this fat, which is a poor conductor, plays a considerable part in retaining the body heat. It also allows free movement of the skin and deeper structures on one another.

The deep fascia is a dense, tough layer deep to the superficial fascia. It forms an investment for the muscles, retaining them in place and preventing them from becoming interlocked during complicated movements. In many situations it gives off sheets, which, passing in to the underlying bone between adjacent groups of muscles, allow the latter to act independent of one another and retain the groups in position. These sheets are called **intermuscular septa.** The deep surface of the deep fascia and the surfaces of the intermuscular septa often serve also for the attachment of some of the fibres of the muscles which they invest (Fig. 18, B).

Fascia, of varying degrees of density, is found, in the form of plugs, filling all spaces in the body, and (as, for example, that round the kidneys) it may play an important part in maintaining the position of and protecting viscera. Such fascial " packing " usually contains a considerable amount of fat.

Muscle Groups

The skeletal muscles can be divided into those of the neck, head, and spinal column, those of the abdomen and thorax, and those of the limbs. In each situation there is sub-grouping of the muscles according to their action and nerve supply, individual groups being separated from others by intermuscular septa.

MUSCLES AND FASCIA OF THE NECK

If a transverse section of the neck be examined (Fig. 18, A) it will be seen that the **cervical vertebral column** forms the foundation of this part. Grouped round it are muscles which can be divided into those **behind the column,** those **lateral to the column,** and those **in front of the column.** The column and these muscles are enclosed by fascia which is called the **prevertebral layer of the deep cervical fascia.**

In the median plane, in front of the osteomuscular column enclosed by the prevertebral fascia, are the viscera of the neck : comprising in the upper part the larynx in front and the pharynx behind ; and in the lower part the trachea in front and the œsophagus behind. In front and at each side of the trachea is the thyroid gland. There is a cleft or groove all the way up the side of the neck, between the viscera medially and the osteomuscular column behind, and in this cleft lie the large blood-vessels of the neck, the carotid arteries and the internal jugular vein. As is usual where vessels lie in clefts among muscles, these are embedded in a mass or plug of fascia, which is called the **carotid sheath.** Stretching from the carotid sheath of one side to that of the opposite side, across the front of the trachea, is the **pretracheal layer** of the deep cervical fascia. This forms a sheath for the thyroid gland.

More superficially, are found the **muscles which,** crossing the deeper structures, **divide the surface of the neck into triangles.** These muscles are the *sternomastoid*, the *trapezius* and a group of smaller ribbon-like muscles associated with the jaw, the hyoid bone, and the thyroid cartilage. The superficial muscles are held in place and ensheathed by the **investing layer** of the deep cervical fascia, which encloses the whole neck from the ligamentum nuchæ behind, to the median plane in front, and from the jaw and the base of the skull above, to the sternum, clavicle, and scapula below. The triangles bounded by these muscles have in their floor the deeper structures of the neck, but it should be noted that the more important vessels are in the vascular cleft which is roofed in by the sternomastoid muscle.

Triangles of the Neck

The *sternomastoid* and *trapezius* muscles crossing the surface of the deeper structures divide the neck into two main triangles. In front of the sternomastoid is the **anterior triangle,** the other two boundaries of which are the jaw above and the median plane of the neck in front (Fig. 19). The anterior triangle is subdivided by the *digastric* and *omohyoid* muscles into the following parts : Submental (below the chin) ; submandibular or submaxillary (below the jaw) ; carotid (between the digastric and omohyoid) ; and muscular (below the omohyoid).

Behind the sternomastoid is the **posterior triangle,** the other two boundaries of which are the trapezius and the clavicle. It is subdivided by the omohyoid muscle into upper and lower parts.

These triangles form useful landmarks in the neck for the localisation of deeper structures.

The trapezius and sternomastoid are supplied by the **accessory** (eleventh cranial) and the **cervical nerves.**

Practical Considerations

The sternomastoid especially, and often other neck muscles, may be the subject of disease or spasm giving rise to the condition of *torticollis* or *wry-neck*. A similar condition may result from irritation of the muscles by inflamed glands, etc., in the neighbourhood.

The fascial planes in the neck are of great importance in determining the spread of infections of this part. An inflammatory process affecting the space between the investing and pretracheal layers will often spread right down into the thorax, where it becomes inaccessible for treatment.

MUSCLES OF THE HEAD

1. Muscles of Facial Expression (Fig. 19).

The muscles composing this group are peculiar in that they are superficial to the deep fascia and are attached to the skin. It is by the movement of the skin that they produce the facial expressions.

On the face they are grouped particularly **round the eye** (*orbicularis oculi*) and **round the mouth** (*orbicularis oris*). One of them, the *buccinator*, forms the muscular substance of the **cheek** and a large part of the **lips.** Also included in this group are the muscles of the **scalp** with the epicranial aponeurosis to which they are attached, the muscles of the **external ear,** and the **platysma** muscle of the neck.

All the muscles of facial expression receive their nerve supply from the **facial (seventh cranial) nerve.**

2. Muscles of the Orbit

These muscles move the eye and raise the upper eyelid.

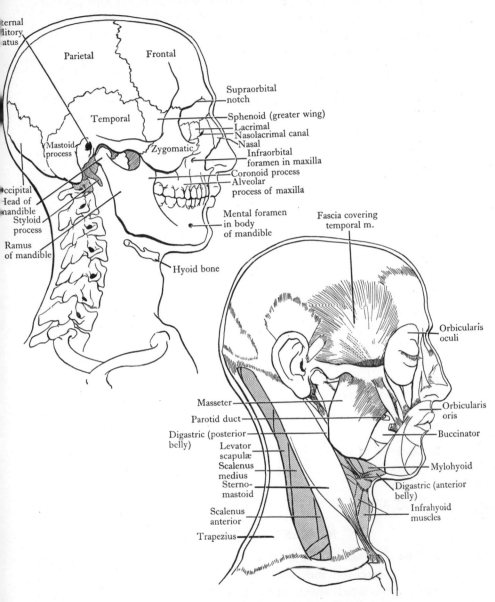

Fig. 19. Muscles of Right Side of Head and Neck. The shaded areas indicate the extent of the anterior and posterior triangles.

Those which move the eye upwards (*superior rectus* and *inferior oblique*), downwards (*inferior rectus*), and inwards (*medial rectus*), and raise the upper lid (*levator palpebræ*) are supplied by the **oculomotor (third cranial) nerve.** The *lateral rectus*, which moves the eye outwards, is supplied by the **abducent (sixth cranial) nerve.** The *superior oblique* muscle, which balances the action of the inferior rectus, is supplied by the **trochlear (fourth cranial) nerve.**

3. Muscles of Mastication (Fig. 19).

The muscles of this group produce the various movements of the jaw in biting and chewing. The side-to-side movements for grinding the food are produced by the muscles of one side acting alternately with those of the other side. The *temporal* muscle, the *masseter* muscle, the *pterygoid* muscles, and the *mylohyoid* muscle, which forms the floor of the mouth, belong to this group.

All the muscles of mastication are supplied by the **mandibular division of the trigeminal (fifth cranial) nerve.**

4. Muscles of the Tongue

There are two groups, extrinsic and intrinsic.

The *extrinsic muscles* have one attachment outside the tongue, and move the tongue as a whole. The *intrinsic muscles* are entirely within the tongue itself, and produce the alterations in shape which result in protrusion and withdrawal of the tongue, and many of the speech movements. All the muscles, intrinsic and extrinsic, are supplied by the **hypoglossal (twelfth cranial) nerve.**

5. Muscles of the Larynx, Pharynx and Palate

These will be discussed with the alimentary and respiratory systems

They are nearly all supplied by the **vagus (tenth cranial) nerve.**

MUSCLES OF THE THORAX

1. The Thoracic Wall (Fig. 22).

The **intercostal muscles** fill the spaces between the ribs. In each intercostal space they form two sheets. The external intercostal muscle, more superficially, consists of fibres running downwards and forwards. The internal intercostal muscle is deep to the external, and its fibres are at right angles to those of the external intercostal.

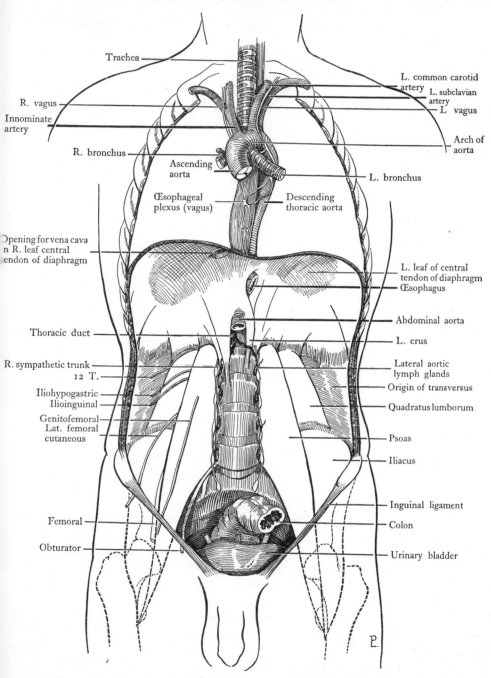

Trachea

L. common carotid artery

L. subclavian artery

L vagus

R. vagus

Innominate artery

Arch of aorta

R. bronchus

Ascending aorta

L. bronchus

Œsophageal plexus (vagus)

Descending thoracic aorta

Opening for vena cava in R. leaf central tendon of diaphragm

L. leaf of central tendon of diaphragm

Œsophagus

Abdominal aorta

Thoracic duct

L. crus

R. sympathetic trunk

12 T.

Lateral aortic lymph glands

Origin of transversus

Iliohypogastric Ilioinguinal

Quadratus lumborum

Genitofemoral Lat. femoral cutaneous

Psoas

Iliacus

Inguinal ligament

Femoral

Colon

Obturator

Urinary bladder

FIG. 20.   Muscles of the Posterior Abdominal Wall.

Deep to the sternum and costal cartilages is the **sternocostalis** (**transversus thoracis**).

These muscles are supplied by the **intercostal nerves.**

2. The Diaphragm (Fig. 20).

This forms the division between the thoracic and abdominal cavities, and is the principal muscle of respiration. It arises by two **crura** from the bodies of the upper lumbar vertebræ, by **digitations** from the deep surfaces of the lower six ribs and costal cartilages, and by two slips from the back of the xiphoid process. The fibres are inserted into a **central tendon** shaped like a clover leaf.

Between the arch formed by the two crura in front, and the lumbar vertebræ behind is the opening transmitting the *aorta* from the thorax to the abdomen. Alongside the aorta in this opening the *thoracic duct* (p. 183) and the *azygos vein* (p. 179) are entering the thorax from the abdomen. The opening allowing the passage of the *inferior vena cava* from the abdomen into the thorax is in the right part of the central tendon, so that the vein is not compressed when the diaphragm contracts.

The *œsophageal opening* is in the muscle just behind the left part of the central tendon.

The other openings in the diaphragm are smaller and less important.

The diaphragm is supplied by the **phrenic nerve.**

Movements of Respiration

Inspiration. The diaphragm, by its contraction, first pushes downwards the abdominal viscera. This descent of the diaphragm can take place to the extent of about 2 inches, when further movement is prevented by the viscera pressing against the anterior abdominal wall. The diaphragm then takes the central tendon as its fixed attachment and further shortening of its fibres pulls up the lower ribs and sternum. As the ribs are oblique, raising their anterior ends also carries the sternum forwards. In these actions the diaphragm is assisted by the intercostal muscles, and, in forced inspiration, by other muscles called the **accessory muscles of respiration.** By the movements of the diaphragm ribs and sternum the vertical, anteroposterior and lateral measurements of the thoracic cavity are increased. The extra space within the thorax is filled by air rushing into the lungs along the trachea, and by blood entering the heart from the great veins.

Expiration. Expiration is due largely to the elastic recoil of the chest wall. Contraction of the anterior abdominal muscles

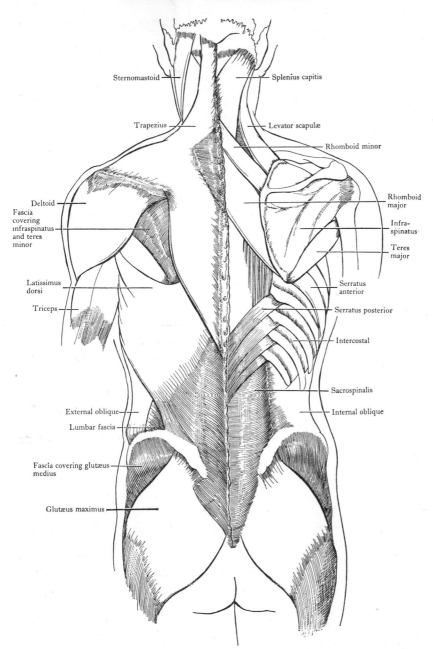

FIG. 21. Muscles of the Back.

pushes the viscera up against the diaphragm and raises it into its expiratory position.

Artificial Respiration. In cases of respiratory failure two methods are used to attempt restoration of breathing.

The **Sylvester** method aims at reproducing the movement of inspiration by raising the arms above the head. This pulls on the muscles passing between the ribs and sternum and the humerus (pectoralis major, etc.), and so lifts the ribs. Expiration is produced by bringing the arms to the side and compressing the thorax by pressure against them.

In the **Schafer** method the subject lies on the face. Forced expiration is produced by pressure against the lower ribs and small of the back, and inspiration depends on the elastic recoil of the thorax.

MUSCLES OF THE SPINAL COLUMN

Reference has been made to the muscles grouped round the cervical part of the vertebral column. Those behind the column belong to a group found the whole length of the spine in this situation. The muscles of the group are known collectively as the **erector spinæ** or **sacrospinalis** (Fig. 21), as they all bend the spine backwards. Some of the muscles of this group also produce rotation of the spine and lateral flexion. The muscle mass fills the groove between the spines and transverse processes of the vertebræ so that only the tips of the spinous processes project on the surface (Figs. 18, A, and 21).

The erector spinæ is supplied by the **posterior primary divisions of the spinal nerves.**

Movements of the Spine

The spine is capable of flexion (bending forwards), extension (bending backwards), lateral flexion (bending to the side) and rotation. The movement between individual vertebræ is small, but, when all the individual movements are added together, the movement in the column as a whole is considerable. Movements are most free in the cervical and lumbar regions, being somewhat hampered by the presence of the ribs in the thoracic part of the column.

Practical Considerations
Curvatures of the Spine

The normal curvatures (p. 17) may be altered either by injury to or disease of the bones and joints, or by weakness or spasm of the muscles moving the spine.

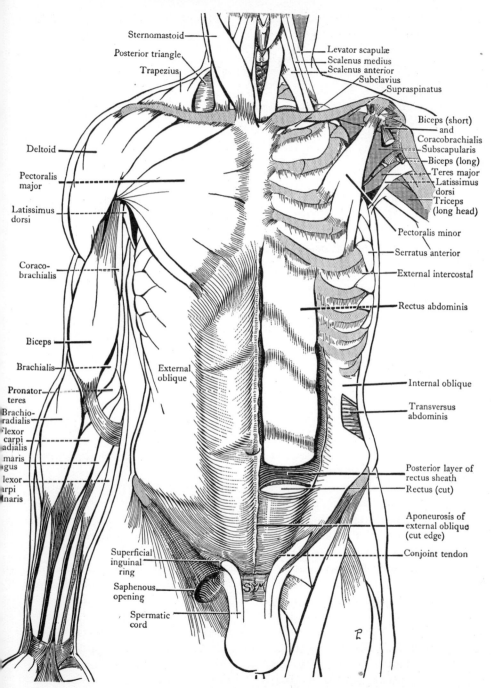

Fig. 22. Muscles of the Front of the Trunk, Neck and Upper Limb.

Injury or disease destroying the bodies of the vertebræ in a limited area, if untreated, usually results in a sharp curvature. Tuberculous disease of the spine is an example. Postural deformities due to weakness or spasm of muscles are usually more gradual curves.

All curvatures are commonly accompanied by a compensatory curve in some other part of the column.

Anteroposterior Curvatures

Kyphosis is an accentuation of the normal thoracic curve producing " humpback."

Lordosis is an increase of the lumbar curve producing " hollow back."

Lateral Curvatures

Scoliosis is a lateral curve usually associated with some rotation.

Torticollis. Reference has been made to this condition in the section on the muscles of the neck.

Fractures and Dislocations of the Spine

Pure dislocation occurs in the cervical region of the spine. Fracture dislocations, in which some part of the vertebra is broken, occur particularly at the junction of fixed and movable parts of the spine. The spinal cord is commonly damaged and results depend on the level of the lesion. "Hanging fracture," which results from judicial hanging, is a dislocation of the atlas on the axis with fracture of the odontoid process. The cord is damaged at such a high level that death is immediate.

MUSCLES OF THE ABDOMEN

The Posterior Wall and the Lumbar Fascia (Fig. 20).

The foundation of the posterior abdominal wall is the lumbar part of the vertebral column. At the upper part are the lower ribs, and below on each side is the ilium, forming the iliac fossa of the false pelvis (Fig. 8).

Filling the gap between the transverse processes of the vertebræ medially, the last rib above, and the crest of the ilium below, is the **quadratus lumborum** muscle. Behind the transverse processes is the **erector spinæ.** Enclosing these muscles is the aponeurotic **lumbar fascia,** the three layers of which, attached to the vertebræ medially, blend with one another at the lateral border of the quadratus lumborum to form an origin for some of the lateral abdominal muscles. At the side of the bodies of the lumbar vertebræ, and in front of the transverse processes and the medial part of the quadratus lumborum, is the **psoas major** muscle. This passes to the brim of the pelvis, where it becomes associated with the **iliacus** muscle arising from the iliac fossa. The psoas and iliacus finally pass out into the thigh beneath the inguinal (Poupart's) ligament and cross in front of the hip joint to reach the femur, where they are inserted into the lesser trochanter.

The Transversalis Fascia and the Lateral and Anterior Abdominal Walls (Fig. 22).

The whole of the interior of the abdominal wall is lined by a continuous fascia which receives different names in different localities. Covering the diaphragm it is called the **diaphragmatic fascia.** Over the psoas and quadratus lumborum it encloses the kidney and is called the **renal fascia.** Over the iliacus it is the **fascia iliaca,** and in the true pelvis the **pelvic fascia.** On the deep surface of the anterior and lateral abdominal walls it is termed the **fascia transversalis.** Where the aorta and iliac vessels lie on the posterior wall this fascial lining of the abdomen is thickened to embed them, and the iliac thickening is prolonged along the vessels when they pass into the thigh to form the femoral vessels, and is here called the **femoral sheath.** Deep to the fascia are the extraperitoneal fat and peritoneum, superficial to it are the muscles of the abdominal wall.

Laterally the abdominal wall is formed by three thin sheets of muscle. The most superficial of these layers is the **external oblique** muscle, and its fibres run downwards and forwards. Just deep to the external oblique is the **internal oblique** with the fibres running upwards and forwards. The deepest is the **transversus** muscle, whose fibres run directly forwards. All these muscles are attached to the ribs above and to the crest of the ilium below, and they form in the anterior part of the abdominal wall flat sheets of tendon called **aponeuroses.** The aponeurosis of the external oblique, somewhat broader than those of the other muscles, has a free inturned lower edge stretching between the anterior end of the iliac crest and the spine of the pubis. This edge is termed the **inguinal ligament** (Poupart's). The aponeuroses of all three muscles finally reach the median plane in front, where they blend with those of the opposite side in the **linea alba** (white line). Just lateral to this they form a sheath for the **rectus abdominis,** a flattened muscle extending from the pubis below to the xiphoid process and lower costal cartilages above.

The muscles of the lateral and anterior abdominal walls are supplied by the **lower five intercostal nerves,** the **twelfth thoracic nerve,** and **branches from the first lumbar nerve.**

The Inguinal Region (Fig. 22).

Above the medial half of the inguinal ligament is situated **the inguinal canal,** which in the male transmits the spermatic cord (p. 294), and in the female the round ligament of the uterus (p. 299). If these structures came straight through the abdominal wall the hole through which they passed would be a weak spot and abdominal contents might find their way through it out of the abdomen. To prevent this the canal for the cord or round ligament is very oblique, its internal opening being about 1½ inches from its external opening. In addition, some of the fibres of the internal oblique and transversus muscles pass in an arched manner from the inguinal ligament to the pubis, first in front of, then above, and then behind the cord to be inserted into the **conjoint tendon.** These **arched fibres** straighten when the abdominal muscles contract and push the cord down against the inguinal ligament, effectively sealing the canal whenever intra-abdominal pressure rises.

Action of the Abdominal Muscles. The psoas and iliacus are flexors of the hip joint.

The remaining abdominal muscles increase the intra-abdominal pressure and are used in such expulsive efforts as defæcation, micturition, parturition and vomiting.

By pressing the viscera upwards and backwards against the inclined plane of the posterior abdominal wall they play an important part in maintaining the position of the organs in the abdomen.

In expiration they press the viscera against the diaphragm and return it to its expiratory position.

Practical Considerations

The Psoas. Tuberculous abscess associated with disease of the lumbar vertebræ may spread into the psoas muscle, and, tracking along its fascial sheath, pass out into the thigh. This condition is called psoas abscess.

Hernia. If the muscles round the inguinal canal be weak, or if a congenital peritoneal sac persist in the canal, the valve mechanism may fail, and abdominal contents enclosed in a sac of peritoneum may bulge out through the canal. This is called *inguinal hernia.* A similar protrusion may occur under the inguinal ligament on the medial side of the femoral vessels. This is *femoral hernia.*

Weakness of the recti muscles may allow extrusion of contents between them through the linea alba. This is a *ventral hernia,* and if occurring near the umbilicus is called *umbilical hernia.*

The Umbilicus

The umbilicus is a fibrous scar in the abdominal wall left by the separation of the umbilical cord (p. 304) after birth. It is at the level of the fourth lumbar vertebra. If separation of the cord be abnormal the umbilicus may be the seat of hernia in the infant.

MUSCLES OF THE ARM

These can be divided into the muscles round the shoulder girdle and those in the free part of the limb.

Muscles Round the Shoulder Girdle (Figs. 21 and 22).

A. Muscles connecting the Scapula to the Trunk

(1) **Pulling the scapula backwards** are the *trapezius* (middle fibres) and the *rhomboid* muscles.

(2) **Raising the scapula** (shrugging the shoulder) are the trapezius (upper fibres) and the levator scapulæ.

These muscles all arise from the vertebral column and are inserted into the scapula. The trapezius, because it is attached also to the skull, can pull the head backwards when the shoulders are fixed.

(3) **Pulling the scapula forwards** are the *serratus anterior* and the *pectoralis minor*, the former running from the ribs to the vertebral border of the scapula, and the latter from the ribs to the coracoid process.

(4) **Tilting the Scapula.** Movement of the arm from the side of the body to a position above the head is a combination of two movements : abduction of the humerus at the shoulder joint ; and rotation of the scapula, carrying the humerus with it, on the surface of the thorax.

This tilting of the scapula is brought about by the lower fibres of the *serratus anterior* and of the *trapezius* (Fig. 21). The rhomboid muscles return the scapula to its original position by pulling the vertebral border of the scapula towards the spinal column.

B. Muscles Connecting the Humerus with the Trunk

(1) **The pectoralis major** adducts the humerus and rotates it medially (Fig. 22).

(2) **The latissimus dorsi** adducts the humerus and carries it backwards (Fig. 21).

C. Muscles Connecting the Humerus with the Shoulder Girdle

(1) The deltoid forms a cap over the shoulder. Its middle fibres produce abduction of the shoulder joint ; its posterior fibres produce extension and external rotation ; its anterior fibres produce flexion and internal rotation.

(2) **The supraspinatus and infraspinatus**, on the back of the scapula, are lateral rotators of the humerus.

(3) **The subscapularis**, on the front of the scapula, is a medial rotator.

(4) **The teres major** is an adductor and a medial rotator of the humerus.

(5) **The teres minor** is an adductor and lateral rotator.

(6) **The coracobrachialis**, of which a large part is in the arm, moves the humerus forwards (flexion at the shoulder joint).

Nerve Supply of the Muscles Round the Shoulder

The **trapezius** by the **spinal accessory** (eleventh cranial) and the **third and fourth cervical** nerves.

The **levator scapulæ** by the **third, fourth and fifth cervical** nerves.

The branches to **all the others** come from the **brachial plexus.**

The latissimus dorsi, the rhomboids, and the serratus anterior are supplied each by its own nerve.

The pectoral muscles are supplied by the medial and lateral pectoral nerves.

The supraspinatus and infraspinatus get their supply from the suprascapular branch.

The coracobrachialis is supplied by the musculocutaneous nerve.

The deltoid is supplied by the circumflex (axillary) nerve.

The Axilla or Armpit

This space is bounded medially by the ribs, the intercostal muscles and the serratus anterior ; laterally, by the humerus and the coracobrachialis ; posteriorly, by the scapula and the subscapularis, teres major and latissimus dorsi muscles ; anteriorly, by the pectoral muscles and the fascia associated with them.

Above, it communicates with the neck by the opening through which the axillary artery and the brachial plexus enter. Below it communicates with the arm.

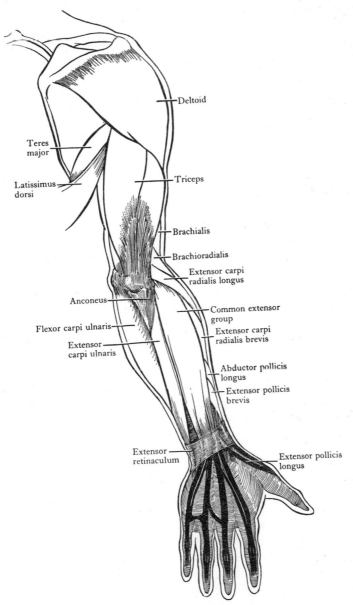

FIG. 23.   Muscles of the Back of the Upper Limb.
Right side.

In its posterior wall are two openings, the *quadrilateral* and *triangular spaces*, the former transmitting the circumflex nerve below the shoulder joint to the deltoid muscle. The axillary space contains the axillary vessels and the brachial plexus of nerves with their branches, and the axillary lymphatic glands, all of them being embedded in fat.

Muscles in the Free Part of the Limb (Figs. 22 and 23).

A. Muscles of the Upper Arm

Flexors.

These are placed on the front of the arm. They are separated from the triceps on the back of the arm by the **medial and lateral intermuscular septa** (Fig. 18, B).

Most superficially is the **biceps** muscle of the arm. It bends the elbow and supinates the hand.

Deep to the biceps are :—

In the upper half of the arm—the **coracobrachialis** which flexes the shoulder joint.

In the lower half of the arm—the **brachialis** which bends the elbow.

The flexor muscles of the arm are all supplied by the **musculo-cutaneous nerve.** (The brachialis gets an additional supply from the radial nerve.)

Extensors.

The **triceps** is the extensor of the arm, *i.e.*, it straightens the elbow. As its name indicates, it arises by three heads. It is supplied by the **radial** (musculospiral) **nerve.**

B. Muscles of the Forearm

Pronators.

The movement of pronation brings the back of the hand to the front, and is brought about by rotating the radius across the ulna. There are two pronators :—

The **pronator teres,** a superficial muscle, running obliquely across the upper third of the forearm.

The **pronator quadratus** is in the lower third of the forearm deep to the tendons of all the other muscles.

The pronators are both supplied by the **median nerve.**

Supinators.

The movement of supination brings the palm of the hand forwards, the bones of the forearm being parallel with one another.

Three muscles perform the movement :—

The **biceps,** which, as already described, flexes the elbow also.

The **supinator,** wrapped round the upper one-third of the radius.

The **brachioradialis** along the lateral side of the front of the forearm.

The biceps is supplied by the **musculocutaneous** nerve. The other two are supplied by the **radial** nerve.

Flexors.

These muscles are found on the front of the forearm and are in three groups, superficial, intermediate, and deep.

Superficial Group. These arise from the medial epicondyle of the humerus by what is known as the **common flexor tendon.** They are :—

The **flexor carpi radialis** producing flexion and radial deviation of the hand.

The **palmaris longus.**

The **flexor carpi ulnaris,** producing flexion and ulnar deviation of the hand.

Intermediate Group. This is formed by one muscle, the **flexor digitorum sublimis** (superficial flexor of the fingers). This splits into four tendons which, after passing through the carpal tunnel (p. 35) and the palm of the hand, go one to each finger. The muscle flexes the second phalanges.

Deep Group. This comprises two muscles :—

The **flexor digitorum profundus** (deep flexor of the fingers), which also divides into four tendons, which run with those of the superficial flexor into the fingers. The muscle flexes the terminal phalanges.

The **flexor pollicis longus** (long flexor of the thumb) flexes the second phalanx of the thumb.

The **flexor muscles** of the forearm are all supplied by the **median nerve** except the ulnar flexor of the wrist and half of the deep flexor of the fingers which are supplied by the **ulnar nerve.**

Extensors.

These are also in superficial and deep groups.

Superficial Group. These arise from the lateral epicondyle of the humerus by the **common extensor tendon.** They are :—

The **extensor carpi radialis longus** and **extensor carpi radialis brevis** (long and short radial extensors of the wrist). These produce extension and radial deviation of the wrist.

The **extensor carpi ulnaris** (ulnar extensor of the wrist), producing extension and ulnar deviation of the wrist.

The **extensor digitorum communis** (common extensor of the fingers), extending the second and third phalanges of all the fingers.

The **extensor digiti minimi** (extensor of the little finger), acting on the little finger alone.

Deep Group. These arise from the posterior surface of the bones of the forearm and the interosseous membrane. They are :—

The **abductor pollicis longus** (long abductor of the thumb), abducting the metacarpal bone of the thumb, *i.e.*, carrying it away from the palm of the hand.

Extensor pollicis longus and **extensor pollicis brevis** (long and short extensors of the thumb), extending the second and first phalanges respectively.

The **extensor indicis proprius** (proper extensor of the index finger), acting on the index alone.

The **extensor muscles** of the forearm are all supplied by the **posterior interosseous branch of the radial nerve.**

The Retinacula (Annular ligaments).

Where the tendons to the digits cross the wrist and the joints in the fingers they are prevented from rising when the joints are bent by thickenings in the deep fascia called retinacula. On the front of the wrist is the **flexor retinaculum** (transverse carpal ligament) which converts the grooved volar surface of the carpus into the carpal tunnel for the tendons. In the fingers the **fibrous sheaths** of the tendons serve a similar function.

On the back of the wrist is the **extensor retinaculum** holding the extensor tendons in place. Retinacula are unnecessary on the back of the fingers as they are never extended beyond a straight line.

Forming a double envelope for the tendons as they lie under these retinacula are the **synovial sheaths.** These permit the tendons to glide easily in the osseofibrous tunnels through which they are passing.

C. Muscles of the Hand

Between the metacarpal bones are the **dorsal interosseous muscles** which abduct the fingers from the line of the middle finger.

Anterior to the metacarpal bones are the **palmar interossei** which adduct the fingers towards the middle finger. The interosseous muscles also flex the first phalanx and extend the second and third phalanges, putting the fingers into the " writing " position.

Grouped round the metacarpal of the thumb are the muscles making up the *thenar eminence*. They are :—

The **abductor pollicis brevis** (short abductor of the thumb).

The **flexor pollicis brevis** (short flexor of the thumb).

The **opponens pollicis,** producing the movement of the metacarpal bone which brings the thumb across the palm to meet the little finger (*i.e.,* opposition).

The **adductor pollicis,** which brings the thumb in towards the side of the palm.

Round the metacarpal bone of the little finger are the muscles of the *hypothenar eminence*, the **abductor, short flexor** and **opponens of the little finger.**

Between the thenar and hypothenar eminences there is a deep hollow in the palm of the hand occupied by the flexor tendons, the lumbrical muscles attached to them, and the palmar vessels and nerves. This hollow is roofed in by the thick fascia called the **palmar aponeurosis,** which further distally splits into slips blending with the fibrous flexor sheaths of the tendons in the fingers.

Nerve Supply of the Muscles of the Hand. Most of the muscles are supplied by the **ulnar nerve.** The abductor, flexor brevis and opponens of the thumb and the radial two lumbrical muscles are supplied by the **median nerve.**

MUSCLES OF THE LOWER EXTREMITY

A. Muscles Round the Hip Joint (Figs. 20, 21, 24 and 25).

Flexion (bringing the leg forwards) is produced by the **psoas and iliacus** muscles which cross the front of the joint.

Extension (carrying the leg backwards) is produced by the **glutæus maximus** which is behind the joint.

Medial rotation and abduction are produced by the **glutæus medius** and **glutæus minimus** which are above the joint.

Lateral rotation is produced by the **piriformis** and the two **obturator muscles,** all of which are underneath the glutæus maximus.

The psoas is attached to the lesser trochanter of the femur and the glutei, piriformis and obturator to the great trochanter.

B. Muscles of the Thigh (Figs. 24 and 25).

Three main groups of muscles are found in the thigh. The

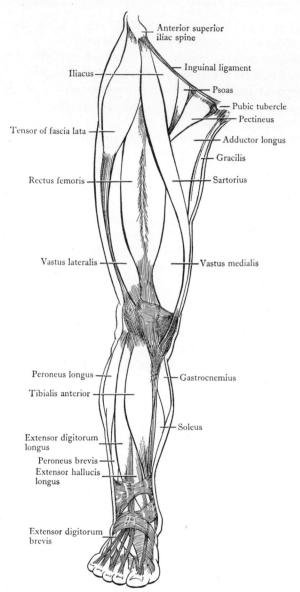

FIG. 24.   Muscles of the Front of the Lower Limb.
Right side.

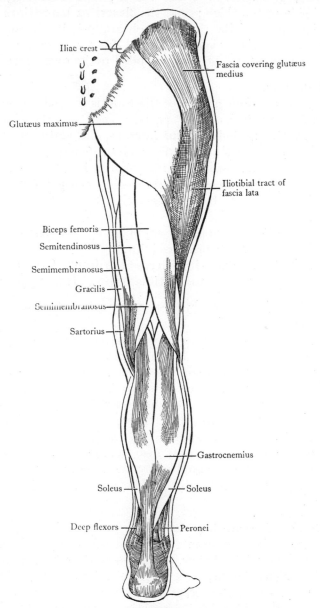

Iliac crest

Fascia covering glutæus medius

Glutæus maximus

Iliotibial tract of fascia lata

Biceps femoris

Semitendinosus

Semimembranosus

Gracilis

Semimembranosus

Sartorius

Gastrocnemius

Soleus

Soleus

Deep flexors

Peronei

FIG. 25.   Muscles of the Back of the Lower Limb.
Right side.

extensors, grouped round the femur ; the adductors, on the medial side of the thigh ; and the flexors or hamstrings, on the posterior aspect of the thigh.   Each group is in a compartment of its own in the thigh, separated from adjacent groups by intermuscular septa, and each supplied by its own nerve.

The Extensors.

The great extensor muscle of the knee is termed the quadriceps femoris because it has four parts.   They are the three vasti muscles, vastus medialis, vastus lateralis, and vastus intermedius, all attached to the femur, and the rectus femoris, which, arising from the hip bone, crosses the hip joint on its way down into the thigh.   All these muscles are attached by the patellar tendon to the tibia, the patella being a sesamoid bone developed in this tendon.

The quadriceps femoris is supplied by the femoral nerve ; it straightens the leg at the knee joint.

The sartorius muscle winds across the front of the quadriceps from the hip bone above to the tibia below.   It is supplied by the femoral nerve.

The Adductors

The muscles of this group arise from the hip bone and spread out in a fan-shaped way to be inserted into the linea aspera on the posterior surface of the femur.   They are arranged in planes, the most anterior being the pectineus and adductor longus muscles, the next being the adductor brevis, and the most posterior the adductor magnus.   Along the medial side of these is the gracilis.   They are supplied by the obturator nerve.   (The adductor magnus gets a supply also from the sciatic nerve, whilst the pectineus is usually supplied by the femoral nerve and only occasionally by the obturator.)   The adductors bring the legs together.

The Flexors or Hamstring Muscles

These muscles arise from the ischial tuberosity and run down the back of the thigh.   Below, two of them, the semi-membranosus and the semi-tendinosus, pass to the medial side to be attached to the tibia, whilst the biceps passes to the lateral side to gain the head of the fibula for its insertion.   The space between the biceps laterally and the semi-membranous medially is bounded below by the two heads of the gastrocnemius muscle and is termed the popliteal space.   The floor of the popliteal space is formed by the femur, the back of the knee joint, and the popliteus muscle covering the upper part of the tibia.

The flexors are supplied by the sciatic nerve ; they bend the knee.

The Vascular Cleft in the Thigh

The vessels in the upper part of the thigh lie in a gutter or groove, the floor of which is formed laterally by the iliopsoas and medially by the adductor muscles. This is the **femoral triangle.** In the middle third the vessels continue in a deep cleft between the quadriceps and adductor groups. This part of the cleft, called the **subsartorial canal** (Hunter), is roofed in by the sartorius muscle, which winds spirally across the front of the thigh. At the lower end of the subsartorial canal the vessels pierce the adductor magnus and pass to the posterior surface into the **popliteal space,** where they become associated with branches of the sciatic nerve which has traversed the posterior compartment of the thigh. In the upper third of the thigh the femoral vessels are enclosed in the **femoral sheath,** a prolongation under the inguinal ligament of the fascia lining the abdomen. A compartment of the sheath medial to the vessels is called the *femoral canal.* It is occasionally the seat of a femoral hernia.

Fascia of the Thigh

The fascia of the thigh is called the **fascia lata.** It is specially thick on the lateral side, where it forms the **iliotibial tract.**

C. Muscles of the Leg (Figs. 24 and 25).

The leg below the knee presents three main groups of muscles :—

The Extensors or Dorsiflexors

These are placed anteriorly. They comprise :—

The **extensor digitorum longus** (long extensor of the toes), which straightens the lateral four toes.

The **extensor hallucis longus** (long extensor of the great toe), which straightens the big toe.

The **tibialis anterior** (anterior tibial muscle), which is one of the invertor muscles, *i.e.*, it turns the sole of the foot inwards towards the median plane.

The extensors are all supplied by the **anterior tibial** (deep peroneal) **nerve.**

The Plantar Flexors

These are found on the posterior surface of the leg. They are in two sub-groups :—

Superficial Flexors. The **soleus, gastrocnemius, and plantaris** muscles all attached to the calcaneum by the "**tendon of Achilles**" on the back of the ankle.

Deep Flexors. The **flexor digitorum longus** (long flexor of the toes) passes round the inner side of the ankle into the sole of the foot. It bends the lateral four toes downwards towards the sole.

The **flexor hallucis longus** (long flexor of the great toe), following the previous muscle into the sole, bends the great toe.

The **tibialis posterior** (posterior tibial muscle) is another invertor of the foot.

The plantar flexors are all supplied by the **posterior tibial nerve.**

The Evertors

These are found on the lateral side of the leg, and they turn the foot outwards. They are :—

The **peroneus longus,** which, after crossing the lateral side of the ankle, passes across the sole of the foot and helps to maintain the transverse arch of the foot (p. 42).

The **peroneus brevis** inserted into the lateral border of the foot.

The peronei are supplied by the **musculocutaneous** (superficial peroneal) **nerve.**

(It will be noted that the evertors of the foot are in a group by themselves, and are separated from the plantar flexors and the extensors by intermuscular septa. The invertors, on the other hand, are included with the flexors and extensors.)

Muscles of the Foot

In addition to the tendons of muscles already described passing into the foot from the leg, there are other muscles situated entirely within the foot.

On the Dorsum. On the extensor aspect (dorsum) of the foot is the **extensor digitorum brevis** (short extensor of the toes) supplied by the **anterior tibial nerve**; it straightens the medial four toes.

In the Sole. In the sole of the foot are a number of short muscles which, in addition to bending the toes, play, with the long flexors and the tibial muscles, an important part in maintaining the longitudinal arching of the foot. They are supplied by the **plantar branches of the posterior tibial nerve.**

The Retinacula. Retinacula, similar to those described in connection with the tendons in the wrist and hand, are found binding down the tendons round the ankle and on the plantar aspect of the toes. They are formed, like those in the upper limb, by thickenings in the deep fascia, and the tendons which pass beneath them are invested by **synovial sheaths.**

PHYSIOLOGY OF MUSCULAR ACTIVITY

It has already been stated (p. 5) that the cells which make up a muscle are elongated to form fibres. Activity of these cells is evidenced by a change of shape resulting in a shortening and broadening of the fibre. The two ends of the muscle (itself composed of a large number of fibres) having certain attachments, shortening of the fibres will approximate the two points of attachment and result usually in movement. The type of movement produced depends on the form of attachment of the particular muscle concerned.

Prime Movers and Antagonists

A muscle acting as a **prime mover** produces a definite movement such as flexion, extension or rotation of a certain part of the body. A great many muscles are usually concerned in the production of any one movement. For instance, in supination of the hand the biceps, supinator, and brachioradialis muscles are all active as prime movers.

The muscles which produce the opposite action to prime movers are called **antagonists.** For example, extensors are antagonists to flexors, pronators to supinators, and *vice versâ*.

It should be noted that if gravity or any other external force will produce the action of a muscle active contraction does not take place. The antagonistic muscle contracts to control the action. For example, in bringing the arm to the side of the body from the abducted position the arm drops by its own weight. The pectoral muscle, which adducts the humerus, does not act unless a resistance is offered to bringing the arm in. Abductors of the shoulder joint prevent the arm from dropping too quickly and control the movement. This is called " action of paradox," and is the principle underlying gravity-aided exercises in the treatment of paralysed muscles.

Some muscles cross more than one joint, and, unless prevented from doing so, would produce movement which might not be wanted.

To prevent unwanted movement other muscles are called into play and act as " muscles of fixation." For instance, in grasping anything in the hand the flexors of the fingers tend also to flex the elbow and the wrist. To prevent this there is coincident contraction of the triceps and the extensors of the wrist, which act as " synergists " in the performance of this movement.

Muscle Tone

Muscles of the body are never entirely relaxed or slack. They are always in a state of tension or **tone.** This is really a partial activity of the muscle brought about by contraction of a certain number of its fibres, the remaining fibres being relaxed.[1]

To illustrate this by an example taken from the muscles moving the elbow joint. If the joint be held in a position midway between flexion and extension, the flexors and extensors are both in such a state of tone (*i.e.*, have just so many fibres contracted) as will maintain that position. A slight movement towards flexion will be brought about by contraction of more fibres of the flexor muscles with a coincident relaxation of *some* of the fibres which were contracted in the extensor muscles to maintain the midway position. As more and more flexion is produced, so more and more fibres of the flexor muscles contract, and fewer and fewer fibres of the extensors are contracted. If the movement be stopped at any point, just that number of fibres continue to be in a state of contraction in the two groups, flexors and extensors, as will maintain the position of the limb until another movement is wanted. Since the position of every part of the body depends in the same way on the relative tone (*i.e.*, partial contraction) of the groups of muscles, this phenomenon is of supreme importance in the maintenance of the postures of the body.

The mechanism of the production of muscle tone is complicated, and its details beyond the scope of the present account. It should be noted, however, that the contraction of fibres which constitutes tone is brought about by impulses from the central nervous system which are themselves set up in response to other impulses reaching the nervous system along afferent nerves. Many of these impulses come from the joints and from the muscles themselves, and are set up by stretching of tendons and ligaments. For this reason muscle tone is one of the examples of " reflex action " of the nervous system (see p. 244).

---

[1] If any fibre contract at all it contracts to its maximum extent. This is called the " *all-or-none law.*" Applied to the collections of fibres which constitute a whole muscle, it follows that the greater the force of contraction of the muscle required the greater is the *number* of fibres called into play.

Stimuli Resulting in Muscle Action

Muscle may be stimulated to contract by the application of heat or cold, and mechanical, chemical, or electrical stimuli, to the muscle itself. It may also be made to contract by electrical stimulation of the nerve which supplies it.

The normal contraction of muscles is, however, a response to impulses reaching them from the central nervous system along their **motor nerves.** These impulses are themselves set up in response to sensory impressions reaching the nervous system from the skin, muscles, joints, ears, eyes, etc. Such impressions *may reach consciousness* and result in **voluntary movement.** Examples of this are seen in response to the prick of a pin to the skin, or the desire to alter the position of a joint which we are aware is uncomfortable or unsuitable for some action required of the part. On the other hand, the sensory impulses arousing the motor nerves of the muscles to activity may not reach consciousness at all. We are, for example, quite unaware of many of the stimuli which result in muscle tone.

Physical and Chemical Changes in Muscles during Contraction

The activity of muscle cells resulting in contraction involves the **breakdown** of the protoplasm of the cells with the production of certain chemical substances. If this breakdown is not made good, and waste products accumulate in the muscle, fatigue results. The muscle protoplasm is restored by the oxidation in the muscle of certain substances (lactic acid) derived from carbohydrates. This latter process also results in the production of carbon dioxide. The *oxygen* necessary for the **restoration** of the muscle protoplasm is brought to the cells by the blood, and the *carbon dioxide* which is formed is removed in a similar manner. During both the breakdown and recovery phases **heat** is produced.

The above series of events is accompanied by **electrical changes** in the muscles.

Since oxygen is necessary for the rebuilding of muscle protoplasm, during muscular exercise there is increased activity of the respiratory system and breathing is deepened and increased in rate.[1]

The **heart rate and output** are also increased during exercise, and the **body temperature** rises slightly.

[1] In severe exercise even this increased breathing may exhibit insufficient oxygen for the recovery phase, and unoxidised lactic acid accumulates in the muscle. This is removed by oxidation during the period of rest following the exercise. (The phenomenon is known as " oxygen debt.")

Practical Applications

Rigor Mortis

After death certain parts of the muscle protoplasm undergo coagulation or clotting, and the muscles will no longer stretch. The result is that the body stiffens and the joints cannot be moved. Subsequent chemical changes soften the fibres so that the rigor passes off. The onset and duration of rigor vary greatly according to the general bodily condition and the cause of death. Its onset may be almost immediate in chronic diseases and in conditions of wasting.

Paralysis

When a certain group of muscles is paralysed the tone of the antagonistic muscles left unopposed will produce deformity of the part. This must be prevented by proper splinting and nursing.

Tetanus

In this condition contraction follows contraction with such rapidity that the fibres cannot relax. It may be localised or general, and may follow infection of wounds with the tetanus bacillus (lockjaw) or strychnine poisoning.

Cramp

This is a painful contraction of muscle due probably to some disturbance in its blood supply.

Convulsions

This is the spasmodic contraction of many groups of muscles, due, as a rule, to some disturbance of the central nervous system.

CHAPTER V

THE ALIMENTARY SYSTEM

THE alimentary system is concerned with the ingestion, digestion, and absorption of foodstuffs, and with getting rid of the waste which remains after digestion is completed.

The tubular structures along which the food passes are grouped collectively as the **alimentary tract** (Fig. 26). In the order in which the food traverses them they are :—

The mouth.

The pharynx or throat.

The œsophagus or gullet.

The stomach.

The small intestine (duodenum, jejunum and ileum).

The large intestine.

THE MOUTH

The oral cavity is concerned with the reception and mastication of the food. It is here also that the saliva is mixed with the food, preparing it for swallowing, and commencing the digestion of cooked starches.

The walls of the mouth are partly muscular and partly bony.

The **cheeks** are formed by the **buccinator muscles**, which further forwards form a large part of the substance of the lips. The **floor of the mouth,** on which rests the tongue, is formed by the **mylohyoid muscle.** The jaws and hard palate are the bony portions of the walls of the mouth. Behind the hard palate is the soft palate, which is also formed of muscles. Hanging down from the soft palate is the **uvula** (Fig. 27).

The cavity is divided into the **vestibule of the mouth** between the gums and the cheeks, and the **cavity of the mouth** proper inside the teeth. The buccinator muscle normally keeps the cheek in contact with the gums and teeth so that the vestibule is a mere chink.

All the structures which form the walls of the mouth are covered with *mucous membrane* which, where it covers the alveolar processes of the jaws, is thick and known as the **gums.**

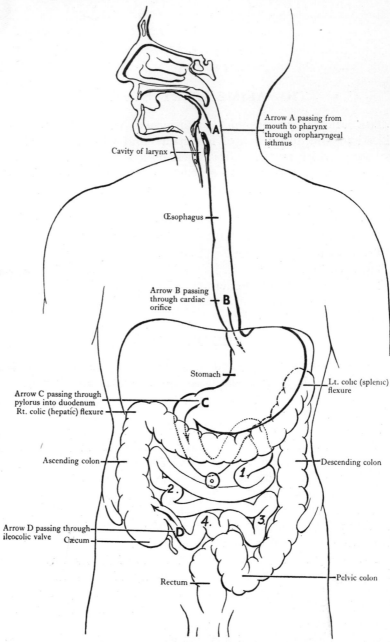

Arrow A passing from
mouth to pharynx
through oropharyngeal
isthmus

Cavity of larynx

Œsophagus

Arrow B passing
through cardiac
orifice

B

Stomach

Lt. colic (splenic)
flexure

Arrow C passing through
pylorus into duodenum
Rt. colic (hepatic) flexure

C

Ascending colon

Descending colon

Arrow D passing through
ileocolic valve
Cæcum

D

Rectum

Pelvic colon

Fig. 26.　A general scheme of the alimentary tract.
1 and 2, Jejunum.
3 and 4, Ileum.

The Tongue (Figs. 27 and 28).

In the floor of the mouth is found **the tongue,** composed of muscles covered by mucous membrane, the latter being reflected off the inferior surface of the organ to the inner aspect of the lower jaw. In the median plane this reflection of mucous membrane is raised into the fold called the **frænum** of the tongue. The base or root of the tongue is placed far back beyond the mouth in the oral part of the pharynx. The upper surface of the tongue is called the **dorsum,** and, in the oral part,

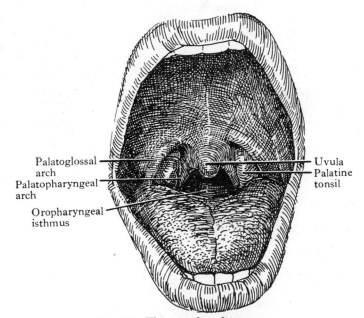

Palatoglossal arch

Palatopharyngeal arch

Oropharyngeal isthmus

Uvula

Palatine tonsil

FIG. 27. The mouth and tongue.

the mucous membrane covering it is velvety in appearance, due to the presence of little projections called **papillæ.** These have names indicating their shape, *e.g.,* circumvallate, conical, fungiform, and filiform. In the mucous membrane of the tongue are found also most of the **taste buds,** in relationship with which are the nerve endings concerned with the appreciation of bitter, sweet, salty and acid tastes. The substances stimulating these endings must be in solution to produce their effects. Flavours, which make up a large part of taste as it is commonly understood, are really appreciated by the organ of smell in the nose. In addition to being concerned with taste, the tongue, by its movements, plays an important part in articulation of speech, in mastication of the food, and in swallowing.

The Teeth

The teeth have already been described (p. 27).

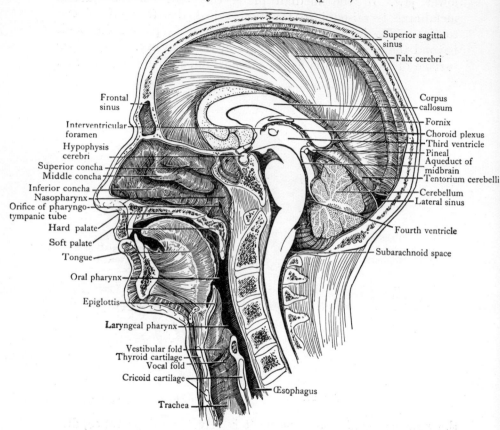

Superior sagittal sinus

Falx cerebri

Frontal sinus

Corpus callosum

Fornix

Choroid plexus

Third ventricle

Pineal

Aqueduct of midbrain

Tentorium cerebelli

Cerebellum

Lateral sinus

Fourth ventricle

Subarachnoid space

Interventricular foramen

Hypophysis cerebri

Superior concha

Middle concha

Inferior concha

Nasopharynx

Orifice of pharyngo-tympanic tube

Hard palate

Soft palate

Tongue

Oral pharynx

Epiglottis

Laryngeal pharynx

Vestibular fold

Thyroid cartilage

Vocal fold

Cricoid cartilage

Œsophagus

Trachea

Fig. 28.   A sagittal section of the head and neck a little to the left of the median plane.   The nasal septum has been removed to expose the lateral wall of the nose.

The Salivary Glands (Fig. 29).

Opening into the mouth are the ducts of the **salivary glands.** These are paired structures, there being three of them on each side.

The Parotid Gland.   The parotid gland is placed below and in front of the ear, wedged into the interval between the jaw anteriorly and the mastoid process and sternomastoid muscle posteriorly. It overlaps considerably on to the face, and its duct (Stenson's duct) pierces the cheek and opens into the vestibule of the mouth opposite the second upper molar tooth.

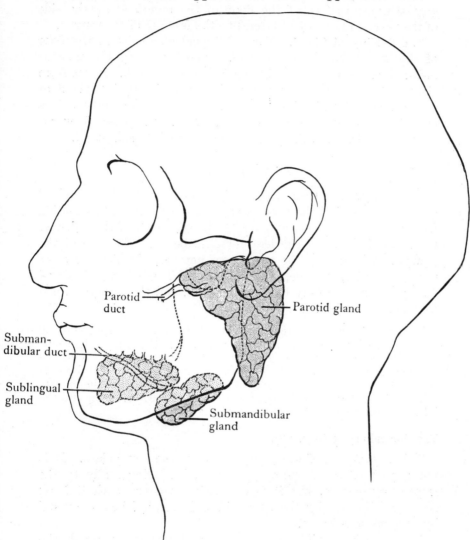

Fig. 29. A scheme of the salivary glands of the right side.

The facial nerve traverses the gland on its way forwards to the face, and the external carotid artery divides into its terminal branches in the gland substance.

The Submandibular or Submaxillary Gland. This gland is

found under cover of the body of the jaw and below the muscular floor of the mouth. It projects considerably below the lower border of the jaw into the neck. Its duct (Wharton's duct) runs on the upper surface of the floor of the mouth along the side of the tongue to open just lateral to the frænum of the tongue.

The Sublingual Gland. The sublingual gland lies in the floor of the mouth below the tongue, covered only by the mucous membrane. It can readily be felt inside the mouth. It has from eight to twenty ducts, some of which open directly into the floor of the mouth by piercing the mucous membrane, whilst others open into the submandibular duct, which, as it passes forwards towards the frænum, lies just beneath the sublingual gland.

THE PHARYNX

The pharynx, or throat, is a cavity in front of the vertebral column and behind the nose, mouth, and larynx, and extending from the base of the skull above to the beginning of the gullet at the level of the sixth cervical vertebra below. The wall of the pharynx is formed by the **constrictor muscles,** of which there are three, superior, middle, and inferior. These are reinforced deeply and superficially by fibrous layers, and the cavity is lined by mucous membrane.

The constrictors are attached posteriorly to a median raphe running down the back of the pharynx from the skull to the gullet. In front, the superior constrictor is attached to the pterygoid process of the sphenoid bone and to the lower jaw, and through these attachments is continuous with the muscle of the cheek and the floor of the mouth.

The middle constrictor is attached in front to the hyoid bone and the inferior constrictor to the cartilages of the larynx.

The Nasopharynx (Fig. 28).

This is the part of the pharynx above the soft palate. It is not a part of the alimentary system, belonging really to the respiratory system, but it is convenient to deal with it here. Its roof is formed by the sphenoid and occipital bones covered by mucous membrane.

Below, it is continuous with the oral pharynx through the opening behind the soft palate. By raising the palate this opening can be closed in such activities as blowing, swallowing, and some of the speech movements.

Anteriorly, the nasopharynx communicates with the nose through the apertures called the **choanæ (posterior nasal apertures).**

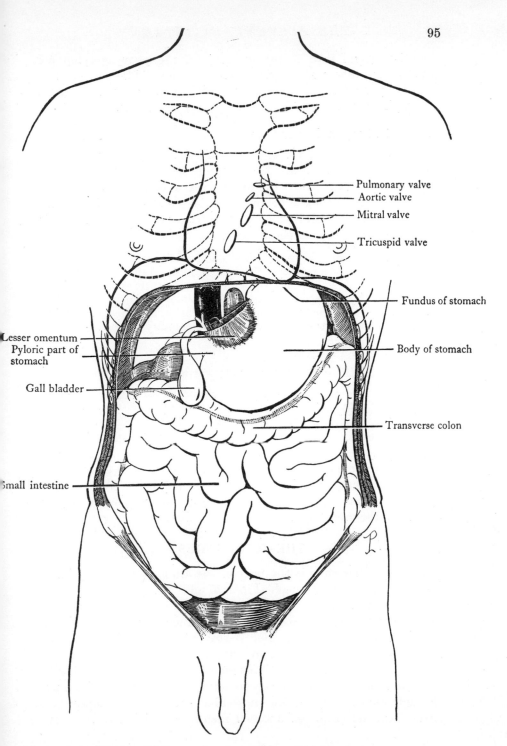

Pulmonary valve
Aortic valve
Mitral valve
Tricuspid valve
Fundus of stomach
Lesser omentum
Pyloric part of stomach
Body of stomach
Gall bladder
Transverse colon
Small intestine

FIG. 30   The stomach, colon and intestines from in front.

In its lateral wall is the opening of the **pharyngotympanic (Eustachian) tube,** which connects it with the middle ear.

In the posterior wall and the roof of the nasopharynx is a mass of lymphoid tissue called the **naso-pharyngeal tonsil.**

The Oral Pharynx (Figs. 28 and 27).

The upper part of this portion of the pharynx can be seen through the open mouth. The aperture between the mouth and the oral pharynx is called the **oropharyngeal isthmus,** and has the palate above, the tongue below, and the **palatine tonsil** laterally on each side. The oral pharynx also extends a little below this level behind the base of the tongue.

The palatine and pharyngeal tonsils and similar masses of lymphoid tissue on the posterior part of the tongue form an incomplete ring of this tissue round the channel by which the air we breathe enters the body. This lymphoid tissue, like that found in the lymph glands (p. 183), has a protective function, forming a first line of defence against infection of the respiratory and alimentary tracts.

The Laryngeal Pharynx

This part is the continuation downwards of the oral portion of the pharynx. It communicates anteriorly with the larynx through an opening termed the laryngeal aperture. At the sides of the **laryngeal aperture** are the **pyriform recesses.** Below, the laryngeal part of the pharynx is continuous with the œsophagus.

The oral and laryngeal parts of the pharynx are common to both the alimentary and respiratory systems, being traversed by air from the nasopharynx on its way to the larynx, as well as by food from the mouth on its way to the gullet.

THE ŒSOPHAGUS

This muscular tube is the part of the alimentary tract joining the pharynx to the stomach (Figs. 20 and 26).

It is about 10 inches long, and lies first in the neck and the upper part of the thorax between the trachea in front and the vertebral column behind. Below the bifurcation of the trachea it lies between the heart and the spinal column and, finally, passing a little towards the left side of the body and crossing in front of the descending thoracic aorta, it enters the abdomen through an opening in the muscular part of the diaphragm. After a further course of about 1 inch in the abdomen it enters the stomach. The opening into the stomach is termed the **cardia,** and is a distance of *16 inches from the incisor teeth*. The muscle in the wall of the œsophagus is striped like that of the pharyngeal constrictors in its upper one-third, whilst in its lower two-thirds it is involuntary. The lining mucous membrane contains a number of mucous glands, the secretion of which lubricates the surface so that food can pass easily down the tube.

THE STOMACH (Figs. 26 and 30)

This is situated in the upper part of the abdomen on the left side of the body, just below the diaphragm. It is related to the liver and diaphragm above, to the pancreas behind, to the spleen on the left, and to the diaphragm and anterior abdominal wall in front. Being suspended from the liver by peritoneum (the gastrohepatic omentum), it moves with that organ during respiration. It varies greatly in position and shape according to the amount of its contents and the general position of the body (whether standing, sitting or lying).

When empty, the stomach is flask-shaped, the narrow end towards the right being called the **pyloric part,** and the wider end towards the left being the **fundus**. The œsophagus enters on the right border just below the fundus, and the part between this and the pyloric portion is called the **body** of the stomach. The two borders of the stomach are called the lesser and greater curvatures, and separate the anterior and posterior surfaces from one another.

The stomach is almost completely invested by peritoneum (p. 108).

When full, and with the subject standing erect, the stomach tends to be lower in the abdomen and somewhat J-shaped.

The Pylorus (Fig. 26)

The pyloric part of the stomach is continuous with the duodenum at the **pylorus,** in which situation there is a thickening of the circular muscle coat (see Structure) forming the **pyloric sphincter**. By its contraction the pyloric sphincter retains the food in the stomach a sufficient length of time to enable gastric digestion to take place. (The stomach is not completely empty until four to six hours after a full meal.)

In respect of function, the stomach may be divided into two parts : The fundus and body act together as a reservoir delivering

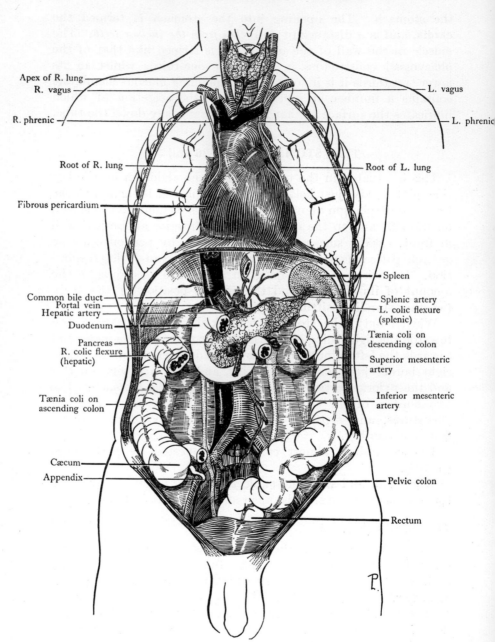

Apex of R. lung
R. vagus
R. phrenic
L. vagus
L. phrenic

Root of R. lung
Root of L. lung

Fibrous pericardium

Spleen

Common bile duct
Portal vein
Hepatic artery
Duodenum
Pancreas
R. colic flexure
(hepatic)

Splenic artery
L. colic flexure
(splenic)
Tænia coli on
descending colon
Superior mesenteric
artery

Tænia coli on
ascending colon

Inferior mesenteric
artery

Cæcum
Appendix

Pelvic colon

Rectum

FIG. 31. The duodenum and pancreas

its contents to the pyloric part, which acts as a churn, driving the contents towards the pylorus and then relaxing to allow them to return, and so mixing them properly with the gastric juice.

Structure. The stomach consists of the following coats or layers : The outer coat is peritoneum and subserous connective tissue. The muscular coat consists of three layers, longitudinal, oblique, and circular. Between the muscle coat and the mucous membrane is the submucous coat. The mucous membrane contains the glands which secrete the gastric juice.

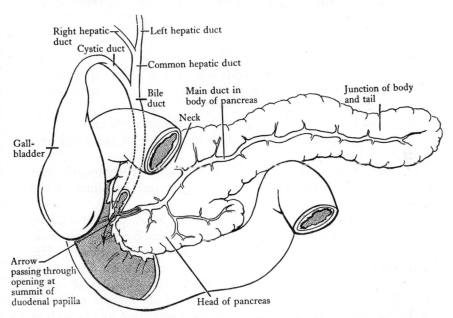

Fig. 32. A scheme of the duodenum, pancreas, and the gall-bladder and bile ducts from in front.

THE DUODENUM, PANCREAS AND LIVER

These viscera must be considered together, as their digestive functions are closely allied.

The Duodenum (Figs. 31 and 32)

This is the first part of the small intestine, differing from the rest in that it is behind the peritoneum of the posterior abdominal wall, and therefore more or less fixed in position. It is about 10 inches long and forms a C-shaped loop in front of the aorta and inferior vena cava. In the concavity of the loop is the head of the pancreas. The duodenum is continuous with the stomach at the **pylorus,** and with the rest of the small intestine at the **duodeno-jejunal flexure.** Entering its middle part are the common bile duct and the two ducts of the pancreas.

It is customary for purposes of description to divide the duodenum into four parts. The first part passes from the pylorus upwards backwards and to the right as far as the neck of the gall-bladder. The second part descends in front of the hilum of the right kidney and the edge of the inferior vena cava to the level of the third lumbar vertebra. The third part crosses the median plane in front of the vena cava and the aorta, and the fourth part passes up on the left of the median plane to the duodenojejunal flexure.

The Pancreas (Figs. 31, 32 and 33)

This is a soft gland situated behind the stomach and the peritoneum on the posterior abdominal wall. It consists of a head, neck, body, and tail.

The **head** is contained in the curve of the duodenum.

The **neck** projects from the anterior surface of the head and joins it to the body.

The **body** passes across to the left side behind the stomach, and is continued into the **tail,** which lies just on the hilum of the spleen.

The gland has two functional elements. First, the gland tissue which forms the **pancreatic juice,** which drains by the pancreatic ducts into the duodenum. The ducts are two in number : The **main duct** drains the whole of the gland except the lower part of the head, and it joins the bile duct before the latter opens into the duodenum. At the common opening for the bile duct and main pancreatic duct there is a slight elevation on the wall of the duodenum called the **duodenal papilla,** and the aperture is guarded by a sphincter muscle. The **accessory pancreatic duct** is much smaller and drains the lower part of the head of the gland. The second functional element in the pancreas consists of groups of cells which pour their secretion into the blood-stream. These are called the **islets of Langerhans** and produce the substance called **insulin,** which controls the fate of sugar in the body (see Ductless Glands, p. 324).

The Liver (Fig. 34)

The liver is the largest gland in the body. It is wedge shaped, the base of the wedge being to the right, and is situated on the under surface of the diaphragm almost entirely under cover of

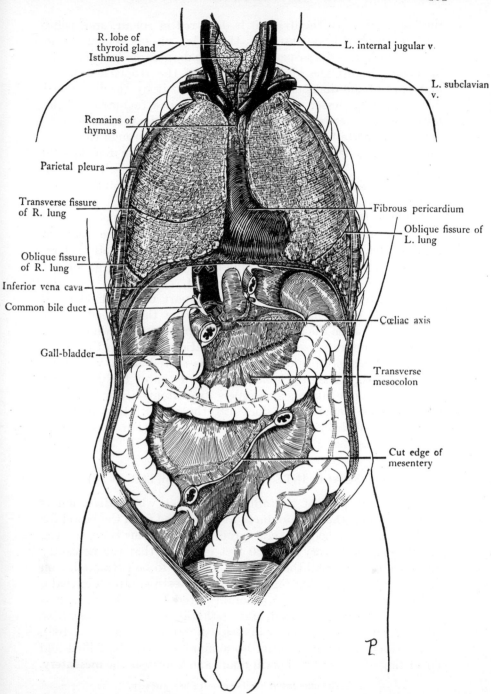

R. lobe of
thyroid gland
Isthmus

L. internal jugular v.

L. subclavian
v.

Remains of
thymus

Parietal pleura

Transverse fissure
of R. lung

Fibrous pericardium

Oblique fissure of
L. lung

Oblique fissure
of R. lung

Inferior vena cava

Common bile duct

Cœliac axis

Gall-bladder

Transverse
mesocolon

Cut edge of
mesentery

FIG. 33.   The colon and the mesenterics.

7*

the lower ribs. In the living it is deep red in colour, and, being soft, its surface is indented by the other viscera which are in contact with it. It is suspended from the diaphragm by peritoneal ligaments, whilst the lesser curvature of the stomach and the first part of the duodenum are attached to it by the peritoneal fold called the **lesser omentum.** The main attachment of the latter to the liver is a cleft on the middle of the inferior surface termed the **porta hepatis,** or gate of the liver. Through the porta the **bile ducts** leave the liver, and the **portal vein and hepatic artery** enter. There are two main branches of each of these structures, one for the left part, or lobe, of the liver, and a larger one for the right lobe.

The Bile Ducts and Gall-bladder. The two bile ducts leaving the liver unite, and the resultant duct is called the **common hepatic duct.** It joins the **cystic duct** or duct of the **gall-bladder,** a muscular bag lying on the under surface of the right lobe of the liver, to form the common **bile duct.** This opens with the main pancreatic duct into the second part of the duodenum. The liver is producing bile continuously, but this is needed only after a meal, when the stomach contents pass into the duodenum. The bile therefore passes from the hepatic duct along the cystic duct into the gall-bladder, where it is stored for a while and concentrated. When the stomach contents enter the duodenum the gall-bladder contracts and expels its contents along the cystic duct and the common bile duct into the bowel. Bile may thus pass in either direction along the cystic duct. (For functions of the liver see p. 327.)

THE SMALL INTESTINE [1] (Figs. 26, 30 and 33)

This is the part of the alimentary tract where digestion is completed and the end-products are absorbed from the bowel for utilisation in the body. These processes take some time, and the small intestine is very long, 20 feet in all, so that the necessary time is allowed for all the useful substances to be extracted from the contents before they reach the large intestine. In order that a tube of such length can be accommodated in the abdomen, it is necessarily very much coiled, and, so that its movements may take place freely, it is completely invested by peritoneum (see p. 109). It is attached to the posterior abdominal wall by the frilled fold consisting of two layers of peritoneum and known as the **mesentery.**

---

[1] The **duodenum** has been described already.

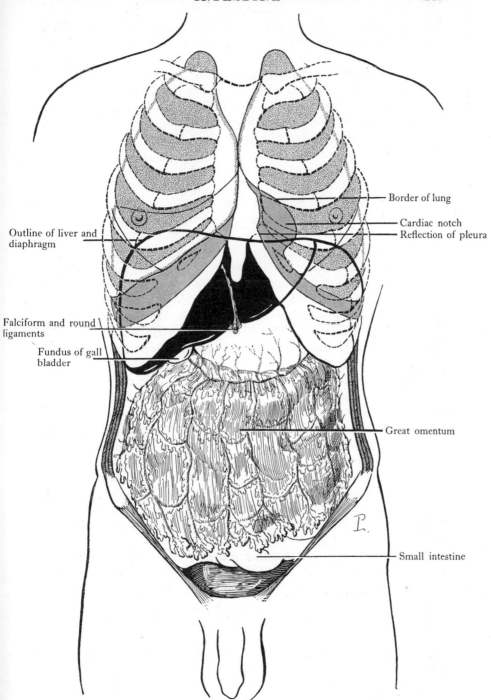

Border of lung

Cardiac notch
Reflection of pleura

Outline of liver and
diaphragm

Falciform and round
ligaments

Fundus of gall
bladder

Great omentum

Small intestine

Fig. 34. The liver, stomach and great omentum.

The mesentery carries vessels, nerves, and lymphatics to and from the gut. The small intestine is divided into two parts. The first, continuous with the duodenum at the duodenojejunal flexure, is called the **jejunum.** There is no definite demarcation of this part from the second portion, which is called the **ileum.** The ileum ends in the right iliac fossa by joining the large intestine. At the point of junction there is a thickening of the circular muscle of the ileum called the **ileocolic sphincter.** The aperture through which the ileum opens into the cæcum has projecting lips which constitute the less important **ileocolic valve.**

Structure of the Small Intestine (Fig. 35)

The wall of the intestine consists of the following coats from within outwards :—

The Mucous Coat. The mucous membrane of the small intestine is thrown into numerous folds running in a circular fashion round the bowel. These infoldings are called the **valvulæ conniventes.** They have the effect of increasing the length of the mucous membrane to considerably more than the 20 feet which the intestine itself measures. This increases the surface area available for absorption of the products of digestion from the intestinal contents. Absorption is further facilitated by the presence of hair-like projections from the mucosa which give the surface an appearance rather like the pile of velvet. These projections are called **villi.** The microscopical structure of a villus is shown in Fig. 35, C. The surface is covered by columnar epithelium, amongst which can be seen clearer " goblet cells " which secrete mucus for the lubrication of the intestine. The villus has a core of connective tissue in the centre of which is a lymphatic vessel called the **lacteal** (see Absorption of Fat, p. 124). Surrounding this is a plexus of capillaries, the blood from which will pass ultimately to the liver _viâ_ the portal vein (see Absorption of Carbohydrates and Proteins, p. 124).

Between the villi are **tubular glands** (crypts of Leiberkühn) which secrete the intestinal digestive juices. The mucosa contains also follicles of **lymphoid tissue,** which have a function similar to that found in lymphatic glands (p. 183).

In the deeper part of the mucous coat is a thin layer of muscle (muscularis mucosæ).

The Submucous Coat. This connects the mucous membrane to the muscle coat, and contains vessels and lymphatics.

The Muscle Coat. The muscle is of the involuntary type

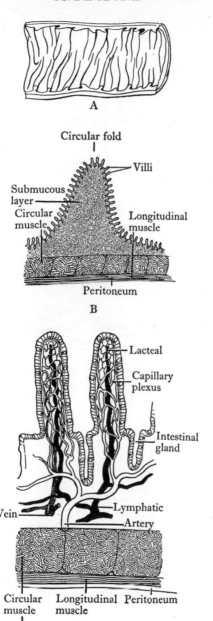

Circular fold

Villi

Submucous layer

Circular muscle

Longitudinal muscle

Peritoneum

B

Lacteal

Capillary plexus

Intestinal gland

Vein

Lymphatic

Artery

Circular muscle

Longitudinal muscle

Peritoneum

C

FIG. 35. Scheme of the structure of the small intestine. A, as seen with the naked eye. B, enlarged view of a section through a circular fold. C, a villus and intestinal glands (greatly enlarged).

and is in two layers, **inner circular** fibres and **outer longitudinal** fibres.

The Serous Coat. This is peritoneum and enables the intestine to move freely on adjacent viscera.

THE LARGE INTESTINE (Figs. 26, 30, 31 and 33)

This is arranged in an arched manner over the small intestine

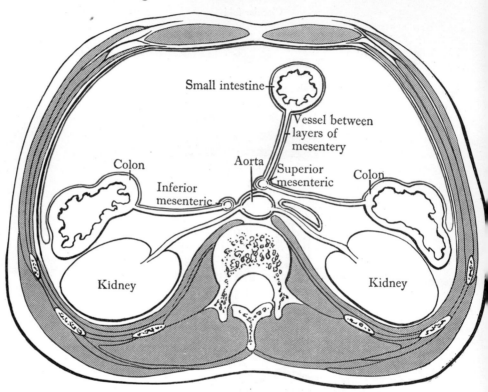

Fig. 36.   A scheme of a section across the abdomen.   The peritoneum is in red.

which lies in the concavity of its curve. It is about 5 feet in length and consists of the following parts :—

The Cæcum

This is a rounded sac, 2½ inches long, lying in the right iliac fossa. It is the part of the colon below the ileocæcal orifice, and above this opening it is continuous with the ascending colon. The **appendix** (vermiform process) springs from its posterior and medial part, about an inch from the ileocæcal junction. The appendix varies much in position and length, the latter being usually from 3 to 4 inches. The lumen of the appendix communicates with that of the cæcum.

The Ascending Colon

This passes from the cæcum below, to the front of the right kidney, where, just below the liver, it bends towards the left to become the transverse colon at the **hepatic flexure.** It is covered only in front and at the sides by peritoneum and is therefore relatively fixed on the posterior abdominal wall.

The Transverse Colon

This forms a wide loop in front of the small intestine. It is suspended from the anterior border of the body of the pancreas by a mesentery, the **transverse mesocolon,** and has applied to its anterior surface the **great omentum,** the apron-like fold of peritoneum hanging down from the greater curvature of the stomach. At the **splenic flexure,** in front of the left kidney, and just below the lower pole of the spleen, it is continuous with the descending colon.

The Descending Colon

This runs from the splenic flexure of the colon to the brim of the pelvis, where it is continuous with the pelvic or sigmoid colon. It has no mesentery, and so is more or less fixed on the posterior abdominal wall.

The Pelvic or Sigmoid Colon

The pelvic colon, continuous above with the descending colon, forms a loop in the upper part of the pelvis, and is attached by a mesentery to the region of the pelvic brim. It is continuous below with the rectum.

The Rectum (Figs. 26, 31, 62, and 63)

The rectum occupies the lower part of the posterior wall of the pelvis, and is supported in its lower part by the muscle of the pelvic floor, the **levator ani.** The latter separates it on both sides from the fat lying in the **ischiorectal fossæ.**

The rectum is not straight, as its name implies, but is curved both anteroposteriorly and from side to side. Below, it bends at a right angle to become continuous with the anal canal. Its lower part is somewhat dilated and called the **rectal ampulla.** The rectum is covered anteriorly by peritoneum in its upper two-thirds, the membrane being reflected in the male on to the back of the bladder to form the rectovesical pouch, and in the female on to the upper part of the posterior wall of the vagina to form the recto-uterine pouch (Douglas).

The Anal Canal (Figs. 62 and 63)

The anal canal is about $1\frac{1}{2}$ inches long and leads from the rectum to the exterior. It pierces the pelvic floor (levator ani muscle), superficial to which it is surrounded by the **external sphincter muscle.** The latter separates the anal canal from the ischiorectal fat, and is the muscle which, after early childhood, exerts a voluntary control over the anus.

Structure of the Large Intestine

The Mucous Coat. There are no villi in the large intestine, they being unnecessary, as only water is absorbed from this part of the bowel. The glands present are of tubular type and secrete mucus, but no digestive juices. In the rectum near the anal canal are vertical folds of mucous membrane joined to one another at their lower ends by little pocket-like folds termed the anal valves.

The Muscle Coat. The longitudinal muscle layer is not found all round the bowel, but in three bands, the **tæniæ coli.** These are shorter than the other coats, so that the latter are puckered rather in the manner of the bellows of an accordian. The bulges are called the **sacculations** of the colon. In the rectum this infolding of the other coats forms shelf-like folds on the internal surface called the valves of Houston.

The circular muscle is thickened at the recto-anal junction to form the internal sphincter of the anus. This is involuntary.

The Serous Coat. This is incomplete except in the transverse and sigmoid parts of the colon. Scattered over the surface of the large bowel are little bags of peritoneum containing fat called the **appendices epiploicæ.**

THE PERITONEUM (Figs. 30, 33, 34 and 36)

The peritoneum is the serous membrane which lines the abdomen and covers the abdominal viscera. Its purpose is to allow the viscera to move freely on one another and on the abdominal walls. The peritoneum has the form of an invaginated closed sac, one layer of which covers the wall of the abdomen and is called the **parietal layer,** whilst the other covers the viscera and is termed therefore the **visceral layer.** The exact relationship of the latter varies in different viscera. Some lie behind the peritoneum and are covered by it only in front, or in front and at the sides. Other viscera occupy a position farther away from the abdominal walls and are therefore pushed farther into the sac from behind so that they come to be suspended from the posterior abdominal wall by double folds of peritoneum called **mesenteries** through which the visceral and parietal layers are continuous with one another (Fig. 36). The peritoneal cavity is divided into two main parts. The **great sac** is the larger of these. The **lesser sac** is a part of the peritoneal cavity which lies mainly behind the stomach, and also extends for some distance below the stomach between the layers of an apron-like fold, the **greater omentum,** which hangs down from the greater curvature of the stomach to overlap the small intestine (Fig. 34).

The Mesenteries (Figs. 33 and 36)

The mesentery of the small intestine is attached obliquely to the posterior abdominal wall from the duodenojejunal flexure above, to the right iliac fossa below. It attaches the small intestine to the posterior wall of the abdomen and carries the vessels, lymphatics and nerves to and from the bowel.

The transverse and sigmoid parts of the colon have mesenteries which serve a similar function for these parts of the gut.

The Omenta (Figs. 30 and 34)

The Lesser Omentum. This is a fold of peritoneum which suspends the stomach from the inferior surface of the liver. It is attached above to the portal fissure of the liver and has between its layers the portal vein, the hepatic artery, the bile duct, and the blood-vessels, lymphatics and nerves to the lesser curvature of the stomach.

The Greater Omentum. This is an apron-like fold consisting of two anterior and two posterior layers of peritoneum, with a part of the lesser sac of the peritoneum between its anterior and posterior walls. The two anterior layers are attached to the greater curve of the stomach, the two posterior layers to the transverse colon. Between the layers of peritoneum which form the great omentum are blood-vessels and lymphatics to the greater curvature of the stomach, and a considerable quantity of fat. It forms one of the fat depôts of the body. Another function of the great omentum is to wrap itself round any focus of infection which may occur in the abdomen and by the production of a barrier round the focus to limit its spread. The whole of the peritoneum exhibits this tendency to produce adhesions between neighbouring parts in the protection of the cavity as a whole when an infection occurs in any one part of it, the adhesions tending to localise the disease to the viscus or part first affected. Because it is so frequently found wrapping up and limiting infective foci in this way, the great omentum has been named " the abdominal policeman " (Rutherford Morison).

The Peritoneal Cavity

The peritoneal cavity is the largest serous space in the body. In life, however, the viscera occupy so much of the space in the abdomen that the cavity is represented only by the chinks between coils of the intestine, etc. The peritoneum secretes fluid which lubricates the surfaces and allows the viscera to move freely one against another.

In the **erect position** the pelvic part of the peritoneum is the lowest part of the sac. With the subject **lying on the back** the lowest part is the recess between the liver and the diaphragm.

Practical Considerations. Owing to its large size, inflammations of the peritoneal membrane (peritonitis) are dangerous to life. The peritoneum has, however, amazing powers of resistance owing to the properties mentioned above. In the nursing of cases of peritonitis the patient should be propped up in bed so that if any localisation of the condition occur the abscess will form in the pelvis, where it is accessible, and not below the diaphragm, where it is difficult to reach. It should be remembered that the female genital tract opens directly into the peritoneal cavity through the uterine tube, and that infections of the uterus may spread to the peritoneum by this route. There is no such communication in the male.

CHAPTER VI

DIGESTION

FOODS

MAN takes in his requirements by a mixed diet, in which the following basic substances are represented :—

Proteins.

Fats.

Carbohydrates.

Mineral salts.

Water.

Vitamins, or accessory food factors.

Proteins. Proteins are used mainly for the rebuilding of the protoplasm of cells which has become broken down in the performance of work. Some of the proteins are essential for growth. Proteins contain nitrogen.

Animal proteins are contained in :—

Lean meat and fish.

Sweetbreads (pancreas or thymus), liver, kidney, tripe, etc.

Milk (as caseinogen).

Eggs (albumin in the white, vitellin in the yolk).

Gelatin.

Vegetable proteins are contained in :—

Cereals. Gluten in wheat is the most important protein in bread. Macaroni and spaghetti are almost pure gluten. Rice, maize, barley, sago and tapioca all contain some protein.

Vegetables. Beans, peas, carrots, and other vegetables, in smaller amounts, all contain protein. Potatoes contain a small amount.

Fruits.

Fats

Fats are used mainly as energy producers in the body. The storage of fat provides the body with a covering which plays a part in the retention of body heat.

Animal fats are taken in :—
Milk, butter and cheeses.
Eggs (in the yolk).
Fat meat.

Vegetable fats in :—
Butter substitutes.
In small amounts in some vegetables.
Cocoa and chocolate.
In frying oils (cocoa butter) and salad oils.

Carbohydrates

The oxidation or combustion of carbohydrates is the greatest source of energy in the body. Carbohydrates are contained :—

As starches : in bread and other cereals, potatoes, and many other vegetables.

As sugars : in cane and beet sugars (sucrose), in milk (lactose), fruit juices, particularly grape juice (dextrose and lævulose), malted foods, etc. (maltose).

Mineral Salts

Common salt is sodium chloride, but most table salts contain other salts as well as this.

Calcium salts are present in milk and vegetables.

Iron is present in red meat, some vegetables, and milk.

Iodine is another inorganic substance necessary in the diet.

Water

In addition to that taken in beverages, water is present in large amounts in many articles of diet, *e.g.*, potatoes.

Vitamins

Although diet may be adequate in the constituents already considered, normal life and growth cannot go on without vitamins. Six are recognised—A, B1, B2, C, D and E.

Vitamin A. This is originally derived from plants growing in air or water, and is soluble in fat. Man ingests it in fats derived from animals or fishes which feed on the plants, in the form of milk, butter, fat meat and eggs, or in oils extracted from the livers of fish (cod- or halibut-liver oil). Dried and condensed milk contain it, but vegetable fats (margarine) do not, unless it be added specially.

Vitamin A is destroyed by heat unless the air is excluded.

Deficiency in vitamin A leads to **lack of growth in young animals,** and to **increased tendency to infections.**

Vitamin B1. This is found in wholemeal flours (not in white flour), egg yolk, yeast, and in minute quantities in milk and meat. It is soluble in water.

Lack of this vitamin causes a disease of the nerves called **beri-beri.**

Vitamin B2. This has sources similar to B1. Lack of it causes dermatitis (inflammation of the skin) or the disease called **pellagra.**

Vitamin C. This is derived from fresh fruit and vegetables, and some seeds. It is abundant in oranges and lemons.

Lack of it leads to the disease called **scurvy** (scorbutis), which was at one time so prevalent in seamen who, on long voyages, were without fresh vegetables. The disease may occur in infants fed on patent foods unless fresh fruit juice or some substitute be added to the diet.

Vitamin D. This is derived from the same sources in the diet as vitamin A, but it *can be produced in the body itself* by irradiation of the skin with sunlight or ultra-violet light. The substance present in the skin from which it is formed is probably ergosterol. This vitamin regulates the absorption of calcium and so has to do with the maintenance of that balance of the relative amounts of calcium and phosphorus in the blood which determines the amount of calcium deposited in bones and teeth. Lack of it causes the disease called **rickets** (rachitis) in which the bones become soft from lack of calcium and bend, and the development of the teeth is impaired. The importance of a diet exhibiting adequate calcium and vitamin D, and of sunlight, in the treatment of rickets is obvious.

Vitamin E. This is not so well understood as the others, but it is probable that lack of it causes **sterility.**

DIGESTION

The articles constituting the food of man, although containing all the substances necessary for the provision of energy and replacement of wear and tear, are in such a form that these substances cannot be assimilated by the body without previous preparation. For example, the vegetable starches are often protected by an envelope of the resistant material called cellulose,

whilst the protein constituents of meat are held in a connective
tissue framework which protects them.   Also, the substances
themselves are too complicated to be absorbed unchanged.

Cooking liberates to some extent the essential substances,
bursting starch grains and rendering cellulose and connective
tissue softer.

Even cooked foods, however, need further preparation before
their protein, carbohydrate and fat constituents can be absorbed
and utilised by the body.   The process of preparation is called
digestion, and entails the breaking down of the complex proteins,
carbohydrates and fats into simpler substances of the same type
by the action upon them of the digestive juices.

The change is brought about by the chemical combination of
water with the more complex substances, so altering their
composition that, as a consequence, they split up into simpler
molecules.   Thus, a molecule of cane sugar and a molecule of
water combined give a molecule of glucose and a molecule of
fructose, the two latter being simpler sugars than the cane sugar.
This process of breakdown with the addition of water is called
hydrolysis.   It is a process which would, given time, take place
spontaneously, but it might take years to do so.   In the presence,
however, of digestive juices it takes place very rapidly, and this
is due to the presence in the juices of substances called **enzymes.**
The enzymes are not themselves used up in the reaction, but they
act as " catalysts " (*i.e.*, assist and hasten a reaction which would
take place much more slowly in their absence).   Since enzymes
are not used up in the processes of digestion, a very small amount
of enzyme is capable of hydrolysing a large amount of the
substrate (the substance on which it acts).   If, however, the
substances which result from the hydrolysis be allowed to
accumulate they stop the action of the enzyme eventually.   This
action of the products of hydrolysis is limited in the alimentary
tract because they are absorbed from the bowel almost as soon as
they are formed and so the enzymes are allowed to go on acting
on the remaining substrate.   The digestive enzymes act best at
the **temperature** of the body.   They are, as a rule, destroyed at a
temperature of 50° C.   The **reaction** of the medium in which
an enzyme acts is of great importance.   Some act in an acid
medium and some in an alkaline medium.   Enzymes act
specifically, that is, on one type of foodstuff only.   Enzymes
which digest carbohydrates, for instance, will produce no action
on proteins.

Digestion involves the mechanical processes which break up the food and knead and mix it with the digestive juices, and the chemical action of the juices themselves. The process begins in the mouth and ends in the small intestine.

Digestion in the Mouth

Mastication, or chewing, is the process in which the food is broken up into small particles and mixed with saliva to form the rounded mass called a **bolus.** The formation of the bolus is brought about by movements of the jaw and tongue moulding the food mass against the palate. The molar teeth are used for grinding the food, the incisors for biting it.

Saliva

Saliva is the digestive juice produced by the parotid, submandibular (submaxillary) and sublingual glands and poured out into the mouth. It is continually being produced, but its amount is increased by the presence of food in the mouth, and by the sight and smell of appetising dishes. Its secretion is a **reflex** response to the above stimuli.

The nerve impulses pass along the sensory nerves from the mouth, nose and eyes to the brain, which then sends impulses along the nerves which supply the parotid, submandibular and sublingual salivary glands. The latter nerves belong to the parasympathetic system (p. 278).

Conditions of severe emotional disturbance may stop the secretion of saliva. The dry mouth of fear is an example of this.

Appearance and Composition of Saliva. Saliva is a slightly opalescent slimy fluid. It consists mainly of water, salts, mucus, and the **starch-splitting enzyme ptyalin.** It is alkaline in reaction.

Action of Saliva

.**Ptyalin** has a chemical action.

This enzyme acts on **cooked starches,** producing the sugar called **maltose,** and **dextrin,** the latter substance being subsequently changed into maltose also. Ptyalin acts in an alkaline medium.

There is not time for all the starch to be acted upon in this way in the mouth, and salivary digestion continues for some time in the stomach after the food is swallowed. The action is eventually stopped by the acid gastric juice.

The ptyalin present in the saliva of infants is not so active, so starchy foods are unsuitable at this early age.

Mucus has a mechanical action.

The mucus lubricates the surface of the food so that it can be swallowed easily. It is produced by some of the cells in the submaxillary and sublingual glands.

Water has both mechanical and chemical actions.

Some of the water is used in the hydrolysis of the starch.

Some is utilised to soften the food.

Some dissolves the substances which stimulate the nerve endings of taste.

Apart from its functions in digestion, saliva keeps the mouth moist, thus assisting the movements of the tongue and lips in speech.

Deglutition or Swallowing

Swallowing takes place in three stages, which follow one another immediately to make one continuous act. The first stage is voluntary, the second and third are involuntary.

Stage 1. The food having been masticated and mixed with saliva to form a bolus, the latter is pressed between the tongue and the palate and pushed backwards towards the oropharyngeal isthmus by movement of the tongue.

Stage 2. This occurs in the pharynx. The bolus having reached the oropharyngeal isthmus, it is pushed on into the oral pharynx by further movement of the tongue and by contraction of the muscles of the palatine arches. At the same time the soft palate is raised into contact with the posterior pharyngeal wall so as to prevent food entering the nasopharynx. The bolus is then gripped by the action of the constrictor muscles which push it on down the pharynx. It is prevented from entering the larynx as follows :—

(a) The tongue and epiglottis overhang the superior laryngeal aperture, and, by the contraction of muscles attached to the hyoid bone, the whole framework of the larynx is raised towards the base of the tongue. This, and the contraction of the muscle round about the superior laryngeal aperture, so reduce the size of the opening that the food is unlikely to pass into it.

(b) The speed at which the bolus is projected by the constrictor muscles carries it past the laryngeal aperture so fast that it is unlikely to enter.

(c) Food touching the posterior wall of the pharynx at once sets up a reflex act by which respiratory movements are inhibited until the food has passed the superior laryngeal aperture.

Stage 3. Once through the pharynx, the food is passed down the œsophagus by the peristaltic contraction of its muscle. Having been passed by peristalsis down the œsophagus, the bolus passes through the cardiac orifice into the stomach.

The above description applies to the swallowing of solids. Fluids are squirted by the pharyngeal constrictors into the œsophagus, which is at the time relaxed or open. Gravity and the "pump" action of the constrictors give the momentum to carry the fluid to the lower end of the œsophagus, and when a sufficient weight of fluid has accumulated here it passes on into the stomach.

Peristalsis

This is the type of movement which propels the contents along the whole of the gut, and also along many other tubes in the body (see Ureter, etc.). A powerful stimulus to its production is the stretching of the muscle in the wall of the tube by the presence of contents within the lumen. It may also be produced by other forms of mechanical stimulation, by stimulation of the motor nerves to the viscus concerned, or by the action of chemicals (purgatives) which either produce increase in the amount of fluid present (salines), or stimulate the nerve endings or the muscle.

Peristalsis consists of a wave of contraction preceded by a wave of relaxation passing progressively along the wall of the gut. The effect produced may be imitated if a cylinder be rolled along a rubber tube filled with fluid.

In the intestine other movements take place which knead and mix the contents. They are called **segmentation** movements.

Digestion in the Stomach

The most important *rôle* played by the stomach is the **initiation of protein digestion.** Digestion of carbohydrate, commenced in the mouth, continues, however, for a time in the stomach, and a very slight action on fats also takes place. Gastric digestion is brought about by the **gastric juice** secreted by the glands in the wall of the stomach, assisted by the movements of the stomach which mix the food thoroughly with the juice.

Gastric Juice. This is produced by the tubular glands in the mucous membrane lining the stomach, partly in response to stimuli reaching the stomach along the vagus nerves, and partly by the presence of chemical substances in the stomach itself.

Nervous Factors. The impulses passing along the vagi are set up in response to stimuli reaching the brain along sensory nerves, mainly those of taste and smell. Thus, starting an appetising meal at once increases the flow of juice. Distasteful food does not evoke this response, hence the importance of tempting the palate in feeding invalids. This " appetite secretion " of juice is another example of reflex action.

Chemical Factors. As stated above (p. 115), one of the products of salivary digestion is the substance called **dextrin.** This stimulates the gastric mucous membrane to produce gastric juice. There is evidence to show also that the hydrochloric acid, which is a normal constituent of gastric juice, produces a substance called **gastrin** when it comes into contact with the mucous membrane of the pyloric part of the stomach. The gastrin is absorbed into the blood-stream from the pyloric mucosa, and, circulating in the blood, stimulates the mucous membrane of the body of the stomach to produce more juice. Thus, the juice produced by nervous stimuli and by dextrin results in the production of gastrin, which stimulates the stomach to produce yet more juice until the contents have been emptied completely into the duodenum.

Composition of Gastric Juice. Gastric juice is an acid fluid containing about 99·4 per cent. of water. The important constituents from the point of view of digestion are the enzymes **pepsin, rennin** and **gastric lipase,** and dilute **hydrochloric acid** (0·02 to 0·2 per cent.). The enzymes are produced from granules previously present in the cells of the gastric mucosa. The way in which the hydrochloric acid is produced is not known, except that it is in some way associated with cells called oxyntic cells, which are present in the upper part of the stomach.

Action of Gastric Juice

1. **Rennin.** **Milk** contains the protein **caseinogen** as well as **fats** (butter), **milk sugar** (lactose), and **salts** (principally **calcium phosphate**). Rennin in some way alters the caseinogen, which is then precipitated, in the presence of calcium salts, to form the insoluble protein **casein.** (This does not take place in the absence of calcium salts.) The casein in its precipitation entangles with it the **fat,** and the resultant coagulum is called **curd.** The liquid **whey** which remains contains the sugar and salts.

The casein formed in this process of curdling of milk is subsequently digested like any other protein (see below).

2. **Pepsin and Hydrochloric Acid.** These two constituents act

together on **proteins,** converting them in progressive stages into simpler protein-like substances called **peptones.** These are still too complex to be absorbed and will undergo further changes in the intestine.

The substances intermediate between proteins and peptones are called metaproteins and proteoses.

3. **Lipase.** A certain amount of fat is digested in the stomach because of regurgitation through the pylorus of duodenal contents containing bile and pancreatic juice. Apart from this, however, a very small quantity of fat is digested by the enzyme **lipase** present in the gastric juice. The protein envelopes of the fat cells are first digested by pepsin and hydrochloric acid, leaving the fat itself free to be acted upon by the lipase.

4. **Hydrochloric Acid alone.** Gastric juice kills, or inhibits the growth of, bacteria swallowed with the food, and thus prevents putrefaction of the stomach contents. This **antiseptic** action is due to the hydrochloric acid.

Hydrochloric acid can also break down **cane sugar** into **fructose** and **glucose.** It has no action on starches.

The Arrest of Salivary Digestion. For some time after the bolus of food reaches the stomach the saliva goes on acting on the carbohydrates contained in it. Soon, however, the hydrochloric acid of the gastric juice stops the action of the ptyalin, which, it will be remembered, acts in an alkaline medium. The action is stopped at once, therefore, in the superficial parts of the bolus, but goes on for longer at the centre to which it takes some time for the hydrochloric acid to penetrate. The dextrin formed by the salivary digestion is a stimulus to the formation of gastric juice.

Movements of the Stomach. The movements of the stomach are, like those of the rest of the gut, quite involuntary. They are co-ordinated so as to mix the food with the gastric juice, and to pass the stomach contents periodically in small quantities into the duodenum.

The food leaving the œsophagus accumulates at first in the upper part of the body of the stomach, which acts as a sort of reservoir, exerting a fairly uniform pressure on the contents and delivering them to the pyloric part. The pyloric part acts as a mill or churn, mixing the contents by means of peristaltic waves passing along it. At each of these peristaltic contractions, which begin in the body and pass towards the pylorus, the pyloric sphincter opens and allows a small amount of chyme (digested stomach contents) to pass through into the duodenum. This sequence of events continues until the stomach is completely emptied. The time taken for complete emptying varies considerably with the type of food taken, being shortest for carbohydrates and longest for fats. After an ordinary meal the stomach should be completely empty in from four to six hours.

The stomach contents being fluid, the position of the organ when full is influenced by posture. In the erect position the fundus is occupied by a bubble of air, which may, if large, press on and embarrass the heart (palpitation).

Practical Considerations

Gastric Ulcer. This condition is often associated with a high acidity of the gastric juice, the exact cause being unknown. The ulcer may erode the wall of the stomach and involve surrounding viscera or blood-vessels, giving rise to vomiting of blood (hæmatemesis), or it may perforate the wall of the stomach and burst into the peritoneal cavity.

Pyloric stenosis, or narrowing, may result from the healing of a gastric or duodenal ulcer. In infants it is usually due to hypertrophy of the muscle of the pyloric sphincter. The stomach being unable to expel its contents into the duodenum, vomiting results.

Vomiting. Usually only the contents of the stomach are vomited, but intestinal contents may regurgitate into the stomach and be brought up also. The usual cause is something in the contents irritating the stomach, but inflammation of the wall (gastritis) or obstruction of the pylorus or intestine may have the same result.

Effect of Exercise. Violent exercise immediately after a meal inhibits the secretion of gastric juice and the movements of the stomach.

Digestion in the Intestine

When the food leaves the stomach to enter the duodenum it is called **chyme.** The reaction of this fluid is acid, due to the presence of the hydrochloric acid of the gastric juice. It contains partially digested carbohydrate and protein. The fat has had the envelopes removed from the cells, and is in the form of oily droplets suspended in the fluid. In the small intestine digestion is completed and the end-products of digestion are absorbed from the gut, the residue being passed on into the large intestine where, by the further absorption of water, the fæces or stools are formed.

The further digestion is brought about by the action of the **pancreatic juice** and the **intestinal juice.** The pancreatic juice is assisted, especially in the digestion of fats, by the **bile.**

Pancreatic Juice

This is an alkaline fluid containing about $97\frac{1}{2}$ per cent. water, inorganic salts, and three enzymes. These enzymes are produced from the granules present in the secreting cells of the pancreas. They are : **Trypsinogen,** which acts on protein ; **amylase,** which acts on starch ; and **lipase,** which acts on fats.

Secretion of Pancreatic Juice. The mechanism of the secretion of pancreatic juice is rather a complicated one. There is evidence to show that **nervous impulses** reaching the pancreas along the **vagus nerves** are responsible for the secretion of some juice. Much of the juice is formed, however, in response to a different stimulus. When the stomach contents pass into the duodenum they set up peristaltic waves there. Coincident with the passage of these waves the sphincter at the lower end of the bile duct relaxes and allows a little bile to pass into the duodenum. Fat is by far the most important of the stomach contents producing this liberation of bile. From the combined action of the bile and the gastric hydrochloric acid the duodenal mucosa produces a substance called **secretin,** which is absorbed into the blood-stream and, reaching the pancreas by this route, results in a further flow of juice.

Action of Pancreatic Juice

Trypsinogen. This enzyme can break down partially digested proteins into **amino-acids,** which are sufficiently simple to be absorbed. This action is intensified by the action of bile and of intestinal juice which convert the relatively inactive trypsinogen into **trypsin,** which can act on *all* proteins.

Amylase. This enzyme converts **starch** (even uncooked starch) into **maltose.** It is found only in very small amount in the juice of infants, so that starch is not a suitable food for very young children.

Lipase. This digests **fat,** converting it into **glycerol and fatty acid.** Some of the fatty acid combines with alkali in the pancreatic juice to form **soaps,** which make an emulsion of the fats. The fat in emulsion is in very small droplets and so is more easily acted upon by the lipase. The action of lipase is also helped by the presence of bile, the salts of which reduce surface tension and allow the fats to be emulsified more easily.

The Intestinal Juice

The intestinal juice is secreted by the tubular glands in the intestinal mucous membrane. Its actions are :—

1. It **activates trypsinogen** (secreted by the pancreas), converting

it into the more powerful enzyme trypsin, which can act on all proteins. This conversion is due to the substance called **enterokinase** present in the intestinal juice.

2. It **digests carbohydrates,** converting them into glucose. **Cane sugar** is acted on by the enzyme **sucrase.** **Maltose** is digested by **maltase.** **Lactose** is digested by the enzyme **lactase.**

3. It **digests proteoses and peptones** (derived from proteins by the action of the gastric and pancreatic juices), converting them into amino-acids. This action is due to the enzyme **erepsin.**

SUMMARY OF THE ACTION OF DIGESTIVE JUICES

Juice.	Enzymes.	Reaction.	Substrate.	Result.
Saliva	Ptyalin	Alkaline	Cooked starch	Maltose and dextrin
Gastric juice	Rennin	Acid	Caseinogen of milk	Casein
	Pepsin	,,	Proteins including casein	Acid metaprotein ǀ Proteoses ǀ Peptones
	Lipase (gastric)	,,	Fat	Glycerol and fatty acid
Pancreatic juice	Trypsinogen (converted into trypsin by enterokinase of intestinal juice)	Alkaline	Proteins Proteoses Peptones	}Amino-acids
	Amylase	,,	Starch	Maltose
	Lipase (pancreatic)	,,	Fat	Glycerol and fatty acids. (Some of fatty acid and alkali form soaps which emulsify fats.)
Intestinal juice	Enterokinase	Alkaline	Trypsinogen	Trypsin
	Sucrase	,,	Cane sugar	Glucose and fructose
	Maltase	,,	Maltose	Glucose
	Lactase	,,	Lactose	,,
	Erepsin	,,	Proteoses and peptones	Amino-acids

PRODUCTS OF DIGESTION

Carbohydrates are broken down to **glucose.**
Proteins are broken down to **amino-acids.**
Fats are broken down to **fatty acids and glycerol.**

ABSORPTION

The end-products of digestion are in solution in the intestinal contents and have to be absorbed so that they can be utilised by the tissues of the body. The glucose and fructose and the amino-acids are absorbed into the capillary blood-vessels of the villi. The fatty acids and the glycerol are reunited to form fat by the epithelium covering the villus, and the fat is then taken up by the central lymphatic vessel or lacteal in the interior of the villus. During these processes the muscle in the villi contracts from time to time. This " pumping " action of the villi may have something to do with absorption, but the main factors are the forces of diffusion and osmosis, and the " vital action " of the intestinal epithelium.

Diffusion and Osmosis

The substances to be absorbed, being in solution, are subject to the physical forces of diffusion and osmosis.

If equal quantities of water and a solution of salt be placed together in the same vessel they will mix until a solution of salt of half the strength of the solution originally added to the water is produced. This is termed **diffusion.**

If the salt solution be placed in a vessel made of parchment or some similar substance, and the whole be suspended in a vessel containing water, it will be found after some time that both vessels contain a salt solution weaker than the original one. This means that salt must have passed out of the salt solution through the parchment into the water, and water from the outer vessel into the interior of the parchment vessel. This is termed **osmosis,** and the salt in solution is said to exert a certain **osmotic pressure** which causes it to behave in this way. The intestinal mucous membrane and the walls of the blood-vessels act in a manner similar to the parchment. The blood or lymph in the vessels in the villi and the solution of the products of digestion contained in the intestine are comparable with the two liquids in the above experiment.

Absorption of Carbohydrates and Proteins

The osmotic pressures of amino-acids and glucose are different in the blood from what they are in the intestinal contents, so that, by a process of osmosis, they pass through the epithelium of the villus and the walls of the vessels in the villus into the blood. This process of **osmosis,** however, accounts for a relatively small part of absorption, and a process which is imperfectly understood, but which is termed the '' **vital activity** '' of the epithelial cells covering the villi, plays a very important part in passing the substances from the intestinal lumen into the blood.   (If these cells be destroyed very little absorption takes place.)

The blood leaving the intestine thus contains the end-products of protein and carbohydrate digestion in the form of amino-acids and glucose respectively.   The veins draining the intestine enter the **portal vein** (p. 177), which goes to the liver and there breaks up into a further set of capillaries, which bring the blood intimately into contact with the gland cells of the liver.   These cells allow as much glucose as is needed at once by the tissues of the body to pass into the blood leaving the liver and thence into the general circulation, the blood-vessels carrying it to the tissues, which thus replenish their store of energy producing material.   The sugar which is not wanted at once is stored by the liver cells as **glycogen.** When sugar is wanted by the body this glycogen is converted back again into glucose by the action of a ferment (glycogenase) on the liver cells.   The glucose mobilised is swept into the general circulation and so finds its way to the tissues.

The amino-acids needed at once by the body for the rebuilding of its tissue proteins are also passed through the liver into the general circulation.   The excess amino-acids over the immediate requirements of the body are changed by the liver cells, with the production of the substance called **urea,** which enters the blood leaving the liver and is carried by the general circulation to the kidneys, where it is excreted as one of the constituents of urine.

In certain circumstances excess glucose and amino-acids can be converted into fat by the liver (see p. 328).

Fats

The fat in the form of fatty acids, glycerol, and soaps is changed by the epithelium of the villi back again into fat as it is absorbed. This fat differs from that taken in the food in that it is now of the variety peculiar to human beings.   This is another example of the vital activity of the epithelial cells.   In the form of minute droplets, the fat is taken up by the lymphatic vessel in the centre of the villus and thence into the lymph vessels draining the intestine. The droplets of fat in the lymph make it look rather like milk, so the lymph vessels draining the intestine are called **lacteals.** The lacteals finally join the main lymphatic vessel of the body, the **thoracic duct** (p. 183), which opens into the junction of the left internal jugular and subclavian veins in the neck. The lymph containing fat here mixes with the blood in these vessels and the fat is carried by the blood into the general circulation. Such of it as is not needed at once to provide a source of energy in the tissues (see Metabolism, p. 211) is first altered by the liver (p. 328) and then carried to the various **fat depots** of the body, where it is stored in cells until required. The main fat depots are the subcutaneous tissues, the space round the kidneys, and the omenta and mesenteries of the peritoneum.

The Function of the Large Intestine

The intestinal contents which pass through the ileocæcal opening into the cæcum have already had almost all the nutritive substances absorbed from them. They are still fluid, and the further extraction of water is necessary to bring them to the consistency of the formed fæces, or stools. This water is absorbed by the vessels in the mucous membrane of the large intestine.

The Fæces

The fæces contain about 75 per cent. of water. The solid matter consists largely of cellulose (which is not digested in the human intestine), bacteria, which are for the most part dead, and desquamated epithelial cells. The presence of a sufficient quantity of indigestible cellulose to form " roughage " in the diet is important in providing the necessary bulk to the fæces to give a stimulus to proper action of the muscle of the large intestine. Such cellulose is present in fruits, vegetables and brown meal, etc. The colour of the fæces is due to the presence of bile pigments, and the characteristic odour to the presence of gases produced by bacterial decomposition in the colon, and to substances called indol and skatol.

The colon is capable of absorbing a few other substances as well as water. Glucose and salts can be absorbed, and this is the rationale of the administration of enemata of these substances in conditions of starvation or shock (rectal feeding and rectal salines). Ether is absorbed from the colon, but, if administered in this way (rectal anæsthesia), it must be mixed with oil so that it does not irritate the mucous membrane. Some substances are also excreted into the colon, *e.g.*, salts of iron, magnesium and calcium.

Contents begin to enter the cæcum four and a half hours after a meal, but do not reach the rectum until eighteen hours after taking the food. During this period the percentage of water is reduced from 90 to 75. Normally the rectum is empty, but shortly after the taking of a meal (usually breakfast) the fæces are passed on from the pelvic colon into the rectum and there stimulate the bowel to contract. This sets up the urge for defæcation.

The act of defæcation itself is brought about by voluntary contraction of the abdominal muscles, the diaphragm, and the muscles of the pelvic floor, which increases the intra-abdominal pressure. This is accompanied by peristalsis in the whole colon and relaxation of the sphincters of the anus, so that the fæces are passed out through the anal canal. If the call to defæcation be resisted or neglected, further absorption of water from the fæces takes place, they become hard, and constipation results.

CHAPTER VII

THE BLOOD

THE blood is a red, viscid, opaque fluid, slightly alkaline in reaction. When shed from the blood-vessels (or in some abnormal conditions in the vessels themselves) it forms a jelly or clot (see Coagulation, p. 133).

Blood consists of two parts, a yellowish fluid called **plasma,** in which are suspended cells of various types, the **blood corpuscles.** The total amount of blood present in the body is about 5 litres, or one-fifteenth of the body weight.

THE PLASMA

The composition of the plasma is as follows :—

Water	90 per cent.
Serum Proteins . . .	Fibrinogen.
	Albumin.
	Globulin.
Salts	Mainly sodium chloride.
	Potassium chloride, and some phosphates of calcium and magnesium are also present.
End-products of Digestion .	Amino-acids.
	Glucose.
	Fats.
Waste Products . . .	Urea and uric acid.
	Creatine and creatinine. Xanthine.
	Carbon dioxide (as sodium bicarbonate).
Secretions	The secretions of the ductless glands.

The concentration of salts in the blood-plasma is of very great importance. The salts preserve the alkalinity of the blood at the correct level, preventing the blood from becoming too alkaline or not alkaline enough. They are therefore called " buffer salts." They also maintain the red cells in proper condition (see

Hæmolysis). Some of the salts are essential for the proper action of tissues, such as muscle, epithelium, etc., whilst calcium salts form an important constituent of bone.

Filtration of the plasma through the walls of capillaries provides the *tissue fluid* necessary for the metabolic exchanges between the blood and the tissues.

THE BLOOD CORPUSCLES

These are of two kinds, red and white (Fig. 37).

Red Corpuscles (Erythrocytes)

These cells function as the **oxygen carriers** of the blood by virtue of the compound of iron called **hæmoglobin** which they

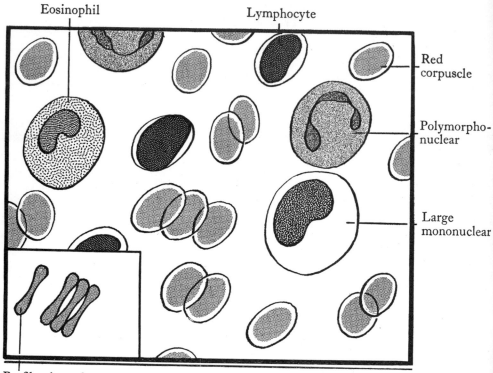

Fig. 37.
Cells of the blood

contain. The hæmoglobin, which is responsible for the red colour of the blood, is contained within an envelope like that of other cells, but the mature red corpuscles differ from other cells in having no nucleus. In form, they are biconcave discs, measuring $\frac{1}{3000}$ of an inch in diameter and about $\frac{1}{12000}$ of an inch thick at the edge. They can alter their shape so as to pass through openings smaller than their diameter, and in whole blood they tend to concentrate in rouleaux like piles of coins.

Number of Red Corpuscles and Colour Index. There are five million red corpuscles in 1 cubic millimetre of blood in males, the number being slightly less in females. The number becomes increased in people living in rarefied air, where there is relative lack of oxygen (*e.g.*, high altitudes).

The efficiency of blood as an oxygen carrier depends on its content of hæmoglobin, and this is expressed by the **colour index** (percentage of hæmoglobin divided by the percentage of red blood corpuscles). Normal blood has a colour index of 1. If the total hæmoglobin content be low and the number of red corpuscles normal, then the colour index becomes a fraction of 1, so that, although the number of corpuscles is normal, the oxygen-carrying power of the blood is seriously impaired.

Origin and Fate of Red Corpuscles. During the whole of extrauterine life red corpuscles are being destroyed and must be replaced. The average life of a red corpuscle in the blood has been estimated at about three to four weeks. The red cells are formed in the red bone-marrow found at the ends of long bones and in the flat bones such as the ribs, scapula and skull bones. The cells from which they are formed are nucleated, but as they become mature and before they are set free into the blood-stream they lose their nuclei.

In conditions of severe anæmia the red bone-marrow increases in amount, and the demand for red cells may be so great that they are set free into the circulation before they become mature and lose their nuclei.

When they become worn out, the red corpuscles are dealt with by the **reticulo-endothelial system.** This system is represented by endothelial cells in the **spleen, liver (Kupffer cells), bone-marrow, lymph sinuses,** etc. The hæmoglobin is set free and the iron is extracted from it by the endothelial cells of the system.

The iron is returned to the bone-marrow and other tissues to be used again. The iron-free part is converted into the pigment **bilirubin,** which gives the colour to the bile.

Hæmolysis. If red corpuscles be placed in solutions of salt more dilute than the blood plasma, osmosis occurs through the cell envelopes, the corpuscles swell up and burst, and the hæmoglobin is set free into the solution. This is termed **hæmolysis** or **laking of the blood.**

Function of Hæmoglobin. Hæmoglobin combines readily with oxygen to form **oxyhæmoglobin.** The compound is not, however, a very stable one, and the oxyhæmoglobin can easily give up its oxygen again.

The blood picks up oxygen as it passes through the capillaries of the lungs and carries it, combined with the hæmoglobin, to the tissues. Here the oxygen leaves the corpuscles and passes, *viâ* the tissue fluid, to the tissue cells which utilise it. The hæmoglobin which has given up the oxygen (reduced hæmoglobin) is darker in colour than the oxyhæmoglobin, so that the venous blood returning from the tissues is bluish in colour. That in the arteries (containing a large percentage of oxyhæmoglobin) is bright red.

White Corpuscles or Leucocytes

These are transparent masses of protoplasm all containing nuclei. Their number varies from 6,000 to 8,000 per cubic millimetre of blood. The number is increased by bodily activity and decreased by rest. Their number is also enormously increased in most infections (see Immunity, p. 131).

Many of these cells possess the power of **amœboid movement** in a marked degree. In this activity the cell alters its shape, the protoplasm flowing from one part to another so as to form processes projecting from the cell body. Having advanced one of these processes, the remaining protoplasm may flow into this process, and the cell moves from its original position into that occupied by the process it advanced. Processes advanced by the cell may surround extrinsic matter such as food, micro-organisms, etc., and in this way such particles are ingested into the cell. The amœboid movement exhibited by the leucocytes is the mechanism by which the body deals with the micro-organisms which produce disease (see Immunity). The varieties, characters, number, and site of origin of the leucocytes are shown in the following table :—

Variety.	Characters.	Percentage of total leucocytes.	Site of origin.
Lymphocytes	Small round cells with small amount of clear protoplasm round the nucleus.	20–25 per cent.	Lymphoid tissue (lymph glands, tonsil, spleen, etc.)
Large mono-nuclear cells	Large round cells, with much clear cytoplasm round the nucleus	1 per cent.	Probably the reticulo-endothelial system
Polymorpho-nuclear cells	Nucleus is lobed or multiple. Cytoplasm contains fine granules staining with neutral dyes	70 per cent.	⎫
Eosinophil cells	Irregular nucleus. Large granules stain with acid dyes	½–4 per cent.	⎬ Bone marrow
Basophil cells	As eosinophil, but granules stain with basic dyes	½ per cent.	
Transition types		2–4 per cent.	⎭

Immunity

Immunity is the power possessed by the body of resisting and overcoming infection. The blood and lymph play an important part in this protection of the body against micro-organisms. The protective function is due partly to the plasma and partly to the white cells of the blood.

Plasma in Immunity. Foreign substances in the blood act as what are called **antigens,** and stimulate the production of bodies inimical to them called **antibodies** [1] in the plasma. These antibodies are of various types, some of the more important being :—

[1] In the union of antigen with antibody a substance called **complement** present in the plasma is used up. This **fixation of complement** is the basis of several blood tests for the presence of diseases, *e.g.*, the Widal reaction in typhoid fever and the Wassermann reaction in syphilis.

Bacteriolysins, which kill the germs themselves.

Agglutinins, which precipitate the germs into clumps.

Antitoxins, which neutralise the poisons produced by the bacteria.

Substances called **opsonins** are also produced in the plasma and alter the bacteria in some way so that the leucocytes can ingest them more easily.

Cells in Immunity. As already stated, the leucocytes, due to their amœboid movement, can ingest micro-organisms. In the process they are often themselves killed by the organisms. The dead cells can be removed by the large mononuclear cells of the blood and by the cells of the reticulo-endothelial system, but if killed in large numbers they form the solid part of the **pus** or matter in the interior of an **abscess.** In most infections the number of leucocytes in the blood increases enormously. This is termed **leucocytosis.**

The **lymphatic system** (p. 181) is another protection for the body against disease.

Artificial Immunity. The occurrences described above follow an attack of the particular disease concerned and are the phenomena of natural immunity. For some years attempts have been made, with varying success, to prevent and treat disease by the administration of antigens or antibodies artificially.

The following are some examples which have been dramatically successful :—

Smallpox. An immunity which lasts several years is conferred by vaccinating the patient with the virus of cowpox, a disease similar to smallpox. This is an example of prevention of the disease.

Typhoid Fever. Preventive inoculation is practised and will guard the patient against the disease for a period of about three years. A suspension of killed typhoid bacilli is injected into the body, and, acting as an antigen in the blood, will result in the production of antibodies against living typhoid bacilli.

In diphtheria and tetanus (lock-jaw) the serum of an animal, which has been rendered immune by the injection of very gradually increased doses of the organisms of the disease, is injected into the patient. This serum contains antibodies against the disease, and, if injected in time, will diminish materially the severity of the attack. These sera are termed **antitoxic sera.**

Many other examples could be quoted if space permitted.

Coagulation or Clotting of Blood

This process is a protection for the body against excessive loss of blood in the injuries which are unavoidable in ordinary life. The process is occasionally deficient in the familial disease called **hæmophilia.** Persons suffering from this disease (bleeders) rarely reach adult age.

Coagulation is due to the conversion of the protein **fibrinogen** into the form called **fibrin.** In its precipitation, the fibrin entangles the cells of the blood and forms the **clot.** The fluid part which remains is the plasma minus the fibrin and is called **serum.** The conversion of fibrinogen into fibrin is brought about by the substance **thrombin.** This is not present, as such, in the blood in the blood-vessels. It is formed by the union of its precursor **prothrombin** with **calcium salts.** This union is probably prevented in the blood-stream by the combination of the prothrombin with another substance, **cephalin.** When blood is shed the damaged tissues and small bodies called **platelets** in the blood set free a substance which combines with the cephalin and thus liberates the prothrombin. The prothrombin thus set free unites with calcium salts of the blood to form thrombin, which, with the fibrinogen, forms fibrin.

The process may be summarised as follows :—

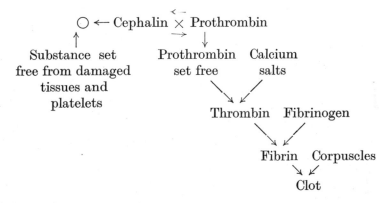

Coagulation Time

The normal time taken for coagulation in man is from seven to eight minutes. The process begins in *two minutes* from the shedding of the blood.

Coagulation is hastened by contact of the blood with foreign substances and by agitation of the blood.

It is retarded by the addition of certain salts (citrates are used to prevent the blood clotting in one method of blood transfusion), and by contact with oiled or waxed surfaces.

Summary of the Functions of the Blood

1. To provide fluid in the tissues.
2. To carry oxygen and foodstuffs to the tissues.
3. To carry carbon dioxide and other waste products from the tissues.
4. To protect the body from disease.
5. To clot when it is shed.
6. To convey the secretions of certain glands (*see* ductless glands, p. 315) to all parts of the body.

CHAPTER VIII

THE CIRCULATORY SYSTEM

THE circulatory system consists of the heart and blood-vessels. The heart acts as a muscular pump driving the blood round the vessels.

THE BLOOD-VESSELS

The blood-vessels are of three types, namely, arteries, capillaries, and veins.

The Arteries

The arteries are branches of two great vessels **leaving the heart**, the **aorta** coming from the left side of the heart and going to the whole body except the lungs, and the **pulmonary artery** coming from the right side of the heart and going to the lungs.

The arteries divide and subdivide, giving off successively smaller branches as they reach the tissues they supply. The smallest are called **arterioles,** and their branches are continuous with the capillaries. Both arteries and arterioles have elastic walls.

The walls of arteries have three layers or coats :—
The outer coat (adventitia) is composed of fibrous tissue.
The middle coat (media) is made up of plain muscle and elastic tissue.
The internal coat (intima) is composed of a single layer of endothelium forming a smooth lining on which the blood will not clot.

The Capillaries

The capillaries are microscopic vessels which bring the blood into intimate relationship with the tissues. They anastomose so freely with one another that they form a **network** which communicates on one side with the arterioles and on the other with the venules.

The walls of the capillaries are formed of a single layer of endothelium, so that the blood is separated from the tissues by a very thin layer. It is through this layer that the exchanges between the blood and the tissue fluid take place. The diameter of the capillaries is uniform, and is just a little larger than that of a red blood corpuscle.

135

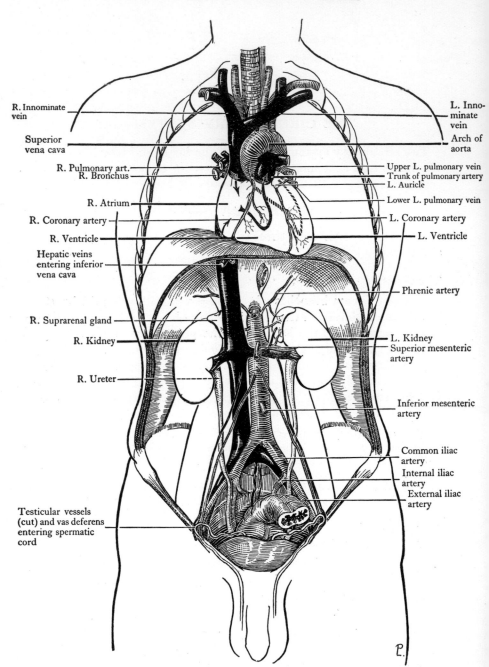

FIG. 38. The heart and great vessels.

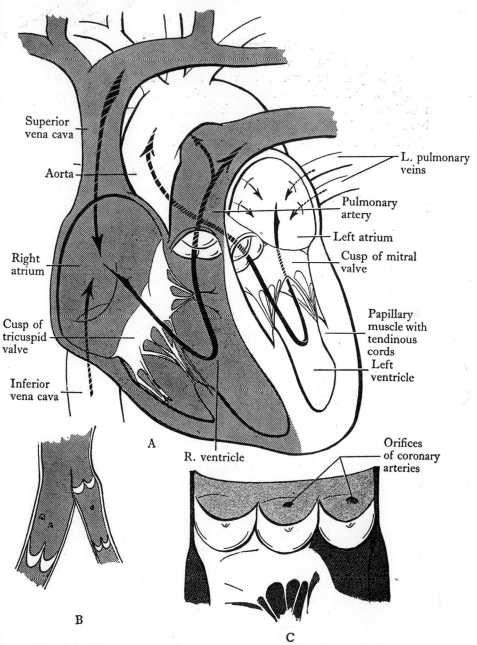

Superior
vena cava

Aorta

Right
atrium

Cusp of
tricuspid
valve

Inferior
vena cava

L. pulmonary
veins

Pulmonary
artery

Left atrium

Cusp of mitral
valve

Papillary
muscle with
tendinous
cords

Left
ventricle

A

R. ventricle

Orifices
of coronary
arteries

B

C

FIG. 39.   A. Interior of the heart.   The shaded part is the right side.
          B. Valves in veins.
          C. The cusps of the aortic valve.   (The aorta has been slit open.)

The Veins

The veins begin in the tissues as **venules,** which are formed by the union of capillaries. Joining with one another to form successively larger vessels, the veins **return the blood to the heart.** The walls of veins are like those of arteries, but contain less muscle and elastic tissue. The blood is prevented from flowing backward along the veins by little pocket-like folds of the endothelial lining called **valves** (Fig. 39B).

The three types of vessels react differently when cut owing to the difference in their structure. The arteries remain tubular in form owing to the firmness of their walls. If cut completely across the internal coat curls up inside the others, partially occluding the lumen. Veins collapse when cut across, partly owing to the relative softness of their walls, and partly to the low blood pressure in their interior. Capillaries ooze when cut, having no tissue to contract or close them.

The thickness of the walls of arteries is determined by the average pressure of the blood they contain.

THE HEART

The heart (Figs. 38 and 39) is the hollow muscular organ responsible for the circulation of the blood. It is about the size of the clenched fist, and is situated in the lower part of the thorax, behind the sternum and costal cartilages, and above the diaphragm. It is enclosed within the pericardium (p. 142), which separates it on each side from the lungs, and behind from the œsophagus.

In shape the heart is more or less conical, with the **apex** pointing downwards, forwards, and to the left, and the **base** facing backwards, upwards, and to the right. The basal part of the heart comprises the **atria** (auricles), the part towards the apex the **ventricles.** The interior is divided into right and left parts by the **septa,** so that there are the following cavities in the heart :—

The **right and left atria.**

The **right and left ventricles.**

At the junction of the atria with the ventricles the heart muscle (myocardium) is interrupted by fibrous rings which surround the atrioventricular orifices, and the surface of the heart shows in this situation the atrioventricular groove (coronary sulcus).

Surface Marking of the Heart (Fig. 30).

The position of the heart can be marked out on the surface of the chest by the following lines :—

The **right border,** a line about 1 inch to the right of the sternum from the third costal cartilage to the sixth costal cartilage.

The **inferior border,** by a line from the sixth right costal cartilage where it joins the sternum to a point in the fifth left intercostal space $3\frac{1}{2}$ inches from the median plane. This point overlies the **apex** of the heart.

The **left border,** by a line from the apex to the second left costal cartilage near where it joins the sternum.

Chambers of the Heart

The Atria

The atria receive blood from the veins and pass it on to the ventricles. The walls of the atria are thin, and, in the living, are bulged out by the contained blood. In front of the anterior concave surface of the atrial part of the heart lie the aorta and pulmonary artery coming from the ventricles. Small parts of the atria (the auricular appendages) overlap these two vessels anteriorly.

The Right Atrium. The right atrium is placed in front and to the right of the left atrium. Opening into its posterior part are the following veins :—

The **superior vena cava,** which drains the blood from the head and neck, the upper limbs, and the thoracic wall.

The **inferior vena cava,** which drains the lower part of the body.

The **coronary sinus,** which drains blood from the heart itself.

Below and in front, the right atrium communicates with the right ventricle through the right atrioventricular orifice, which is guarded by the **tricuspid valve.**

On the septum separating the right atrium from the left is a depression called the **fossa ovalis,** which indicates the situation of the obliterated foramen ovale, which during fœtal life transmits blood from the right atrium to the left.

The Left Atrium. The left atrium occupies a position behind and to the left of the right atrium.

Entering it are the **four pulmonary veins** (two from each lung). The left atrium communicates with the left ventricle through the left atrioventricular orifice, which is guarded by the **bicuspid** or **mitral valve.**

The Ventricles

The ventricles are responsible for driving the blood into the arteries. They have, therefore, more work to do than the atria and their muscular walls are very thick.

The Right Ventricle. The right ventricle forms a large part of the anterior surface of the heart. It receives blood from the right atrium through the right atrioventricular orifice. The interior of most of the ventricle has walls which are marked by numerous muscular ridges. Three small conical masses of muscle, the **papillary muscles,** also project into the interior. These muscles are connected each to two of the cusps of the tricuspid valve by **tendinous cords** (cordæ tendineæ). The papillary muscles and tendinous cords prevent the valve cusps being turned inside out into the atrium when the pressure in the ventricle rises. The outlet from the right ventricle leads into the **pulmonary artery,** the orifice being guarded by the **pulmonary valve.**

The Left Ventricle. The left ventricle is separated from the right ventricle by the interventricular septum. As it has to drive the blood round the whole body, except the lungs, its walls are thicker than those of the right ventricle. Blood enters from the left atrium through the mitral valve, the two cusps of which are connected by **tendinous cords** to two **papillary muscles** projecting into the interior of the ventricle. The outlet from the left ventricle leads into the **aorta** through the **aortic valve.**

The Valves of the Heart

The valves are formed by infoldings of the endothelial lining of the heart strengthened by a small amount of fibrous tissue.

The **atrioventricular valves** (tricuspid and mitral) prevent the reflux of blood from the ventricles to the atria when the former contract. They have to withstand great pressure, as the muscle of the ventricles is very thick and strong. These valves are therefore provided with tendinous cords and papillary muscles to prevent them from being turned inside out.

The **aortic and pulmonary valves** have each three cusps rather like watch-pockets. When blood enters the aorta and pulmonary artery these vessels are distended or stretched. The elastic recoil of their walls tends to squeeze the blood backwards as well as forwards along these vessels when the ventricles have ceased contracting. Reflux into the ventricles is prevented by closure of the valves. The elastic recoil is then expended in propelling the blood along the vessels.

Blood-vessels of the Heart

The heart is supplied with blood by the right and left **coronary arteries,** which arise from the ascending aorta. Blockage of the lumen of one of the coronary arteries may cause sudden death due to the cutting off of the blood supply to a large part of the heart muscle.

The veins of the heart drain mainly into the **coronary sinus,** a venous channel occupying the posterior part of the atrioventricular groove on the heart. Many small veins (venæ cardiæ minimæ), however, open directly into the right atrium.

Nerves of the Heart

Near the entry of the superior vena cava into the right atrium is a collection of tissue forming the **sinuatrial node.** This node sends out rhythmic impulses to the surrounding muscle and excites it to contract. The rate of contraction depending thus on these impulses, the sinuatrial node has been called the " pace-maker " of the heart. The beat spreads across the atrial walls and finally reaches another collection of nerve cells at the junction of the atria and ventricles called the **atrioventricular node.** The impulse cannot pass across the fibrous rings at the atrioventricular junction, so a special bundle of modified muscle, the **atrioventricular bundle of His,** is provided to conduct the impulse across and make the ventricles beat at the same rate as the atria. The bundle begins at the atrioventricular node and passes down the septum of the heart to reach the ventricles. Damage to the bundle prevents the impulses from passing, and the ventricle then beats at its own inherent rate, which is slower than that of the normal heart beat. This condition is called heart-block.

The sinuatrial node, and other parts of the nervous tissue of the heart, can be influenced by impulses from the sympathetic and vagus nerves.

Stimulation of the **sympathetic** nerves **increases the rate** of the heart.

Stimulation of the **vagus** nerves **slows** the heart.

The Pericardium (Fig. 31)

The heart and small portions of the vessels entering and leaving it are enclosed in the **pericardium**. This consists of two parts, the fibrous and the serous.

The Fibrous Pericardium. The fibrous pericardium is a tough resistant bag enclosing the heart. As it cannot be stretched, it prevents over-distension of the cavities of the heart.

The Serous Pericardium. The serous pericardium enables the heart to move freely within the fibrous pericardium. It consists of a **parietal** layer lining the inner surface of the fibrous pericardium, and a **visceral** layer, sometimes known as the epicardium, which covers the heart. The two layers are continuous with one another along the great vessels. Between the layers is a film of fluid which allows them to rub against one another without friction.

PHYSIOLOGY OF THE HEART

The Cardiac Cycle

The heart muscle contracts in beats throughout the whole of life, waking and sleeping. Muscle, after a period of activity, must have a period of rest to recover. No prolonged rest is possible for the heart, so it takes its rest in short periods after each contraction. The period of contraction at each beat is called **systole**, and the period of rest, during which the heart muscle is relaxed, is termed **diastole**. The two periods together form one complete **cardiac cycle**.

There being normally seventy-two beats of the heart per minute, each cardiac cycle lasts about 0·8 of a second, of which systole occupies less than one-half and diastole more than one-half. If the heart beat faster, each cycle is shorter, but the time is saved by shortening diastole, systole remaining about the same length as normal. This means that the heart gets less rest when it beats faster.

Diastole. During this period blood is flowing into the heart from the great veins—into the right side of the heart from the caval veins, and into the left side from the pulmonary veins. At first the blood flows into the atria, but as these fill, the atrioventricular valves being open, the blood flows through into the relaxed ventricles. This venous filling of the heart is assisted by the negative pressure in the thorax (see Respiration). When the atria and ventricles are full, systole begins.

Atrial Systole occurs before that of the ventricles. The atrial muscle contracts, squeezing the blood into the already full ventricles, distending them a little more. Blood is prevented from flowing back into the veins during atrial contraction because the muscle round the orifices of these vessels is the first part of the atrial muscle to contract, and this constricts the orifices.

Ventricular Systole. Contraction of the ventricles follows immediately the contraction of the atria. The rise of pressure in the ventricles resulting from contraction of the muscle closes the atrioventricular valves. For the moment, therefore, the ventricles are closed cavities, both the atrioventricular and the watch-pocket valves on the aorta and pulmonary artery being closed. Because of the continued contraction of the ventricular muscle, the pressures in the ventricles become greater than those in the aorta and the pulmonary artery, and the valves guarding these vessels open, allowing the blood to pass into them from the ventricles. Thus the pressures in the aorta and pulmonary artery rapidly become greater than those in the ventricles (which have emptied themselves into these vessels), and this causes the valves guarding them to close and prevent the reflux of blood into the ventricles during diastole.

Note that *both* atria contract together and *both* ventricles contract together, although the right and left sides of the heart serve somewhat different functions (see Pulmonary circulation).

Summary of the Events of the Cardiac Cycle

Diastole (Fig. 40 A).
Aortic and pulmonary valves closed.
Atrioventricular valves open.
Blood flowing from veins into atria and through into ventricles.
Muscle of heart relaxed.
Systole (Fig. 40 B).
1. **Atrial contraction** drives blood into ventricles.
   Atrioventricular valves begin to close.
2. **Ventricular contraction** :—
(*a*) Closes atrioventricular valves.
(*b*) Opens aortic and pulmonary valves.
(*c*) Empties ventricles into aorta and pulmonary artery.
   Rise of pressure in aorta and pulmonary artery closes their valves.
   Fall of pressure in ventricles allows atrioventricular valves to open.

144

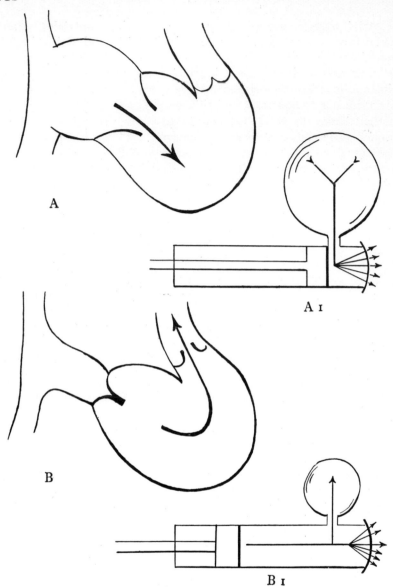

FIG. 40.

A. *Diastole.* Semilunar valve (aortic or pulmonary) closed to prevent reflux
   of blood into ventricle ; blood is flowing from veins, through atrium, through
   open atrioventricular valve, into ventricle.
B. *Systole.* Atrial contraction is completed and ventricle is beginning to
   contract ; atrioventricular valve is closed to prevent reflux of blood into
   atrium (tendinous cords are omitted).
   Semilunar valve (aortic or pulmonary) is open.
B1. *Systole.* Force of piston (contraction of ventricular muscle) expended
   partly in squirting fluid through rose of syringe (arterioles), partly in
   distending rubber bag (elasticity of arteries).
A1. *Diastole.* Piston has reached limit of traverse (ventricular contraction
   over) ; flow of fluid through rose (arterioles) is kept up by recoil of distended
   rubber bag (elastic recoil of arterial walls).

Rate and Output of the Heart

When the tissues of the body, particularly muscle, are very active they need an increased supply of oxygen to satisfy their demands. This increase in oxygen is provided by increase in respiration, but in order that the extra oxygen may reach the tissues, more blood carrying it must flow through the capillaries in a given time. There must be an increase in the *amount* of blood delivered to the blood-vessels in conditions of activity, that is to say, there must be an increase in the output of blood from the heart.

Increase in the output can be brought about by filling the heart more at each beat, or by increasing the number of beats per minute. Increase in the heart rate can increase the output only if sufficient blood is provided to fill the heart properly at each beat. Increase in venous return to the heart is thus absolutely necessary to increase its output. If the heart beat very fast there is not time during the short diastole for it to fill completely with blood, and, in spite of the increased rate, the output may actually be diminished.

The Heart Rate is increased by :—

1. Higher **temperature** of the blood warming the sinuatrial node (pacemaker). This accounts for the increase in rate in fever, and to some extent for that in exercise.

2. **Increased venous inflow** distending the right atrium causes stimulation of nerves in its wall and **reflex** increase in rate by reduction of the activity of the vagi and increase in that of the sympathetic nerves (see p. 276).

3. The setting free of **adrenaline** into the blood (see p. 321).

4. Stimulation from the **higher centres** of the brain. Pain, emotion, etc., bring about this action by increasing sympathetic activity, and decreasing vagal activity.

The Venous Inflow into the Heart is increased by :—

1. Increased respiration sucking more blood into the great veins in the thorax.

2. Increased activity of the muscles propelling blood more quickly along veins in the limbs (see p. 150).

The Heart Sounds and Apex Beat

Listening over the heart, two sounds can be heard, which have been likened to the spoken words, "lubb-dupp."

The first sound (lubb) is caused mainly by the contraction of the ventricular muscle and the impact of the apical region against the chest wall consequent on the hardening of the heart muscle. The closure of the atrioventricular valves contributes to the sound.

The second sound (dupp) is caused by the closure of the semilunar valves (aortic and pulmonary). If these valves be incompetent the sound may be replaced by a hiss or murmur.

The Apex Beat. The apex beat can be seen in the fifth left intercostal space 3½ inches from the median plane.

It is caused by the stiffening of the heart muscle pushing the apex against the chest wall.

CIRCULATION OF THE BLOOD

The blood pumped out by the left ventricle is carried by the aorta and its branches all over the body except to the lungs. The blood is returned from the body by the veins entering the right side of the heart. This is the **systemic circulation.** From the right side of the heart the impure venous blood is pumped into the pulmonary artery, which carries it to the two lungs, where it is purified. The pure blood is returned to the left side of the heart *viâ* the pulmonary veins. This is the **pulmonary circulation.**

Blood from the intestine is not returned at once to the great veins, but drains into the portal vein which passes to the liver, where it breaks up into capillaries. This is termed the **portal circulation,** and differs from the systemic system in that the blood goes through two sets of capillaries before regaining the heart.

Circulation in the Arteries

The impulse given to the blood by the contraction of the ventricles is the initial force responsible for the circulation of blood along the arteries. As the arteries divide, their branches become progressively smaller, the final ramifications, the arterioles, being very tiny. An analogy may be drawn to the ordinary garden syringe in considering the effects of this, although there are very marked differences in the circulation. In squirting water through the tiny holes in the rose of the syringe the pumping force is the plunger operated by the hand. This is represented in the circulation by the pumping force of the heart; the holes in the rose represent the arterioles. During the operation of squirting, the pressure in the syringe rises and water leaves the rose at a pressure sufficient to project it a considerable distance over the flower-beds being watered. When the plunger is fully depressed (corresponding to the end of systole of the heart) the pressure falls, and the flow from the syringe ceases. Blood, however, continues to flow through the blood-vessels during diastole of the heart as well as during systole. Where, then, is to be found the difference in the circulatory system from the syringe ? It lies in the capacity of the arteries and arterioles to stretch, and it is this which maintains the pressure of blood in the vessels at a level sufficient to keep the flow going during diastole. We can modify the syringe to make it more like the circulation by fitting at the side a distensible rubber bag (Fig. 40). A part of the force imparted by the plunger will now be utilised in squirting water through the holes in the rose, and a part in distending the bag with water. At the end of the traverse of the plunger the elastic recoil of the walls of the bag will keep on squirting water through the rose for a considerable time longer. In the same way the force imparted by the heart beat is utilised partly in driving the blood through the peripheral vessels, which, because of their small lumen, offer a considerable **peripheral resistance** to the flow of blood. The remainder of the force is expended in distending the muscular walls of the arteries and arterioles all over the body. When the semilunar valves close at the end of ventricular systole the elastic recoil of the vessel walls keeps up the flow through the arterioles during diastole. The elasticity in the system is generalised over the arteries and arterioles of the whole body, and is not localised as in the experiment with the syringe.

Blood Pressure

Since blood is flowing continuously through the arterioles it is obvious that the blood in the arterial system must be under considerable pressure. This is called the **blood pressure.**

The more easily blood can flow through the arterioles, *i.e.*, the less the peripheral resistance, the lower this pressure will be. Variation in the tone of the muscle in the walls of the arterioles is therefore one of the main factors in raising or lowering the blood pressure. If the arterioles be constricted the pressure rises ; if they be dilated the pressure falls.

Since the flow through the arterioles is continuous, it follows that at each heart beat the pressure in the whole of the arterial system must rise, as more blood enters it during systole. This extra blood is accommodated partly, but not entirely, by distension of the arteries, so that the difference in blood pressure during systole from that during diastole is not so great as might be expected. The actual values in man are :—

Systolic pressure, 110 to 135 millimetres of mercury.

Diastolic pressure, 60 to 80 millimetres of mercury.

The difference between systolic and diastolic pressures is termed the **pulse pressure.**

Thus blood pressure depends on the following factors, variation in any of which will alter the pressure :—

1. The total volume of fluid in circulation.
2. The output of the heart.
3. The elasticity of the arteries.
4. The peripheral resistance offered by the arterioles.

The arterioles contract or dilate in response to impulses reaching them from the sympathetic nervous system (p. 276). The effects are co-ordinated by the **vasomotor centre** in the hindbrain.

The blood pressure rises during exercise due to increase of the heart output and constriction of the arterioles.

As age advances the walls of the blood-vessels lose their elasticity (hardening of the arteries). This loss of elasticity brings about a rise in systolic pressure, as the extra blood pumped into the arterial system during systole cannot be accommodated by stretching of the arteries. The diseased vessel walls may not be capable of with-standing the increased pressure and they may give way. When occurring in the small arteries of the brain this causes the condition called cerebral hæmorrhage (apoplectic stroke).

The Pulse

The sudden distension of the arteries during systole gives rise to an impulse felt over the artery and called the **pulse.** This can be elicited most easily over the radial artery at the wrist, as this vessel is very superficial at this point.

The rate of the pulse is an indication of the rate of the heart.

The strength gives an indication of the output of the heart.

The tension, or pressure necessary to stop the pulse, is an indication of the blood pressure.

The average pulse rate is seventy-two per minute, but this may vary considerably in different individuals.

The pulse rate is increased in conditions such as muscular exercise, fever, etc., in which the heart is quickened.

When the heart output is increased the pulse is full and bounding in character.

Circulation in the Capillaries

As the blood enters the capillary network it is subject to the rhythmic variations in pressure due to the heart beat. In the capillary network, however, the blood becomes spread out over a wide area as compared with the area occupied in the arterioles. The capillaries therefore do not pulsate, and the pressure within them is constant. Owing to the enormous ramification of the capillaries and their successive branching into vessels *which are all of the same size*, and not smaller than those which preceded them, the blood pressure in the capillaries becomes much lower than that in the arterioles, there being little resistance to the passage of the blood through these vessels.

The capillaries can contract and dilate, the mechanism by which they do so being incompletely understood.

It may be taken as a general rule that they dilate during activity of a tissue and contract during rest.

The capillaries of the skin contract under the influence of cold and dilate when the skin is warmed, this being part of the heat-regulating mechanism (see p. 313).

In **shock** the capillaries dilate enormously, especially in the viscera. The increase in total capacity of the capillaries is so great that they drain blood away from other vessels to fill themselves, and the general blood pressure falls. This leads eventually to failure of the circulation, as the heart does not receive sufficient blood to keep it working properly.

As the blood flows through the capillaries it gives up oxygen to the tissues and takes up the carbon dioxide produced as a result of cell activity. Some of the fluid part of the blood passes through the walls of the capillaries partly by filtration and osmosis, and partly by the activity of the endothelial cells which form the capillary walls. This fluid is the tissue fluid, or **lymph,** which bathes the cells and forms the medium through which the **metabolic exchanges** take place between the blood and the tissues. If the tissue fluid were not removed the tissues would become waterlogged. After taking up waste products from the cells and giving up nutritive material to them, some of the fluid is returned to the capillaries. The remainder is collected by the lymphatic vessels (p. 181), and is eventually returned to the blood *viâ* the thoracic duct and the right lymph duct.

In conditions where there is over-production of tissue fluids due to increase in the capillary pressure from obstruction of veins, or when there is deficient drainage into the lymphatics, the fluid stagnates in the tissues. This is termed **œdema**, or dropsy.

Circulation in the Veins

The flow of blood in the veins, like that in the capillaries, is continuous, and is not subject to the pulse variations.

The pressure in veins is low, and gradually decreases from the periphery towards the heart. The great veins entering the heart are subject to the effects of the negative intrathoracic pressure.

The flow of blood along the veins depends on :—

1. The blood delivered to them from the capillaries.

2. The action of muscles " milking " the blood along the veins towards the heart. Flow away from the heart is prevented by the valves on the veins.

3. The suction exerted by the negative intrathoracic pressure.

If one of the veins near the heart be cut, air may be sucked in because of the negative pressure. This may produce serious effects on the circulation (air embolism).

Hæmorrhage. Infusion. Transfusion

When blood-vessels are cut, bleeding occurs until it is naturally or artificially arrested.

In *arterial hæmorrhage* the blood, being oxygenated, is bright red in colour, and it escapes in spurts synchronous with the heart beats.

Capillary hæmorrhage is a steady oozing of bright red blood from the cut surface.

Venous hæmorrhage is characterised by the welling of dark blood from the wound.

Effects of Hæmorrhage

If a large amount of blood be lost the blood pressure falls, and the skin becomes pale because of lack of blood in its capillaries. As many red cells are lost the oxygen-carrying power of the blood is impaired and respiration becomes deep and sighing in character.

Arrest of Hæmorrhage

Natural Arrest. This is brought about by :—

1. Fall in blood pressure.

2. Collapse of veins, or curling up of the inner coat of arteries (p. 135).

3. Coagulation of blood in the cut end of the vessel. This clot is subsequently converted into a scar which seals the end of the vessel permanently.

Artificial Arrest. This is aided by :—

1. Pressure. Pressure must be applied on the side of the wound nearer the heart if the vessel be an artery, and on the side farther from the heart if a vein. In all cases local pressure by a dressing over the wound assists.

2. Posture. The part affected should be raised so as to drain as much blood as possible away from it.

3. Coagulation can be hastened by chemicals termed styptics (*e.g.*, alum) or by the action of heat (the actual cautery, or hot solutions).

Infusion

Subcutaneous or intravenous injection of normal saline solutions will make up the fluid lost, but is more useful in shock (p. 149) than in hæmorrhage.

Blood Transfusion

Transfusion of blood is injection of the blood of one person, the donor, into the blood vessels of another, the recipient. It is carried out in the treatment of severe bleeding and in certain other conditions. Care must be taken to ascertain by tests performed beforehand that the blood is a suitable one. Some individuals are universal donors and can give their blood to anyone else. Most people, however, belong to other blood groupings, and if their blood be injected into other people it may be destroyed, or may even result in the death of the recipient, unless the tests to which reference has been made above be carried out.

CHAPTER IX

THE PRINCIPAL BLOOD-VESSELS OF THE BODY

THE SYSTEMIC ARTERIES

The Aorta (Figs. 39, 41 and 46)

THE aorta arises from the left ventricle and carries arterial blood all over the body, except to the lungs.

The Ascending Aorta. This is the first $2\frac{1}{2}$ in. of the vessel. It is entirely within the pericardium and passes in front of the root of the right lung. It arises from the left ventricle and is continuous with the arch of the aorta. The **coronary arteries,** right and left, which supply the heart arise from it.

The arch of the aorta, the continuation of the ascending aorta, passes across the front of the trachea and, arching first above and then behind the root of the left lung, finally is continuous with the descending thoracic aorta (p. 163) at the left side of the body of the fourth thoracic vertebra. The arch is directed almost directly antero-posteriorly.

The arch of the aorta gives off the innominate, the left common carotid, and the left subclavian arteries in that order from right to left.

The innominate artery arises from the arch of the aorta as that vessel lies in front of the trachea. It passes upwards, backwards and to the right to reach the side of the trachea, and behind the right sternoclavicular joint it divides into the subclavian and common carotid arteries for the right side.

The **left subclavian** and the **left common carotid** arteries arise directly from the arch of the aorta, and have a short intrathoracic course before passing into the neck behind the left sternoclavicular joint.

ARTERIES OF THE HEAD AND NECK

The Common Carotid Artery (Figs. 41 and 42)

This vessel arises on the right side from the innominate and on the left from the arch of the aorta. Entering the neck from

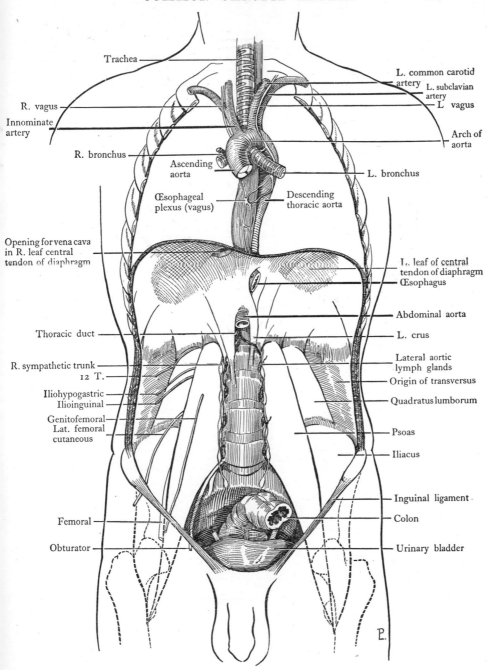

Trachea

L. common carotid artery

L. subclavian artery

R. vagus

L. vagus

Innominate artery

Arch of aorta

R. bronchus

Ascending aorta

L. bronchus

Œsophageal plexus (vagus)

Descending thoracic aorta

Opening for vena cava in R. leaf central tendon of diaphragm

L. leaf of central tendon of diaphragm

Œsophagus

Abdominal aorta

Thoracic duct

L. crus

R. sympathetic trunk

Lateral aortic lymph glands

12 T.

Origin of transversus

Iliohypogastric
Ilioinguinal

Quadratus lumborum

Genitofemoral
Lat. femoral cutaneous

Psoas

Iliacus

Inguinal ligament

Femoral

Colon

Obturator

Urinary bladder

Fig. 41.   The aorta.

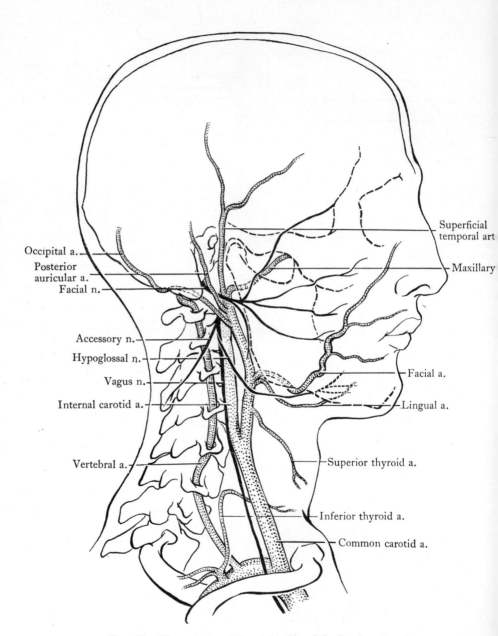

Occipital a.

Posterior
auricular a.

Facial n.

Accessory n.

Hypoglossal n.

Vagus n.

Internal carotid a.

Vertebral a.

Superficial
temporal art

Maxillary

Facial a.

Lingual a.

Superior thyroid a.

Inferior thyroid a.

Common carotid a.

FIG. 42.   The arteries of the right side of the head and neck.

behind the sternoclavicular joint on each side, the vessel runs up the cleft underneath the sternomastoid muscle, embedded in the fascia called the **carotid sheath.** Lateral to it lies the internal jugular vein, with the vagus nerve in the interval between the two vessels posteriorly. At the level of the upper border of the thyroid cartilage (fourth cervical vertebra) it divides into its only branches, the internal and external carotid arteries.

Pressure Point. The common carotid artery can be compressed against the transverse process of the sixth cervical vertebra (carotid tubercle). The manœuvre is not without risk, as the vagus nerve may be pressed at the same time and the action of the heart impaired.

The Internal Carotid Artery (Fig. 42)

This artery continues in the line of the common carotid to the base of the skull. There it enters the carotid canal in the temporal bone and passes into the inside of the skull to give the main supply to **the brain.** The ophthalmic artery to the orbit and **eye** is also given off from the internal carotid.

The External Carotid Artery (Fig. 42)

The external carotid emerges from the cleft under the sterno-mastoid muscle and curves upwards to a point just behind the angle of the mandible, where it enters the parotid gland. In the gland just in front of the ear it divides into its terminal branches.

Branches of the External Carotid

Superior thyroid . . .	To the thyroid gland and larynx.
Lingual	To the tongue.
Occipital	To the back of the scalp.
Posterior auricular . . .	To the back of the ear.
Facial	To the face.
Terminal { **Maxillary** . .	To the muscles of mastication.
{ **Superficial temporal** .	To the side of the scalp.

Pressure Points. There are no points where the internal and external carotid arteries can be compressed efficiently.

The branches of the external carotid can be compressed as follows :—

Lingual : by pulling the tongue bodily forwards.

Facial : as it crosses the jaw two fingers' breadths in front of the angle.

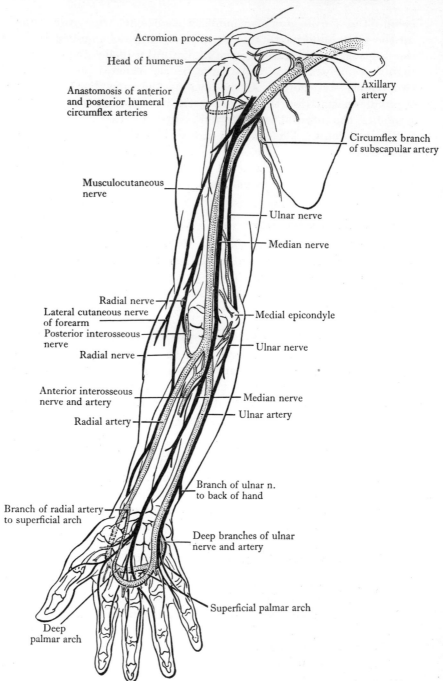

FIG. 43. Arteries and nerves of right upper limb, anterior aspect.

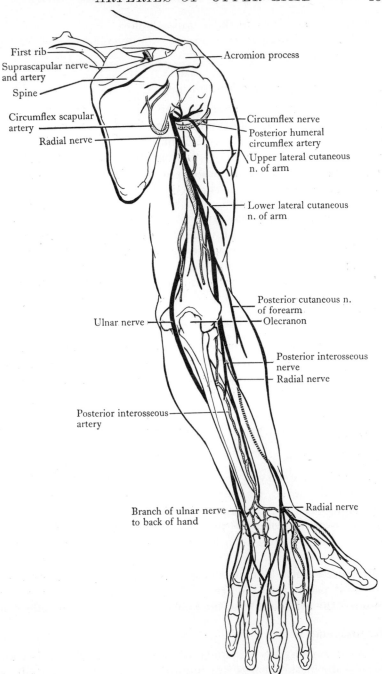

First rib

Suprascapular nerve
and artery

Spine

Circumflex scapular
artery

Radial nerve

Acromion process

Circumflex nerve

Posterior humeral
circumflex artery

Upper lateral cutaneous
n. of arm

Lower lateral cutaneous
n. of arm

Posterior cutaneous n.
of forearm

Olecranon

Posterior interosseous
nerve

Radial nerve

Ulnar nerve

Posterior interosseous
artery

Branch of ulnar nerve
to back of hand

Radial nerve

FIG. 44. Arteries and nerves of right upper limb, posterior aspect.

Occipital : as it lies on the occipital bone.

Superficial temporal : as it crosses the zygomatic arch just in front of the ear.

The Subclavian Artery (Figs. 41 and 42)

The subclavian artery arises on the right from the innominate and on the left from the arch of the aorta. On each side it emerges into the root of the neck from behind the sternoclavicular joint and arches a little above the medial half of the clavicle. Finally, passing behind the middle of the clavicle, it crosses the first rib and is continued as the axillary artery.

Branches of the Subclavian Artery

Vertebral. This passes through the foramina in the transverse processes of the cervical vertebræ and through the foramen magnum to supply the brain.

Thyrocervical. This supplies muscles of the neck and shoulder, and gives off the inferior thyroid to the thyroid gland.

Internal Mammary.
Costocervical. } These supply the chest wall.

Pressure Point. The subclavian can be compressed as it crosses the first rib. Pressure must be made deeply in the hollow above the middle of the clavicle, and the head inclined to the same side to relax the muscles.

ARTERIES OF THE UPPER LIMB (Figs. 43 and 44)

The Axillary Artery

The axillary artery is the continuation of the subclavian. It passes in a curved manner through the axillary space and is surrounded by the nerves of the brachial plexus.

It gives off branches to the walls of the axilla, to the shoulder and the breast. It is continued into the arm as the brachial artery.

Pressure Point. The vessel can be compressed only in its lower part as it passes into the arm. Placing a pad in the armpit and bringing the arm closely to the side of the body may be effective.

The Brachial Artery

The brachial artery is a continuation of the axillary artery and extends down the arm to the middle of the bend of the elbow, where, opposite the neck of the radius, it divides into radial and

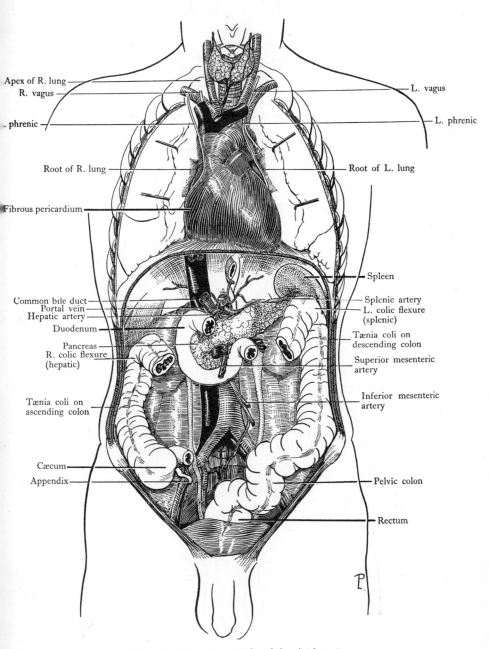

Apex of R. lung

R. vagus

. phrenic

Root of R. lung

Fibrous pericardium

Common bile duct

Portal vein

Hepatic artery

Duodenum

Pancreas

R. colic flexure
(hepatic)

Tænia coli on
ascending colon

Cæcum

Appendix

L. vagus

L. phrenic

Root of L. lung

Spleen

Splenic artery

L. colic flexure
(splenic)

Tænia coli on
descending colon

Superior mesenteric
artery

Inferior mesenteric
artery

Pelvic colon

Rectum

FIG. 45. Branches of the abdominal aorta.

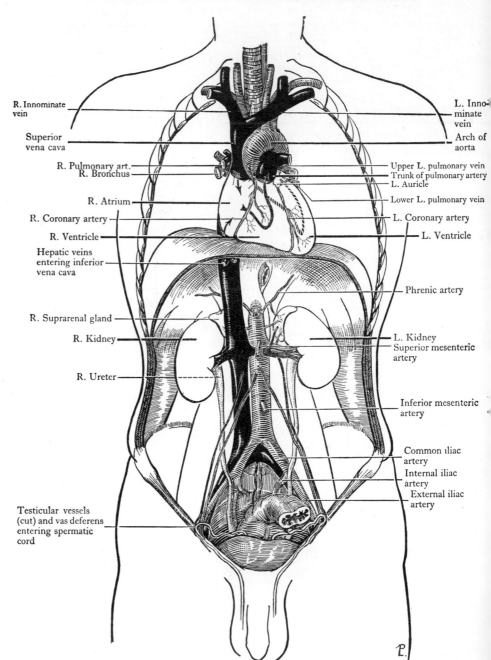

R. Innominate vein

Superior vena cava

R. Pulmonary art.
R. Bronchus

R. Atrium

R. Coronary artery

R. Ventricle

Hepatic veins entering inferior vena cava

R. Suprarenal gland

R. Kidney

R. Ureter

Testicular vessels (cut) and vas deferens entering spermatic cord

L. Inno-minate vein

Arch of aorta

Upper L. pulmonary vein
Trunk of pulmonary artery
L. Auricle

Lower L. pulmonary vein

L. Coronary artery

L. Ventricle

Phrenic artery

L. Kidney
Superior mesenteric artery

Inferior mesenteric artery

Common iliac artery
Internal iliac artery
External iliac artery

FIG. 46   The aorta and its branches.

ulnar arteries. In its course through the arm it lies first medial to the humerus on the triceps muscle. At the middle of the arm it passes on to the front of the humerus over the coracobrachialis muscle, and in the lower half of its course it lies on the brachialis muscle. It is overlapped on the lateral side by the biceps muscle and is accompanied by two companion veins which lie one on each side of the vessel.

The brachial artery gives off muscular branches, and vessels which descend to the elbow joint and there anastomose with branches of the vessels in the forearm.

Pressure Points. The brachial artery can be compressed against the humerus almost anywhere along its course. It can be felt just along the medial border of the biceps muscle. At its lower end it can be compressed by placing a pad over the bend of the elbow and flexing the forearm on the pad.

ARTERIES OF THE FOREARM AND HAND

The Radial Artery

The radial artery begins as a branch of the brachial at the middle of the bend of the elbow. It passes distally over the muscles attached to the front of the radius to the styloid process of that bone. It next winds round the lateral side of the wrist, crossed by the tendons going to the thumb. Reaching in this way the back of the wrist, it finally dips through the first intermetacarpal space to reach the palm of the hand, where it forms, with the deep branch of the ulnar artery, the deep palmar arterial arch. In its course through the forearm the radial artery is placed very superficially, being almost immediately beneath the skin. Its superficial position at the front of the wrist makes it a suitable vessel for timing the pulse.

Branches of the radial artery in the region of the elbow run backwards to anastomose with branches of the brachial artery; in the forearm branches are given to the surrounding muscles; at the wrist and in the hand the radial artery gives off branches which form with similar branches of the ulnar artery a series of arterial arches for the supply of these parts.

The Ulnar Artery

The ulnar artery is the other branch of the brachial artery at the bend of the elbow. It runs obliquely medially at first,

ANATOMY. 11

covered by the flexor muscles attached to the medial epicondyle. In the lower two-thirds of the forearm it follows the front of the ulna, becoming more superficial in the lower third. At the wrist it passes into the hand by crossing the flexor retinaculum superficially, and it divides finally into deep and superficial branches which form, with branches of the radial artery, the deep and superficial palmar arterial arches.

Branches of the ulnar artery are similar to those of the radial. It gives off also a branch which divides into the anterior and posterior interosseous arteries which run on the corresponding surfaces of the interosseous membrane.

Arterial Arches of the Wrist and Hand

Carpal Arches. At the wrist the radial and ulnar arteries give off branches which cross the front and the back of the lower ends of the bones, and anastomose to form the anterior and posterior carpal arches. The dorsal carpal arch and the radial artery itself give small branches to the posterior surface of the hand and the thumb and fingers. These are the dorsal metacarpal arteries.

Palmar Arches. The thumb and the lateral side of the index finger are supplied by branches of the radial artery, and the ulnar side of the little finger is supplied by the ulnar artery. The palm of the hand and the remainder of the digits are supplied by the deep and superficial palmar arches. The deep palmar arch is formed by the terminal part of the radial artery anastomosing with the deep branch of the ulnar. The superficial arch is formed mainly by the superficial branch of the ulnar, but a small branch of the radial on the front of the wrist contributes a part.

The superficial palmar arch is on the superficial surface of the flexor tendons in the palm of the hand, covered by the thick fascia in the central part of the palm called the palmar aponeurosis. It gives off three branches, the common digital arteries, which run distally to the webs between the fingers, where they join branches of the deep arch.

The deep arch is between the tendons and the metacarpal bones and muscles attached to them. It gives off three palmar metacarpal arteries which run distally to the webs, where they join the common digital arteries from the superficial arch.

The vessels formed in the webs from the union of the palmar metacarpal and common digital arteries divide each into two branches which run along the adjacent sides of the fingers to supply them.

Pressure Points. The vessels in the forearm and hand form such free anastomoses with one another that, if pressure over the bleeding point fail to arrest hæmorrhage from them, compression of the brachial artery is the only measure likely to be effective.

THE DESCENDING THORACIC AORTA

The continuation of the aorta beyond the arch is termed the descending thoracic aorta. Beginning at the left side of the fourth thoracic vertebra, it runs downwards immediately on the left of the œsophagus. In the lower part of the thorax it approaches the median plane, crossing as it does so behind the œsophagus, and finally passes through the aortic opening in the diaphragm to become the abdominal aorta. The descending aorta gives off branches to the posterior parts of most of the intercostal spaces (the posterior intercostal arteries), and to the œsophagus and other neighbouring structures.

Practical Considerations

The close proximity of the œsophagus to the aorta makes it imperative to ascertain before passing a stomach tube or similar instrument that there is no aneurism of the vessel. The wall of the œsophagus may be eroded by such an aneurism and become so thin that instruments may easily perforate it, with the result that the patient bleeds to death through the opening made.

ARTERIES OF THE ABDOMEN AND PELVIS

The Abdominal Aorta (Figs. 45 and 46)

This part of the vessel lies in front of the lumbar vertebræ slightly to the left of the median plane. A continuation of the thoracic aorta, it enters the abdomen by passing through the aortic opening in the diaphragm at the level of the twelfth thoracic vertebra, and ends by dividing into the two common iliac vessels in front of the body of the fourth lumbar vertebra. In front, the abdominal aorta is related to the viscera, a large part of it being covered by peritoneum.

Branches of the Abdominal Aorta

Some of the branches go to the abdominal wall; these are called parietal branches. Some go to abdominal viscera; these are visceral branches: and some of them are paired, others are unpaired. Finally the vessel gives off the two common iliac arteries.

11—2

Parietal Branches. Four pairs of **lumbar arteries** supply the posterior abdominal wall.

A pair of **inferior phrenic** arteries supply the inferior surface of the diaphragm.

Visceral Branches

Paired. The **renal arteries** supply the kidneys. As the aorta lies to the left of the median plane the right renal artery is longer than the left, and to reach the kidney has to pass behind the inferior vena cava, which is running up the posterior abdominal wall just to the right of the aorta. The renal artery enters the kidney through the opening at the medial border of the gland called the hilum. As it enters it is between the renal vein in front and the ureter (p. 221) behind.

The **suprarenal arteries** supply the suprarenal glands.

The **testicular arteries,** present in the male, supply the testes. They reach the glands through the spermatic cords (p. 294).

The **ovarian arteries,** present in the female, supply the ovaries.

Unpaired. (1) **The cœliac artery.** The cœliac artery supplies the stomach and lower end of the œsophagus, the first half of the duodenum, the liver and gall-bladder, and the spleen and most of the pancreas. It arises from the aorta just beyond where it enters the abdomen through the aortic opening in the diaphragm. It is a very short vessel, and divides almost at once into three main branches :—

The hepatic artery runs to the right to reach the upper border of the first part of the duodenum, where it turns upwards with the portal vein and the bile duct to run in the edge of the lesser omentum to the porta hepatis (p. 102).

At the upper border of the duodenum the hepatic artery gives off the *right gastric artery,* which runs to the left along the lesser curve of the stomach, and the *gastroduodenal artery,* which passes down behind the first part of the duodenum and divides into the *right gastro-epiploic* running to the left along the greater curve of the stomach and the *superior pancreaticoduodenal* supplying the head of the pancreas and the first half of the duodenum. In the portal fissure of the liver the hepatic artery divides into *left and right branches* to the corresponding lobes of the liver. From the branch to the right lobe is given off the *artery to the gall-bladder* (cystic artery).

The splenic artery. The splenic artery runs to the left from the cœliac axis along the upper border of the pancreas, to which it gives some branches. At the tail of the pancreas it passes to the spleen. It supplies the spleen and also gives branches to the greater curve of the stomach, called the *short gastric* and *left gastro-epiploic* arteries.

The left gastric artery. The left gastric branch of the cœliac axis runs up to the œsophageal end of the stomach and then turns down between the layers of the lesser omentum, running along the lesser curve of the stomach from left to right. The left gastric artery gives some branches to the lower end of the œsophagus.

(2) **The Superior Mesenteric Artery.** The superior mesenteric artery supplies the gut from the middle of the duodenum to the left flexure of the colon. It arises from the aorta behind the pancreas, and then, crossing the third part of the duodenum, runs in the root of the mesentery of the small intestine to the right iliac fossa. It gives off *jejunal and ileal* branches, which pass between the layers of the mesentery to the small intestine. These branches are peculiar in that they form in the mesentery a series of arcades or arches one with another before they reach the gut.

Another branch, the *middle colic*, passes to the transverse colon between the layers of the transverse mesocolon. On reaching the bowel this vessel divides into two branches; one runs to the left to anastomose at the splenic flexure with the upper left colic branch of the inferior mesenteric, and the other to the right to anastomose at the hepatic flexure with the right colic artery.

The other branches of the superior mesenteric pass behind the peritoneum on the posterior abdominal wall to reach the cæcum, appendix, and ascending colon. They are the *right colic* and *ileocolic arteries*. Along the gut they anastomose with each other, and the right colic anastomoses with the middle colic artery.

(3) **The Inferior Mesenteric Artery.** The inferior mesenteric artery supplies the bowel from the splenic flexure of the colon to the anal canal. It arises from the aorta about $2\frac{1}{2}$ inches above its bifurcation into the two common iliac arteries, and runs down on the posterior abdominal wall behind the peritoneum to end by passing into the pelvis to supply the rectum. Its branches are:—

The *upper left colic artery*, which supplies the descending colon and anastomoses with the middle colic at the splenic flexure.

The *lower left colic branches* to the sigmoid colon. These arteries anastomose with the upper left colic artery above and with the superior rectal below.

The *superior rectal* (hæmorrhoidal) artery is the continuation of the terminal part of the inferior mesenteric down into the pelvis. It runs behind the rectum and divides into branches which run in the wall of the rectum to the anal canal, where they anastomose with those of the middle and inferior rectal arteries.

The terminal branches of the abdominal aorta are the two common iliac arteries.

The Common Iliac Arteries (Fig. 46)

The common iliac arteries arise from the aorta at the level of the fourth lumbar vertebra. Each runs downwards and laterally to the sacroiliac joint, where it divides into the **internal** and **external iliac** vessels.

The internal iliac passes down the lateral pelvic wall giving branches to the buttock and thigh (the **gluteal** and **obturator** arteries), to the perinæum (the internal **pudendal** artery), and to the pelvic viscera. The visceral branches are : the **vesical** to the bladder ; the **rectal** (hæmorrhoidal) to the rectum and anal canal ; in the female the **uterine** and **vaginal** arteries.

The External Iliac. This runs on the psoas muscle near the pelvic brim, and finally passes beneath the inguinal ligament to become the femoral artery. Just before it goes into the thigh it gives off the **inferior epigastric** artery to the lower part of the abdominal wall.

ARTERIES OF THE LOWER LIMB

The region of the buttock is supplied by the gluteal vessels from the internal iliac artery. The whole of the rest of the limb is supplied through the femoral artery (Figs. 47 and 48).

The Femoral Artery

The femoral begins as a continuation of the external iliac artery at the inguinal ligament. At first, in the upper one-third of the thigh, it lies in the floor of the femoral triangle. In the middle third of the thigh it passes more on to the medial side in the canal roofed in by the sartorius muscle (the subsartorial or adductor canal). At the junction of the middle and lower thirds of the thigh it passes through the adductor magnus muscle to the back of the thigh, where it becomes the popliteal artery.

The femoral gives off one very large branch called the **profunda** artery of the thigh. This gives off vessels which, because they

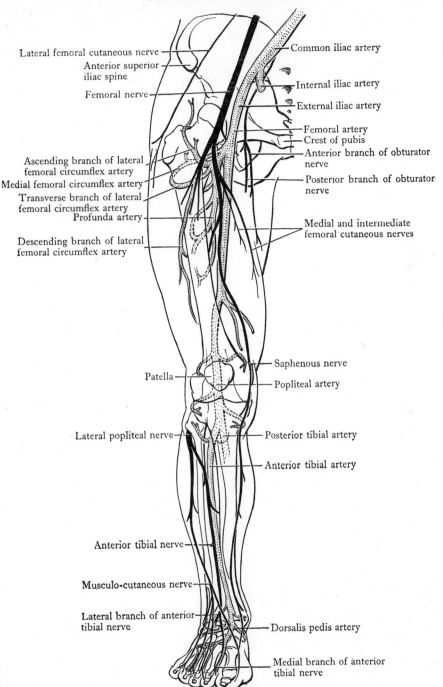

Lateral femoral cutaneous nerve

Anterior superior
iliac spine

Femoral nerve

Common iliac artery

Internal iliac artery

External iliac artery

Femoral artery
Crest of pubis

Anterior branch of obturator
nerve

Posterior branch of obturator
nerve

Ascending branch of lateral
femoral circumflex artery

Medial femoral circumflex artery

Transverse branch of lateral
femoral circumflex artery

Profunda artery

Medial and intermediate
femoral cutaneous nerves

Descending branch of lateral
femoral circumflex artery

Patella

Saphenous nerve

Popliteal artery

Lateral popliteal nerve

Posterior tibial artery

Anterior tibial artery

Anterior tibial nerve

Musculo-cutaneous nerve

Lateral branch of anterior
tibial nerve

Dorsalis pedis artery

Medial branch of anterior
tibial nerve

FIG. 47.   Arteries and nerves of right lower extremity, anterior aspect.

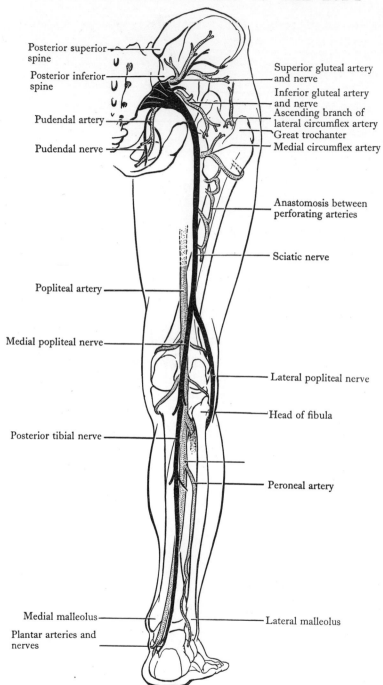

Posterior superior spine

Posterior inferior spine

Pudendal artery

Pudendal nerve

Superior gluteal artery and nerve

Inferior gluteal artery and nerve

Ascending branch of lateral circumflex artery

Great trochanter

Medial circumflex artery

Anastomosis between perforating arteries

Sciatic nerve

Popliteal artery

Medial popliteal nerve

Lateral popliteal nerve

Head of fibula

Posterior tibial nerve

Peroneal artery

Medial malleolus

Plantar arteries and nerves

Lateral malleolus

Fɪɢ. 48.   Arteries and nerves of right lower limb, posterior aspect.

wind round the medial and lateral surfaces of the femur, are called the **medial** and **lateral femoral circumflex** arteries. Through these branches the femoral supplies the front and medial side of the thigh and the hip and knee joints. Vessels pass through to the back of the thigh (the perforating arteries), to anastomose with branches of the gluteal and popliteal arteries.

The smaller branches of the femoral artery supply the superficial structures of the thigh and lower part of the abdominal wall.

The Popliteal Artery

The popliteal artery is a continuation of the femoral and runs behind the knee joint into the leg, where, opposite the upper part of the tibia, it divides into anterior and posterior tibial arteries. The other branches of the popliteal are concerned mainly with the supply of the knee joint.

The Anterior Tibial Artery

The anterior tibial artery arises as a terminal branch of the popliteal artery, behind the upper end of the tibia. Passing through an opening in the interosseous membrane, it runs down in the anterior compartment of the leg among the extensor muscles to the middle of the front of the ankle joint. Beyond this it is continued as the dorsalis pedis artery on the dorsal surface of the foot. It supplies the extensor compartment of the leg and the knee and ankle joints.

The Dorsalis Pedis. This artery is the continuation of the anterior tibial on the dorsum of the foot. It runs from the middle of the front of the ankle to the proximal end of the first inter-metatarsal space, where it dips between the bones into the sole of the foot to form the plantar arterial arch.

Branches of the dorsalis pedis supply the dorsum of the foot and toes.

The Posterior Tibial Artery

The posterior tibial is the other terminal branch of the popliteal artery. It passes down the flexor compartment of the leg between the deep and superficial groups of muscles. In the lower third of the leg, where the superficial flexors are inserted into the tendo calcaneus, the vessel lies on the posterior surface of the tibia and, crossing first behind and then on the medial side of the ankle joint, it enters the sole of the foot on the medial side and divides into the medial and lateral plantar arteries.

In the calf, shortly after its origin, the posterior tibial artery gives off the large **peroneal artery,** which runs down in contact with the fibula to emerge finally to supply the lateral side of the heel. Other branches supply the muscles in the flexor compartment, the knee and ankle joints, and the medial side of the heel.

The plantar arteries are the terminal branches of the posterior tibial.

The Medial Plantar Artery. This runs along the inner side of the sole and supplies branches to the medial three and a half toes.

The Lateral Plantar Artery. This first crosses the sole from the medial to the lateral side under the short flexor of the toes. At the lateral side it divides into a deep branch which contributes to the formation of the plantar arch, and a superficial branch which supplies the lateral one and a half toes.

The **plantar arterial arch** is formed by the deep branch of the lateral plantar artery and the perforating part of the dorsalis pedis. It lies deep to the ·flexor muscles on the bases of the metatarsal bones and supplies branches to the toes.

Pressure Points. The femoral artery can be compressed against the brim of the pelvis just below the inguinal ligament.

The popliteal can be controlled by placing a pad in the popliteal fossa and flexing the knee strongly.

The anterior and posterior tibial arteries can be compressed in the lower third of the leg against the tibia.

The dorsalis pedis can be compressed against the tarsal bones, but the anastomoses are so free that the method will not always control bleeding in its distribution.

THE VEINS

The veins of the head and neck and the two extremities are in two main groups ; the deep veins, which run with the arteries supplying the part, and which are underneath the deep fascia ; and the superficial veins, which are in the subcutaneous tissue, and which do not necessarily correspond to arteries in position. The superficial veins terminate by piercing the deep fascia and joining the deeper trunks.

The veins of the abdomen are in two great subdivisions : those which correspond to the paired branches of the abdominal aorta, and which drain directly into the inferior vena cava, and those which correspond to the unpaired branches of the aorta, and which drain into the **portal vein.** The portal vein breaks up in the liver so that the blood in it, which has already been through one set of capillaries in the intestine, goes through a second set of capillaries in the liver before it gets back to the heart. This second circulation through the liver is called the **portal circulation.** The other veins of the body, apart from those of the lungs, which will be considered later, belong to the **systemic circulation.**

VEINS OF THE SYSTEMIC CIRCULATION

VEINS OF THE HEAD AND NECK

Deep Group

The veins from the brain and the interior of the skull drain into venous channels enclosed between layers of the dura mater (see p. 256). They are called **venous sinuses.** The most important sinuses are the superior sagittal, the two lateral (transverse) sinuses, and the two cavernous sinuses.

The superior sagittal sinus runs in the median plane from the frontal to the occipital region on the deep surface of the bones of the cranial vault. In the occipital region it communicates with both lateral sinuses, but more freely with that of the right side. It drains the blood from the upper part of the brain.

The Lateral Sinuses. These are found *one on each side* of the skull. Each runs on the deep surfaces of the occipital, parietal, and temporal bones to the jugular foramen at the base of the skull, where it passes outside the skull to form the internal jugular vein. The lateral sinus drains the blood from the lower part of the brain, and also receives the blood from the sagittal and cavernous sinuses.

As the lateral sinus crosses the temporal bone it lies very close to the mastoid antrum, a cavity communicating with the middle ear (see p. 288). In some cases of middle-ear disease the antrum becomes affected and the infection occasionally spreads through the bone to the lateral sinus, where it produces clotting of the contained blood. Portions of the infected clot may become detached and find their way *viâ* the internal jugular vein into the general circulation, and result in the formation of secondary abscesses all over the body (pyæmia).

The Cavernous Sinuses. These are placed at the sides of the body of the sphenoid bone. Each receives blood from the base of the brain and from the eye and orbit. The blood drains backwards from it through narrow channels into the lateral sinus and the internal jugular vein of the same side.

Through the veins of the orbit the cavernous sinus communicates with veins on the face, so that severe infections of the region of the cheek and the root of the nose may sometimes spread backwards and cause clotting of the blood in the sinus like that of the lateral sinus in ear conditions. Cavernous sinus thrombosis is nearly always fatal.

The blood from the sagittal and cavernous sinuses drains into the lateral sinuses, and the lateral sinus forms on each side the internal jugular vein.

The Internal Jugular Vein. The internal jugular vein is formed as a continuation of the lateral sinus at the jugular foramen. It is a very large vein and runs down the side of the neck underneath the sternomastoid muscle embedded, with the carotid artery and the vagus nerve, in the carotid sheath. Behind the inner end of the clavicle it joins the subclavian vein to form the innominate vein (Fig. 46).

Tributaries of the Internal Jugular. The internal jugular vein receives the following tributaries :—

The *lingual* vein, from the tongue.

The *common facial* vein, formed by branches from the face.

The *superior and middle thyroid* veins, from the thyroid gland. Veins from the *pharynx.*

The Subclavian Vein. The subclavian vein is the continuation of the axillary vein. It lies behind the medial part of the clavicle a little below and in front of the subclavian artery. With the internal jugular it forms the innominate vein.

The subclavian vein receives the external jugular and sometimes the anterior jugular vein.

Superficial Group

The External Jugular Vein. The external jugular is formed just behind and below the ear. It crosses the sternomastoid muscle superficially, and ends by piercing the deep fascia in the lower part of the posterior triangle of the neck and entering the subclavian vein.

The external jugular receives tributaries from the muscles of the neck, and usually the anterior jugular vein.

The Anterior Jugular Vein. The anterior jugular begins in the region just below the chin. It runs down the neck just lateral to the median plane and pierces the deep fascia in the lower part of the anterior triangle. It drains the superficial tissues of the anterior part of the neck and ends in the external jugular or the subclavian vein.

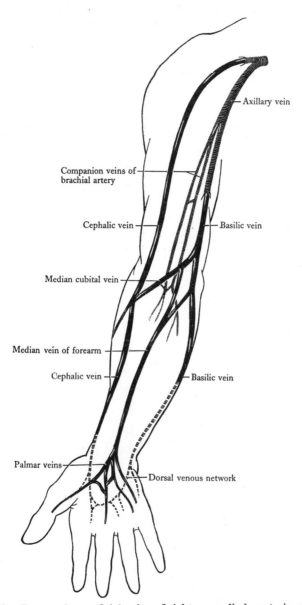

FIG. 49.   Deep and superficial veins of right upper limb, anterior aspect.

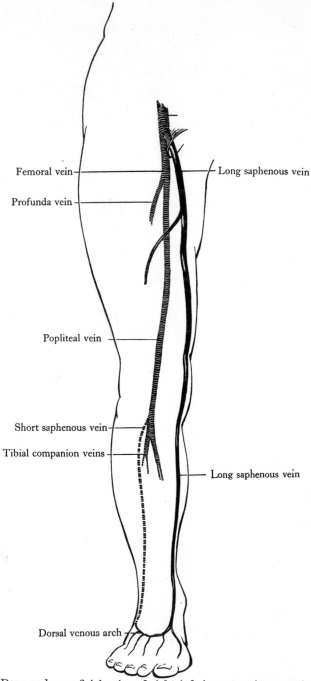

Femoral vein

Profunda vein

Popliteal vein

Short saphenous vein

Tibial companion veins

Dorsal venous arch

Long saphenous vein

Long saphenous vein

FIG. 50. Deep and superficial veins of right inferior extremity, anterior aspect.

VEINS OF THE SUPERIOR EXTREMITY (Fig. 49)

Deep Group

The superficial and deep palmar arches and the **radial, ulnar, interosseous** and **brachial** arteries are each accompanied by a pair of companion veins. The two companion veins of the brachial artery join the single axillary vein medial to the axillary artery. The **axillary** vein becomes the subclavian at the lateral border of the first rib.

These veins receive tributaries corresponding to the arteries.

Superficial Group

The veins on the dorsum of the hand drain into the **basilic vein** on the medial side and the **cephalic vein** on the lateral side. Veins from the palm of the hand drain into the **median vein of the forearm,** which joins the basilic vein near the elbow.

The basilic vein runs up the medial side of the forearm and the arm superficial to the deep fascia. It pierces the fascia in the upper part of the arm and its continuation forms the axillary vein.

The basilic vein receives the median vein of the forearm and the median cubital vein from the cephalic near the elbow.

The cephalic vein runs up the lateral side of the forearm and arm superficial to the deep fascia. In the neighbourhood of the elbow it gives off the median cubital vein, which joins the basilic. The cephalic vein remains superficial to the deep fascia until it reaches the shoulder region, where it dips into the interval between the deltoid and pectoralis major muscles to enter the upper part of the axillary vein.

VEINS OF THE INFERIOR EXTREMITY (Fig. 50)

Deep Group

The arteries of the foot and the **anterior and posterior tibial** arteries and their branches are all accompanied by pairs of companion veins. Those with the tibial arteries unite in the popliteal fossa to form the **popliteal** vein which is continued up the thigh as the femoral vein. At the inguinal ligament the **femoral** vein lies on the medial side of the artery, and is continuous with the external iliac vein.

Superficial Group

On the dorsum of the foot is a venous arch which receives veins from the toes. From the medial end of the arch arises the great saphenous vein, while from the lateral end arises the small saphenous.

The great saphenous vein runs up the medial side of the leg and thigh, and just below the inguinal ligament passes through an opening called the fossa ovalis in the fascia lata of the thigh. It ends by joining the femoral vein.

The small saphenous vein runs round the lateral side of the ankle to the back of the leg. It pierces the deep fascia in the popliteal fossa to enter the popliteal vein.

Practical Considerations

The veins of the lower limb have to support a very long column of blood, and if their valves become incompetent they dilate and thicken. The condition is called varicose veins.

VEINS OF THE ABDOMEN

The Iliac Veins (Fig. 46)

The continuation of the femoral vein into the abdomen forms the **external iliac vein** which runs with the corresponding artery along the brim of the pelvis. At the sacroiliac joint it is joined by the **internal iliac vein** draining the pelvis, the vein formed by their union being the **common iliac.** The common iliac veins of the two sides unite in front of the right side of the body of the fifth lumbar vertebra to form the inferior vena cava.

The Inferior Vena Cava (Fig. 46)

Formed by the union of the two common iliac veins, the inferior vena cava runs upwards on the posterior abdominal wall on the right of the abdominal aorta. It lies slightly to the right of the median plane, first on the bodies of the lumbar vertebræ and the right psoas muscle, then on the right crus of the diaphragm, on which it crosses the right renal artery. It passes finally through an opening in the right part of the central tendon of the diaphragm and immediately enters the pericardium and ends in the lower part of the right atrium of the heart (Fig. 39).

Tributaries of the Inferior Vena Cava. The inferior vena cava receives the veins which correspond to the paired branches of the abdominal aorta. It also drains the blood from the liver *viâ* the hepatic veins.

The common iliac veins have been described already.

The lumbar veins correspond to the lumbar arteries and drain the posterior abdominal wall.

The renal veins drain the kidneys. The left renal vein is much longer than the right and crosses in front of the aorta. It receives also the **left suprarenal and testicular** (ovarian in the female) veins.

The right suprarenal and testicular veins drain directly into the vena cava.

The hepatic veins drain the blood which has reached the liver by both the hepatic artery and the portal vein (see Portal circulation).

The Portal System of Veins (Fig. 51).

The veins corresponding to the unpaired visceral branches of the abdominal aorta terminate in the **portal vein** which goes to the liver, where it breaks up into branches which finally form capillaries. These capillaries join those derived from the hepatic artery at the margins of the lobules of the liver to form vessels which run between the columns of cells of which the lobule is composed. They have incomplete walls, so that the blood comes into intimate contact with the liver cells which deal with the end-products of digestion carried in the portal blood. At the centre of each lobule these sinusoidal vessels enter an intralobular vein, and the intralobular veins unite with one another to form tributaries of the hepatic veins. The **hepatic veins,** from four to six in number, leave the posterior surface of the liver and enter the inferior vena cava. The blood supplied to the stomach, intestines, and the spleen thus passes through two sets of capillaries before being returned to the vena cava which carries it to the heart.

There are no valves on the veins of the portal system. Systemic veins form anastomoses with radicles of the portal vein in a number of situations, the most important of which are at the œsophageal end of the stomach and in the anal canal. In cirrhosis of the liver, where the portal capillaries are obstructed, these anastomoses dilate so that the blood which normally goes through the liver finds its way back to the heart by other channels.

The Portal Vein. The portal vein is formed behind the neck of the pancreas by the union of the superior mesenteric and splenic veins. It passes up behind the first part of the duodenum and reaches the portal fissure of the liver *viâ* the lesser omentum

ANATOMY. 12

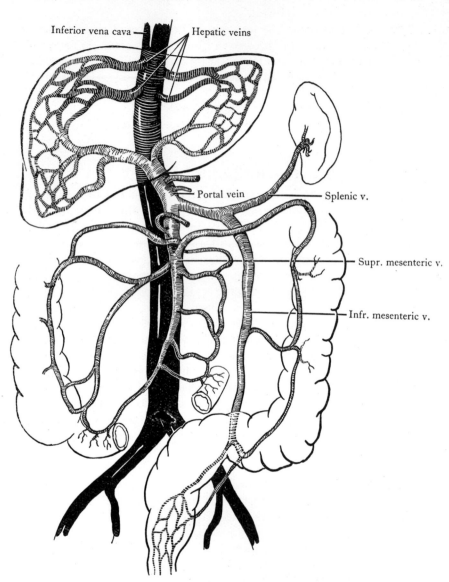

FIG. 51. Scheme of the portal system of veins. The veins from the stomach
are cut short.

(p. 109). In the portal fissure and in the omentum it lies behind the bile ducts and the hepatic artery and its branches. It divides finally into right and left branches distributed to the corresponding lobes of the liver.

Tributaries of the Portal Vein. The Superior Mesenteric Vein. The superior mesenteric vein lies on the right of the superior mesenteric artery. Like that vessel, it is in the root of the mesentery of the small intestine. It receives jejunal, ileal, and middle colic, right colic and ileocolic tributaries and drains the blood from the bowel between the lower part of the duodenum and the left flexure of the colon. After crossing in front of the third part of the duodenum it joins the splenic vein to form the portal vein behind the neck of the pancreas.

The Splenic Vein. The splenic vein begins at the hilum of the spleen and runs to the right behind the body of the pancreas, finally to join the superior mesenteric behind the neck of the pancreas. At the hilum of the spleen it receives the veins from the left half of the greater curvature of the stomach. Behind the body of the pancreas it receives the **inferior mesenteric vein.** This drains the blood from the descending colon, the pelvic colon and the rectum. The splenic vein also receives radicles from the pancreas.

The Right and Left Gastric (Coronary) Veins. These drain the lesser curvature of the stomach and enter the portal vein in the lesser omentum.

The Right Gastro-epiploic Vein. This drains the right half of the greater curvature of the stomach and may enter the portal vein directly or the superior mesenteric.

VEINS OF THE THORAX

The Thoracic Wall

The thoracic wall is drained posteriorly by the azygos system of veins, and anteriorly by the internal mammary veins. The former drain into the superior vena cava and the latter into the innominate veins.

Deeper Veins

The Innominate Veins (Fig. 46)

The innominate vein is formed on each side by the junction, behind the medial end of the clavicle, of the internal jugular and subclavian veins. The course of the vein is somewhat different on the right and left sides.

The **left innominate vein** passes obliquely downwards and to the right behind the manubrium sterni, and joins the right innominate vein at the level of the lower border of the first right costal cartilage to form the superior vena cava.

The **right innominate vein** runs down just to the right of the innominate artery. It is shorter than the left vein.

The Superior Vena Cava (Fig. 46)

The superior vena cava drains the blood from the head and neck and both arms *viâ* the innominate veins, and from the thoracic wall *viâ* the azygos vein.

It is about $3\frac{1}{2}$ inches long and is formed by the union of the two innominate veins. It runs down behind the first and second intercostal spaces on the right side, crossing in front of the root of the right lung to enter the upper part of the right atrium. Its terminal part is inside the pericardium.

THE PULMONARY CIRCULATION

The vessels carrying blood to and from the lungs are considered in the section on the respiratory system (see p. 202).

CHAPTER X

THE LYMPHATIC SYSTEM

IT has already been stated that the fluid which bathes the tissue cells is exuded into the tissue spaces from the capillaries. Whilst in the tissue spaces it forms a medium through which substances in the blood can reach the cells to nourish or stimulate them, and also takes up waste products from the cells. Some of the fluid finds its way back again into the capillary vessels, but a considerable part of it does not return by this route to the bloodstream. It is absorbed from the tissue spaces into the **lymphatic vessels** which begin as minute blind-ended tubes or in plexuses of lymphatic capillary vessels whose walls are formed by a single layer of endothelium. These vessels possess the power of taking up substances of such a form that they cannot pass in solution in the tissue fluid through the walls of the blood capillaries. Examples of such substances are carbon particles which have found their way with the inspired air into the alveoli of the lungs, foreign substances, such as micro-organisms invading the tissues, and fat absorbed by the villi in the small intestine. Such substances are taken up by the endothelial cells which line the lymphatics and transferred to the fluid absorbed into the lymphatics from the tissue spaces. Once absorbed into the lymphatic vessels this fluid, carrying with it the substances mentioned above, is called **lymph.** The lymph coming from the small intestine after a meal contains fat, and is called **chyle,** the vessels carrying it being known as **lacteals** because of the milky appearance of the fluid. The walls of all but the largest lymphatic vessels are so thin that the contents can be seen traversing them. The lymphatic vessels beginning in this way in the tissues in some ways resemble capillaries, although they start as blind-ended tubes and not as a continuation of other vessels. They form a plexus or network with similar vessels, and from the plexus the lymph is collected by lymphatics which unite with one another to form larger vessels rather like the veins in structure, but of much smaller calibre. These larger lymphatics possess valves which prevent the lymph flowing backwards along them, and they ultimately join one of two main

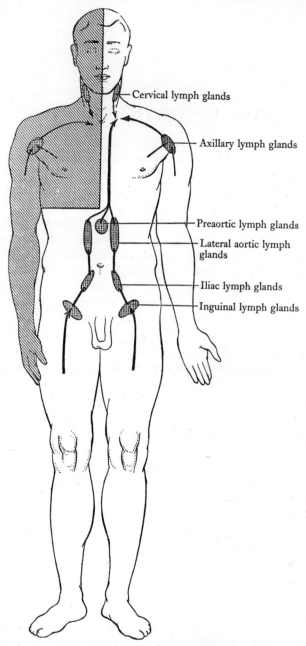

FIG. 52. The main groups of lymphatic glands. Lymph from the shaded area is returned to the blood by the right lymphatic duct; that from the unshaded area by the thoracic duct.

lymphatic channels called the **thoracic duct** and the **right lymphatic duct.** The thoracic duct drains the lymph from the whole of the body except the right side of the head and neck, the right arm, and the upper and right part of the thorax, the right lung, and parts of the diaphragm and the right side of the heart. These exceptions are drained into the right lymphatic duct (Fig. 52). The thoracic duct finally enters the junction of the internal jugular and subclavian veins on the left side of the root of the neck, whilst the right lymphatic duct opens similarly on the right side of the body. In this way the lymph is returned to the blood going back to the heart.

The lymph returning from the tissues, however, contains many substances which would be harmful if they found their way into the blood. These are removed by the **lymph glands** found along the course of the lymphatics. The glands contain large numbers of endothelial cells which take up the harmful constituents of the lymph, and, as it were, filter it before it is returned to the blood. The lymph glands also add to the lymph small round cells called **lymphocytes,** and so they form the main source of these cells in the blood.

It is obvious, from what has been stated, that there is no mechanism like the heart for pumping the lymph along the lymphatic vessels. It flows along partly because of the " milking " action of the movement of surrounding parts, such as muscles, retrograde flow being prevented by the valves in the vessels. Since the thoracic and right lymphatic ducts enter veins near the root of the neck, the lymph is sucked into these veins by the action of the negative intrathoracic pressure.

The cells lining the lymph spaces in the lymph glands belong to the **reticulo-endothelial system.** The function of this system as a whole is the same as that of the lymphatics, namely, the " scavenging " of substances of such a nature that they cannot be dealt with by the blood. The system is also represented by liver and bone-marrow. The reticulo-endothelial system is also concerned with the breakdown of worn-out red blood corpuscles and the formation of the bile pigment (p. 130).

THE PRINCIPAL LYMPHATIC VESSELS AND GLANDS

The Thoracic Duct

The thoracic duct drains the left side and the lower part of the right side of the body. It begins in the upper part of the abdomen in the sac called the **cisterna chyli,** which is situated just to the right of the aorta in the aortic opening in the diaphragm. Entering the thorax through this opening, it runs up in front of the thoracic vertebræ at first to the right of the median plane. At the level of the fifth thoracic vertebra it crosses over to the left side and runs upwards to the root of the neck. It finally arches laterally to join the junction of the left subclavian and internal jugular veins. The duct is about $\frac{1}{8}$ inch in diameter, and has a beaded appearance due to the presence of numerous valves along its interior.

The Cisterna Chyli. This sac, which forms the beginning of the thoracic duct, is about $2\frac{1}{2}$ inches long and $\frac{1}{4}$ inch wide. It receives a lymphatic trunk from the front of the aorta and one from each side of the aorta. These drain the pre-aortic and the two lumbar chains of glands respectively.

Tributaries of the Thoracic Duct. In the thorax the thoracic duct communicates with the right lymph duct, and in the root of the neck it receives the left jugular and subclavian trunks which drain respectively the neck and the upper limb.

The Right Lymphatic Duct

This is much shorter than the thoracic duct, being only about $\frac{1}{2}$ inch long. It enters the junction of the right subclavian and internal jugular veins, and receives the right jugular and sub-clavian lymphatic trunks draining the right side of the neck and the right upper limb. It also receives a vessel which drains the thoracic viscera.

The Lymphatic Drainage of the Head and Neck

The lymph vessels draining the head and neck pass through glands situated along the internal jugular vein and called the **deep cervical glands.** The efferent vessels from these glands enter the jugular trunk which ends in the thoracic duct on the left side and in the right lymph duct on the right.

The vessels from many parts of the head and neck go straight into the deep cervical glands, as, for example, those of the posterior part of the tongue and parts of the larynx and pharynx. From other parts, however, the vessels first traverse other groups of glands before reaching the deep cervical group. These other groups are :—

The **occipital group,** draining the posterior part of the scalp.

The **mastoid group,** draining the ear and scalp.

The **parotid group,** draining the ear and the temporal region and the eyelids.

The **submandibular group** (submaxillary) are important glands found just below the lower jaw. They drain the nose, the cheek, the upper lip, part of the lower lip, the lower jaw, the side of the tongue and the teeth.

The **submental** glands drain the tip of the tongue, the lower lip and the floor of the mouth.

The **external and anterior jugular groups** are found along the veins of the same names.

The efferents from all the above groups drain into the deep cervical lymph glands.

Lymph Drainage of the Upper Limb

The lymph from the upper limb passes through the **axillary group** of glands situated along the course of the axillary vein. These glands also drain the breast and the superficial layers of the back, as well as the arm. The efferent vessels leaving them pass up into the root of the neck, where they join to form the subclavian trunk, which drains into the thoracic duct or the right lymph duct.

In addition to the axillary lymph glands there are a few scattered glands along the course of the main veins of the upper limb, of which one constant gland is found just above the medial epicondyle of the humerus on the course of the basilic vein. This is the **supratrochlear** gland.

The Lymphatic Drainage of the Lower Limb

Groups of glands are found in the **popliteal** fossa and in the **inguinal** region, through which the lymphatic vessels of the lower limb pass. From the inguinal group efferents pass under the inguinal ligament to the iliac group at the brim of the pelvis.

The Lymphatics of the Abdomen

Along the lateral side of the aorta are found the **lateral aortic group** of lymphatic glands. These glands receive vessels from the posterior abdominal wall, the kidneys, the testicles in the male and the ovaries in the female, and the lymphatics from the iliac groups of glands.

The **iliac group,** found along the iliac vessels, receives lymph from the lower limb, and from the contents of the pelvis and the pelvic wall.

Anterior to the aorta are the **pre-aortic** glands grouped round the origin from the aorta of the **cœliac, superior mesenteric** and **inferior mesenteric** arteries. These groups are concerned with the drainage of the intestine supplied by the arteries with which they are in relation, and the cœliac group receives the lymph from the stomach, liver and spleen.

The efferent vessels from the lateral aortic groups and the pre-aortic group drain into the cisterna chyli. The lymph from the intestine after a meal contains absorbed fat and is called chyle.

Lymphatics of the Thorax

The lymph from the thoracic wall drains into either the thoracic duct or right lymph duct, with the exception of the anterior part which drains into the **internal mammary glands** behind the costal cartilages. From the internal mammary group, which also drain the medial part of the breast, lymphatics pass to the lower deep cervical glands.

The thoracic viscera drain mainly into groups of glands near the roots of the lungs called the **tracheo-bronchial glands.** From these, vessels drain either into the main lymphatic ducts or independently into the veins at the root of the neck.

CHAPTER XI

THE RESPIRATORY SYSTEM

THE respiratory system constitutes the passages and organs by which the oxygen necessary for bodily activity is taken in and transferred to the blood, and carbon dioxide, water, and occasionally other substances are excreted.

THE RESPIRATORY PASSAGES

Under this heading are included the nose, the nasopharynx, the oral and the upper part of the laryngeal pharynx, the larynx, the trachea and the bronchial tree.

The Nose

The nose contains the organ of smell as well as being a part of the respiratory system.

The external nose forms a pyramidal projection on the face. The framework of it is formed partly by bone (the two nasal bones and the frontal processes of the maxillæ) and partly by the nasal cartilages.

The Nasal Cavity (Fig. 53). The nasal cavity is the channel leading from the nostrils to the nasopharynx. It is separated into two halves by the nasal septum, and each half opens anteriorly at the nostril and posteriorly, into the naso-pharynx, through the posterior nasal aperture or **choana**.

The septum is formed partly of bone and partly of cartilage. The bones are the vertical plate of the ethmoid and the vomer. These form the posterior part of the septum, whilst the anterior part is composed mainly of the septal cartilage. The septum forms the **medial wall** of each half of the nasal cavity.

The roof is formed from before backwards by the nasal, frontal, ethmoid, and sphenoid bones. In the ethmoid bone are the openings for the transmission of the filaments of the olfactory nerve. It also presents the opening of the sphenoidal air sinuses.

The floor is formed by the bones of the hard palate which separates the nose from the mouth.

The lateral wall of each half presents three projections formed by the **turbinate bones** or **conchæ**. Below the inferior concha is the space called the **inferior meatus**; below the middle

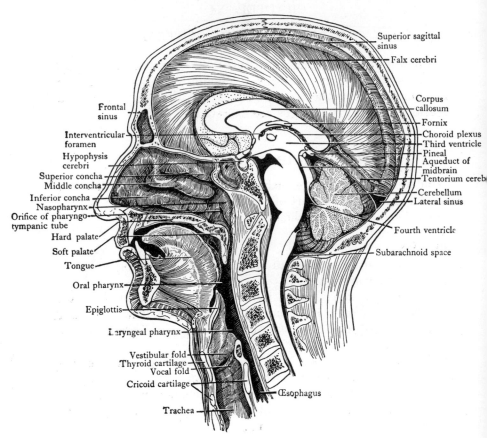

Frontal sinus

Interventricular foramen

Hypophysis cerebri

Superior concha
Middle concha

Inferior concha
Nasopharynx
Orifice of pharyngo-tympanic tube

Hard palate

Soft palate

Tongue

Oral pharynx

Epiglottis

Laryngeal pharynx

Vestibular fold
Thyroid cartilage
Vocal fold

Cricoid cartilage

Trachea

Superior sagittal sinus

Falx cerebri

Corpus callosum

Fornix
Choroid plexus
Third ventricle
Pineal
Aqueduct of midbrain
Tentorium cereb

Cerebellum
Lateral sinus

Fourth ventricle

Subarachnoid space

Œsophagus

FIG. 53. A sagittal section of the head and neck a little to the left of the median plane. The nasal septum has been removed to expose the lateral wall of the nose.

concha, between it and the inferior, is the **middle meatus**; between the superior and middle conchæ is the **superior meatus**; between the superior concha and the roof of the nose is the **spheno-ethmoidal** recess.

Opening on the lateral wall of the nose are the apertures from the frontal, ethmoidal, and maxillary air cells or sinuses, and the nasolacrimal duct which conveys excess of tears into the nose (see p. 284).

The nasolacrimal duct opens at the anterior part of the inferior meatus of the nose.

The frontal, maxillary, and anterior and middle ethmoidal air sinuses open into the middle meatus.

The posterior ethmoidal cells open into the superior meatus.

The sphenoidal air sinus opens from the roof of the nose into the spheno-ethmoidal recess.

Lining of the Nose. The part of the nasal cavity immediately inside the nostril is called the vestibule, and is lined by skin bearing hairs.

The remainder of the cavity is lined by mucous membrane, which is continuous posteriorly with that of the nasopharynx, and, through the openings mentioned above, with that lining the air sinuses and the nasolacrimal duct. Over most of the surface the mucous membrane is like that lining the rest of the respiratory tract, in that it is covered with a layer of **ciliated columnar cells** and contains numerous mucous glands. The mucus secreted by these glands keeps the surface moist and, being sticky, entangles dust, micro-organisms, etc., which may enter with the inspired air. The cilia covering the mucosa move this film of contaminated mucus towards the nostrils, where it is got rid of when the nose is blown. In this way the whole of the respiratory tract protects itself from harmful things in the inspired air.

In infections of the nose this nasal secretion is much increased in amount, and is altered in character.

The **olfactory region,** which is limited to the upper part of the lateral wall and the upper part of the septum of the nose, is covered by rather different epithelium. It is yellowish in colour, and contains the nerve cells which give origin to the fibres of the olfactory nerves, supported in a framework of other cells. The peripheral processes of these cells project on the surface of the mucous membrane as the olfactory hairs. The central processes collect into bundles which traverse the foramina in the perforated plate of the ethmoid bone and join the olfactory bulb (p. 280).

The Nasal Air Sinuses. In many of the bones surrounding the nose are spaces lined by a continuation of the nasal mucous membrane. These cavities open into the nose and contain air. Their purpose is to lighten the bones and to give resonance to the voice.

The **maxillary sinuses** are in the body of the maxilla, one on each side. (The maxillary sinus is also known as the antrum of Highmore.)

The **frontal sinuses** are found, one on each side of the median plane, in the frontal bone near the root of the nose.

The **ethmoid sinuses** are found on each side in the lateral part of the ethmoid bone. They are in three groups, anterior, middle, and posterior, and they make up together the ethmoid labyrinth.

The **sphenoidal sinuses** are located in the body of the sphenoid bone. They open on the roof of the nose in the neighbourhood of the spheno-ethmoidal recesses.

After repeated attacks of inflammation due to spread of infection from the nose or teeth, the lining mucosa of the nasal sinuses may be so damaged that the cilia disappear. The mucus may then accumulate in the sinus instead of draining out through the opening into the nose. The infected contents may then have to be removed by surgical methods.

The Pharynx

The oral and laryngeal parts of the pharynx are shared by both the alimentary and respiratory systems. They have been described already (p. 96).

The Nasopharynx. The nasal part of the pharynx is situated behind the nasal cavity and above the soft palate. In its wall is the superior constrictor muscle, but owing to the fact that the muscle is attached above to the base of the skull, and at the sides to the pterygoid processes of the sphenoid bone, this part of the pharynx cannot be constricted so much as the other parts and is always an open cavity. Its roof is formed by the sphenoid and occipital bones covered with respiratory mucous membrane. Posteriorly and at the sides is the superior constrictor lined by mucous membrane, and separating the cavity from the upper two cervical vertebræ which lie behind it.

Anteriorly the nasopharynx communicates with the nose through the **posterior nasal apertures (choanæ)**, whilst below it leads into the oral pharynx. The aperture by which it communicates with the latter is guarded by the soft palate, which can be lifted upwards and backwards so as completely to close the opening when necessary. The aperture, which is called the **pharyngeal isthmus,** is closed in efforts which require blowing through the mouth and in the enunciation of certain consonants in speech.

The lateral wall of the nasopharynx presents the pharyngeal

aperture of the **pharyngotympanic (Eustachian) tube** which leads to the middle ear. The aperture is partially surrounded by a rounded ridge called the **tubal elevation** or **Eustachian cushion.** In the mucous membrane of the upper part of the posterior wall and the roof of the nasopharynx is a mass of lymphoid tissue called the **naso-pharyngeal tonsil.**

Hypertrophy of the naso-pharyngeal tonsil occurs fairly frequently in children. The condition is called **adenoids** and because of the blockage of the airway through the nose leads to mouth-breathing. This results in the mouth being continually open, giving a peculiarly vacant expression. Because the tongue is not kept in contact with the palate, due to the mouth being open, the palate becomes highly arched and narrowed, cramping the teeth so that they develop irregularly. The pharyngotympanic tube is a frequent pathway for the spread of infection from the pharynx to the middle ear. Adenoids obstructing the aperture of the tube predispose to this.

After traversing the nose and the nasopharynx, air going to the lungs passes through the **oral and laryngeal parts of the pharynx,** and from the latter through the superior laryngeal aperture into the larynx.

The Larynx

The larynx is that part of the respiratory system which contains the vocal cords for the production of the voice. It lies in front of the laryngeal part of the pharynx, with which it communicates above, and below it is continuous with the trachea. It is larger in the adult male than in the female. The larynx is composed of the laryngeal cartilages, with their associated ligaments and muscles.

The Laryngeal Cartilages

Two of these form parts of the walls of the larynx, they are the thyroid and the cricoid cartilages.

The thyroid cartilage is the largest laryngeal cartilage, and it projects forwards in the neck to form the " Adam's apple." It is V-shaped in form, consisting of two flat plates or laminæ, which are blended with one another in front, but are widely separated behind so as to accommodate the cricoid cartilage. The cricoid and thyroid cartilages are connected by joints which permit the thyroid to tilt backwards and forwards on the cricoid.

The cricoid cartilage is shaped like a signet ring, the seal of the ring being posterior. The cricoid reaches a lower level in the neck than the thyroid so that its ring can be felt below the thyroid almost immediately under the skin. Below, the cricoid cartilage is attached to the first ring of the trachea.

The epiglottis is a leaf-shaped cartilage with its base just below the back of the tongue and its apex attached to the anterior part of the thyroid cartilage. It overhangs the superior laryngeal aperture and is bent during swallowing so as to prevent food entering the larynx.

The arytenoid cartilages are found one on each side just behind the superior laryngeal aperture. They are pyramidal in shape and articulate with the upper border of the posterior part of the cricoid cartilage. At these joints the arytenoid cartilages can move towards one another and each can rotate round its own vertical axis. These rotatory movements are responsible for the abduction and adduction of the vocal folds which are attached to the arytenoid cartilages anteriorly.

The cricovocal membrane is the name given to the membranous structure which forms the foundation of the two vocal folds (vocal cords). Below, the membrane is attached along the upper border of the cricoid cartilage ; above, it is attached to the thyroid cartilage on its deep surface near the median plane, and in the rest of its extent ends above as two free edges each running from the junction of the laminæ of the thyroid in front to a projection on the arytenoid cartilage (the vocal process) behind. These free edges are thickened and form the foundation for the vocal fold on each side.

The Interior of the Larynx (Fig. 53). The cavity of the larynx extends from the superior aperture, where it communicates with the laryngeal part of the pharynx, to the point where it communicates with the trachea below.

The superior aperture is oblique, bounded above by the epiglottis, at the sides by the folds running from the epiglottis to the arytenoid cartilages, and below and behind by the fold connecting one arytenoid cartilage with the other. At the superior aperture the mucous lining of the pharynx is continuous with that of the larynx. In the oral and laryngeal parts of the pharynx, which are also traversed by food on its way to the œsophagus, the mucous membrane is not of the respiratory type, but is covered by stratified squamous epithelium. In the larynx it again changes to the ciliated columnar covering except over the vocal fold. On each side of the cavity of the larynx are two folds called the vocal and vestibular folds.

The **vocal fold** (vocal cord) is the lower of the two folds and is separated from the upper fold, the **vestibular fold** (false cord) by an elongated depression called the sinus (ventricle) of the larynx. The interval between the vocal folds is called the **glottis** and can be varied by movements of the vocal folds so as to produce the various notes of the voice. The fold is adducted towards its fellow, and is tightened in the production of a high note, and is abducted from its fellow in the production of a low note. The vestibular fold

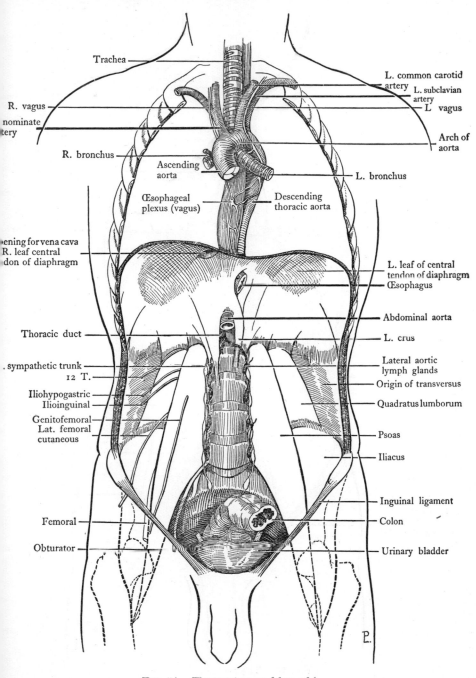

Trachea

L. common carotid artery
L. subclavian artery
L vagus

R. vagus
nominate
tery

Arch of aorta

R. bronchus

Ascending aorta

L. bronchus

Œsophageal plexus (vagus)

Descending thoracic aorta

ening for vena cava
R. leaf central
don of diaphragm

L. leaf of central tendon of diaphragm
Œsophagus

Abdominal aorta

Thoracic duct

L. crus

. sympathetic trunk
12 T.

Lateral aortic lymph glands
Origin of transversus

Iliohypogastric
Ilioinguinal

Quadratus lumborum

Genitofemoral
Lat. femoral cutaneous

Psoas

Iliacus

Inguinal ligament

Femoral

Colon

Obturator

Urinary bladder

P.

FIG. 54. The trachea and bronchi.

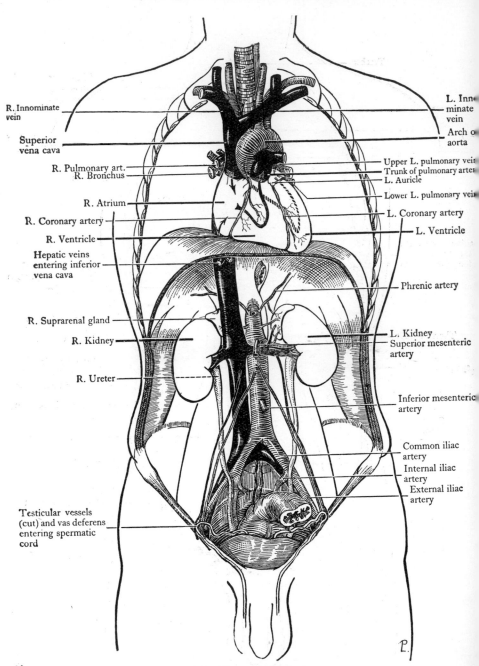

R. Innominate
vein

Superior
vena cava

R. Pulmonary art.
R. Bronchus

R. Atrium

R. Coronary artery

R. Ventricle

Hepatic veins
entering inferior
vena cava

R. Suprarenal gland

R. Kidney

R. Ureter

Testicular vessels
(cut) and vas deferens
entering spermatic
cord

L. Innominate
vein

Arch of
aorta

Upper L. pulmonary vein
Trunk of pulmonary artery
L. Auricle

Lower L. pulmonary vein

L. Coronary artery

L. Ventricle

Phrenic artery

L. Kidney
Superior mesenteric
artery

Inferior mesenteric
artery

Common iliac
artery
Internal iliac
artery
External iliac
artery

FIG. 55.   The roots of the lungs.

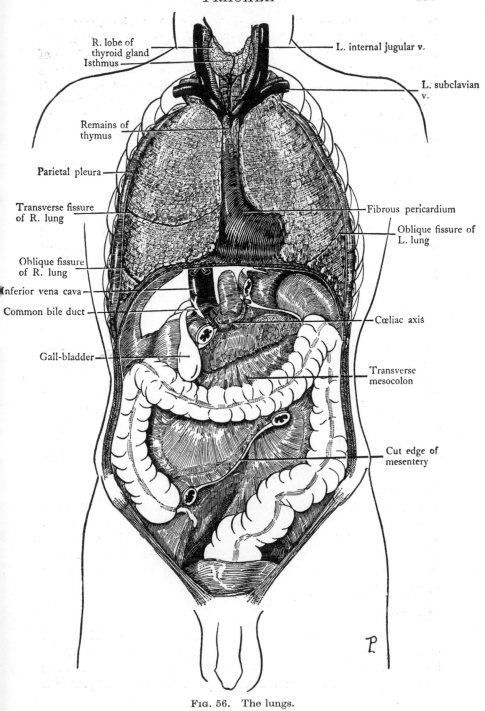

R. lobe of
thyroid gland
Isthmus

L. internal jugular v.

L. subclavian
v.

Remains of
thymus

Parietal pleura

Transverse fissure
of R. lung

Fibrous pericardium

Oblique fissure of
L. lung

Oblique fissure
of R. lung

Inferior vena cava

Common bile duct

Cœliac axis

Gall-bladder

Transverse
mesocolon

Cut edge of
mesentery

FIG. 56. The lungs.

13—2

is not movable and its purpose is to protect the vocal fold. During swallowing the whole of the larynx is raised by muscles attached to its exterior so that it comes to lie nearer the base of the tongue. At the same time the tongue is rolled back so that the vertical measurement of the superior laryngeal aperture is still further reduced. The epiglottis becomes kinked by the pressure from above and below so that a hump, convex backwards, is produced on its posterior surface, and over this the food is projected rapidly past the opening into the larynx.

The nerves of the larynx are branches of the vagus (tenth cranial) nerve.

The Trachea

The trachea or windpipe is a tube about 5 inches long and $\frac{3}{4}$ inch in diameter, continuous above with the larynx, and dividing below at the level of the fifth thoracic vertebra into the two bronchi (Figs. 54, 55 and 56).

The larger air tubes, being subject to pressure from surrounding structures, would collapse unless adapted structurally to withstand this pressure. They are reinforced by rings of cartilage connected one to another by membranous portions, rather like reinforced water hose.

In the wall of the trachea the rings are incomplete posteriorly, where the wall is membranous, and on this account the trachea is not quite cylindrical, being flattened posteriorly (Fig. 18).

Throughout its length the trachea lies just in front of the œsophagus. In the neck the isthmus of the thyroid gland covers its second and third rings, and the lateral lobes of the gland lie at the sides of the trachea. Just above its bifurcation the arch of the aorta crosses in front of the trachea, and the innominate left common carotid, and left subclavian arteries which arise from the arch lie first in front and then at the sides of the tube. Those parts of the sides of the thoracic portion of the trachea which are not related to these vessels are in direct contact with the pleura and lung. The trachea is lined by mucous membrane of the respiratory type.

The Bronchi

The bronchi are the tubes into which the trachea divides and one passes to each lung, forming one of the constituents of the lung root. The right bronchus divides before it reaches the lung into an eparterial branch for the upper lobe of the lung, and a

main branch which is distributed to the middle and lower lobes.
The left bronchus does not divide until it reaches the lung.

THE GENERAL ARRANGEMENT OF THE VISCERA IN THE THORAX

THE MEDIASTINUM

The thoracic cavity is bounded in front by the sternum and
costal cartilages, behind by the vertebral column and the posterior

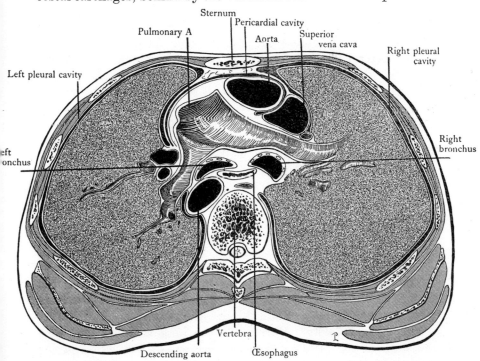

Fɪɢ. 57.   Transverse section of thorax to show the mediastinum and pleural sacs.

parts of the ribs, and at the sides by the ribs.   Its floor is formed
by the diaphragm, whilst above, it communicates with the root
of the neck through the thoracic inlet.   The space so bounded is
divided into two parts by a septum, or partition, known as the
mediastinum.   The **mediastinum** is made up of the pericardium,
the heart and the great vessels entering and leaving it, the trachea
and œsophagus, the vagus and phrenic nerves, as well as
lymphatic glands and a number of smaller and less important
structures.   This mediastinal septum separates the two lungs

from one another, each lung being enclosed in its own pleural sac to facilitate its movement; the pleura on each side covers the lateral surface of the mediastinum (Fig. 57).

The Pleuræ

The pleural sacs are the serous membranes which enable the lungs to move freely in the cavities in which they lie. Each is in the form of an invaginated sac, one layer of which covers the lung and the other the walls of the cavity which the lung occupies. The layer covering the lung is called the **visceral or pulmonary pleura**, the layer covering the walls is the **parietal pleura**. These two layers are continuous with one another along the lung root.

The Visceral Pleura. This layer covers the surface of the lung to which it is intimately adherent. It dips into the fissures between the lobes of the lung, and is reflected from the medial surface of the lung along the lung root, to become continuous with the parietal pleura covering the mediastinum.

The Parietal Pleura. This is divided into parts named according to the portion of the wall of the cavity covered.

The **costal** pleura is that part of the parietal pleura which covers the deep surface of the ribs and the intercostal spaces.

The **diaphragmatic** part covers the upper surface of the diaphragm.

The **cervical** part of the parietal pleura projects up into the root of the neck. It is dome-shaped and the subclavian artery passes across it to reach the first rib.

The **mediastinal** portion of the parietal pleura covers the surface of the mediastinum and is continuous with the visceral pleura over the lung root and through the pulmonary ligament.

The Pleural Cavity. During life the lung is in contact with the walls of the cavity it occupies because of the action of the negative intrathoracic pressure. The two layers of the pleura, visceral and parietal, are therefore in contact with one another and separated by only a very thin film of fluid secreted by the pleura. This fluid enables the two layers to glide freely one on another so that the lung is not hampered in its movements. If the chest wall be opened and the parietal pleura incised the negative pressure within the thorax is abolished and air will rush into the pleural cavity and separate the two layers and convert what is normally only a potential cavity into an actual one. In pathological conditions of the pleura such as pleurisy an excessive amount of fluid may be produced by the pleura and separate the

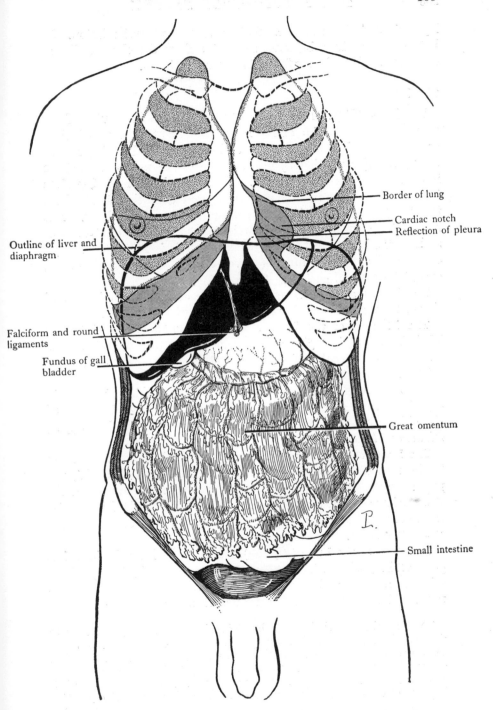

Border of lung

Cardiac notch
Reflection of pleura

Outline of liver and
diaphragm

Falciform and round
ligaments

Fundus of gall
bladder

Great omentum

Small intestine

FIG. 58. The relation of the lungs and pleuræ to the surface of the chest.

layers in a similar manner. This is termed pleural effusion. In both cases the lung becomes separated from the chest wall and collapses against the surface of the mediastinum.

The Lungs

The lungs (Figs. 31, 33 and 58) are placed in the cavity of the thorax one on each side of the mediastinal septum to which they are connected by the lung roots. Each is conical in shape with the **apex** projecting slightly into the root of the neck, and the **base** in contact with the diaphragm. Each lung has a **medial surface** in contact with the mediastinum and presenting the **hilum** where the structures constituting the root enter and leave the lung. The mediastinal surface is marked also by impressions for the structures such as the heart, aorta, etc., with which it is in contact. The entire surface of the lung is covered with the visceral pleura, except for a small part near the root.

The two lungs differ from one another slightly in their general shape, the right being shorter and wider than the left.

The Fissures of the Lungs. The **left lung** is divided into two lobes by an *oblique fissure* extending right through from the lateral to the medial surface, except at the lung root.

The **lobes** are termed *upper and lower*.

The **right lung** shows an *oblique fissure* like the left, but has in addition a *transverse fissure* passing from the anterior border into the oblique fissure. It is thus divided into three *lobes, upper, middle and lower*.

The Roots of the Lungs. The roots of the lungs connect them to the mediastinum and are made up of the main bronchi, the pulmonary vessels and the bronchial vessels for the supply of the interstitial tissue of the lung. They also contain the lymphatics and nerves of the lungs. There are slight differences in the roots of the two sides.

Structure of the Lung (Fig. 59). Inside the lung the **bronchus** gives off branches which pass ventrally and dorsally into the lung substance. These branches divide and subdivide, the small terminal branches being called **bronchioles**.

The bronchi and their main branches have a structure similar to that of the trachea, with cartilaginous plates reinforcing the walls. This cartilage becomes less and less in amount as the smaller branches are reached, until finally, in the bronchioles, it disappears altogether. Plain muscle is present in the walls of the bronchioles, and is capable of constricting the lumen of these small tubes and so cutting

down the amount of air which can pass through them. Spasm of this
muscle occurs in asthma. The bronchioles are lined by respiratory
epithelium.

Each bronchiole opens into a space called a **vestibule,** which
divides into several channels called **atria.** Each atrium in its turn
divides into two or more **infundibula** and from each infundibulum

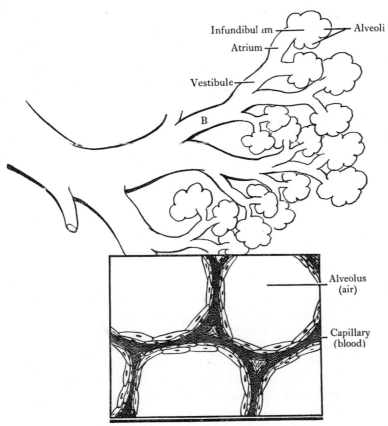

FIG. 59.   Scheme of the structure of a lobule of the lung.
B = bronchiole.

along its whole length project tiny vesicular air spaces called
alveoli. The walls of the vestibule, atria, infundibula and alveoli
are lined by flattened epithelium, their walls being formed of a
single layer of cells.   Each bronchiole with its vestibule and its
subdivisions constitutes a **lobule** of the lung, and adjacent lobules
are connected together by interstitial connective tissue to make

up the substance of the whole lung. The bronchi are accompanied by branches of the pulmonary artery and veins, and by lymphatics and nerves, and branches of these are distributed to every lobule of the lung. The capillaries derived from the branches of the pulmonary artery form a network in the interstitial tissue between the walls of adjacent alveoli, so that the blood in these vessels is separated from the air in the alveoli by only two layers of cells, the endothelium of the capillary wall and the flattened epithelium forming the wall of the alveoli.

The Pulmonary Circulation

This comprises the system of blood-vessels through which the impure blood from the right side of the heart is carried to the lungs to take up oxygen and lose its carbon dioxide, and by which the purified blood is returned to the left side of the heart. The system is made up of the pulmonary artery and its right and left branches and their divisions inside the lung, the lung capillaries and the four pulmonary veins and their radicles (Figs. 38 and 39).

The Pulmonary Artery. This is the only artery in the body which carries deoxygenated blood. It arises from the right ventricle of the heart and is within the pericardium. At its origin it lies in front of the ascending aorta, but soon comes to lie on the left side of that vessel. Just in the concavity of the arch of the aorta it divides into its right and left branches.

Each branch runs into the corresponding lung root. The right branch passes behind the ascending aorta and the superior vena cava, and before it reaches the lung gives off a special branch to the upper lobe. The left branch passes, with the other structures making up the lung root, in front of the descending thoracic aorta.

Within the lung the branches of the pulmonary artery accompany the bronchi and finally give rise to capillaries which ramify in the walls of the alveoli.

The Pulmonary Veins. The venous radicles collecting the blood from the lung substance ultimately form two pulmonary veins on each side. These end by entering the left atrium.

The interstitial tissue of the lung and the walls of the bronchi are supplied by branches which belong to the systemic circulation. They are termed the bronchial vessels, and must not be confused with the vessels of the pulmonary circulation.

The lymphatics drain into glands in the root of the lung and the neighbouring part of the mediastinum called the tracheo-bronchial. The lymph after passing through these goes to the thoracic and right lymph ducts.

The nerves of the lung come from the pulmonary plexuses on the anterior and posterior surfaces of the lung root. They are derived from the vagus and the sympathetic chain.

PHYSIOLOGY OF RESPIRATION

We must now study the means whereby the oxygen entering the body in the inspired air reaches the tissues, and how the carbon dioxide produced in the tissues as a result of activity is got rid of from the body.

The gases are transported between the tissues and the lungs by the blood, and before we can understand the process it is necessary to see how they are carried in the blood, and what factors induce the blood to take up oxygen in the lungs and to give it up in the tissues, and to take up carbon dioxide in the tissues and give it up in the lungs.

Oxygen Carriage in the Blood

We have already seen that oxygen is necessary for muscle contraction (p. 87). It is likewise necessary for the activity of any tissue in the body, for example, secretion by glands and excretion by the kidney (Chapter XIII). The oxygen required by the body tissues to perform their work is carried to them by the blood. The source of this oxygen is the air inspired into the lungs during respiration.

Oxygen is a very insoluble gas and very little of it enters into physical solution in the blood-plasma. The major part of the oxygen is carried by the **hæmoglobin** of the red blood corpuscles in the form of a bright red compound called **oxyhæmoglobin.** This accounts for the colour of arterial blood.

Carbon Dioxide Carriage in the Blood

As a result of tissue activity the oxygen supplied to the tissues is used up, heat and energy being liberated and carbon dioxide formed. In order that the tissues may continue their activity, the carbon dioxide produced during metabolism must be removed from the tissue cells. Once again the blood is the medium by which this removal is effected.

Carbon dioxide, unlike oxygen, is a very soluble gas, and readily dissolves in the blood-plasma to form **carbonic acid.** This acid interacts with other constituents of the plasma to form

sodium bicarbonate, and it is in this latter form that carbon dioxide is carried in the blood back to the lungs. In the lungs the bicarbonate is reconverted to carbon dioxide and this gas is expelled from the body in the expired air.

Changes occurring in the Tissues. Tissue Respiration

When a tissue is about to perform active work its blood supply is increased. This additional arterial blood arriving in the tissues ensures an adequate supply of oxygen.

The hæmoglobin of arterial blood is almost completely saturated with oxygen, whilst the tissue fluid and tissue cells have a low oxygen content. This difference of oxygen tension makes oxygen diffuse from the blood, through the capillary walls and tissue fluid, into the tissue cells. As a result of this process the tissues are supplied with oxygen and the oxyhæmoglobin of the blood is deprived of its oxygen, being converted into the dark red compound called **reduced hæmoglobin.** This accounts for the colour of venous blood.

Being supplied with oxygen, the tissues can carry out their work (muscle contraction, glandular secretion, etc.), and as a result of this work carbon dioxide is produced. The carbon dioxide content of the active tissues is thus high, but the carbon dioxide content of arterial blood is low, and therefore carbon dioxide diffuses from the tissue cells, through the tissue fluid and capillary walls, into the blood-plasma. Here it dissolves in the plasma, forming carbonic acid.

Now the reaction of the blood-plasma is normally slightly alkaline and the body endeavours as far as possible to maintain this reaction, gross variations on either the acid or alkaline sides being dangerous to life. The entrance of carbonic acid into the blood, however, tends to make the blood acid in reaction, and therefore the body carries out certain chemical readjustments in order to prevent this change. This phenomenon is called " buffering."

The carbonic acid reacts with the sodium chloride of the blood-plasma to form sodium bicarbonate, and chloride is liberated. This chloride leaves the plasma and passes into the red blood corpuscles, where it enters into combination with the reduced hæmoglobin. This phenomenon, which prevents the blood becoming acid in reaction, is called the " chloride shift." The blood containing carbon dioxide in the form of sodium bicarbonate then passes through the lungs.

Changes occurring at the Lungs

Deoxygenated blood, arriving in the pulmonary capillaries, is dark red in colour (due to its hæmoglobin being in the reduced form). In the lungs it comes into close contact with the air inspired into the pulmonary alveoli, the air and blood being separated only by the thin alveolar and capillary endothelial walls (Fig. 59). Changes now take place which are the exact reverse of those occurring in the tissues.

The inspired air in the alveoli is rich in oxygen, whilst the venous blood has lost most of its oxygen in the tissues. There is thus a higher oxygen tension in the alveoli, and oxygen diffuses from the alveoli into the blood, where it combines with the reduced hæmoglobin to reform the bright red oxyhæmoglobin.

Being oxygenated again, the hæmoglobin is no longer able to " hold " the chlorine with which it combined as a result of the chloride shift in the tissues. The liberated chlorine now passes out of the corpuscles into the plasma, where, reacting with the sodium bicarbonate, sodium chloride is reformed and the carbon dioxide is once more liberated, *i.e.*, a reversal of the changes which took place in the tissues.

The carbon dioxide content of the plasma thus becomes high, whilst that of the alveolar inspired air is low. Carbon dioxide therefore diffuses from the blood into the alveoli until equilibrium is reached, and the gas is expelled from the body in the expired air. Thus expired air contains much more carbon dioxide than inspired air. The composition of inspired air and expired air is shown in the following table :—

Inspired Air		Expired Air	
	Per cent.		Per cent.
Oxygen . . .	20·96	Oxygen . . .	16·50
Nitrogen . .	79·40	Nitrogen . .	79·40
Carbon dioxide .	0·04	Carbon dioxide .	4·10

The air leaving the lungs (expired air) has a lower oxygen content and a higher carbon dioxide content than the air entering the lungs (inspired air). The nitrogen is an inert gas and takes no part in the respiratory exchanges.

It should be noted that in the lungs the blood takes up as much oxygen as is possible, but in ordinary respiration it does not lose *all* its carbon dioxide. The carbon dioxide which remains in the blood is, we shall see, an important stimulus in the maintenance of respiration.

Summary

The chemical changes occurring in the process of respiration may be summarised as follows :—

Arterial blood, bright red in colour, carries oxygen to the tissues. In the tissues the blood gives up its oxygen, takes up the carbon dioxide produced in the tissues, and becomes converted into the dark red venous blood.

The venous blood, after passing through the right side of the heart, passes to the lungs. In the lungs the blood takes up oxygen from the alveolar air and gives up its carbon dioxide. The arterial blood so formed is returned to the left side of the heart, whence it is redistributed to the tissues.

Respiration in the lungs, therefore, provides the oxygen required by the tissues and removes the waste product of tissue metabolism, carbon dioxide. The blood is the essential connecting medium between the lungs and the tissues.

The Cause of Respiration, and the Mechanism of Variation of the Respiratory Movements

The rhythmic movements of respiration are under the control of a centre in the brain called the **respiratory centre,** the exact position of which is uncertain, but is probably somewhere in the hindbrain. This centre sends out impulses which pass down the spinal cord and stimulate into activity the nerves (phrenic, etc.), which supply the respiratory muscles. It is probable that both inspiratory and expiratory movements are initiated in this way. It is then obvious that whatever influences the activity of this respiratory centre, or alters its irritability, will have a corresponding effect on respiration.

The respiratory centre is sensitive to four main alterations in its environment. These are : First, the amount of acid, particularly carbon dioxide, in the blood. Second, the amount of oxygen in the blood. Third, nervous impulses which reach the centre from other parts. Fourth, the blood supply of the brain itself.

The Amount of Carbon Dioxide in the Blood. Increasing the amount of carbon dioxide in the blood at once causes increased respiration. Conversely, a decrease in the amount leads to diminished respiratory movements. *Increase* of the blood CO_2

occurs in muscular exercise, and this increase arouses the respiratory centre to increased activity. *Decrease* of the blood carbon dioxide can be brought about by voluntarily increasing the pulmonary ventilation by taking a number of excessively deep breaths. This is followed by an actual cessation of respiration (**apnœa**) for some time until the percentage of CO_2 in the blood rises again because it is not being excreted by the lung. When a normal amount of CO_2 is again present it stimulates the respiratory centre and breathing begins again.

The Amount of Oxygen in the Blood. The effect of lack of oxygen in the blood is probably to increase the sensitivity of the respiratory centre to carbon dioxide.

Nerve Impulses Acting on the Respiratory Centre. As already stated, the lung is supplied by the vagus nerve. The passage of air over the respiratory mucous membrane during inspiration causes impulses to pass along the vagus nerves which inhibit or depress the respiratory centre. So that each inspiration really stops itself by this reflex action of the vagus. The cessation of respiration during swallowing is probably a similar action on the respiratory centre by impulses set up in the glossopharyngeal nerve by the food touching the back of the pharynx. Impulses coming along sensory nerves from other parts may also affect the centre. For instance, the stimulation of the skin from plunging into cold water results in a deep gasping respiration. The higher centres of the brain can influence respiration, as, for instance, in emotional disturbance.

The Blood Supply of the Brain. Cutting off the blood supply to the respiratory centre leads ultimately to failure of respiration.

The Normal Respiratory Rhythm and its Variations. The normal respiration rate in an adult is from fourteen to eighteen breaths per minute. The rate is increased during exercise and conditions of emotional stress because more oxygen is needed by the tissues, and is decreased by rest and during sleep. In a child the rate is higher. Normally as the respiration rate rises the heart rate rises more or less proportionately, the ratio between respiration and pulse being about one to four or five. In respiratory diseases both the pulse rate and the respiration rate commonly increase, but the normal pulse respiration ratio is not maintained, and the rise in respiration rate is disproportionately large.

Vital Capacity. This is the quantity of air which can be expelled from the lungs after taking the largest breath possible.

It is reduced in many diseases, the normal amount in an adult is about 230 cubic inches (3,000 to 4,500 cubic centimetres).

Effects of Respiration on the Circulation. Each inspiration decreases the intrathoracic pressure, and, in addition to drawing air into the lungs, this tends to suck blood from the great veins into the right side of the heart. This in turn increases the output of the heart and leads to an increase in the general arterial blood pressure. Muscular exercise is the usual cause of all these phenomena.

Special Respiratory Acts. **Coughing and sneezing** are sudden respiratory acts produced reflexly by stimulation of the mucous membrane of the respiratory tract due to the presence of some irritant. The sudden expulsion of air leads to the clearing away of the offending substance.

Dyspnœa. This means difficult breathing. Its cause may be obstruction of the air passages from inside or outside. Breathlessness may also be caused by diseases of the blood or the heart leading to deficient elimination of carbon dioxide or diminished carrying power of the blood for oxygen.

Asphyxia. This is the train of events which follows when an animal is deprived of air, either by obstruction of the air passages or by the breathing of suffocating gases. In the first stages the accumulation of carbon dioxide in the blood leads to very greatly increased respiratory efforts. In the second stage there are general muscular convulsions, and in the third exhaustion of the muscles and total cessation of respiration. In suffocation due to obstruction of the air passages the skin becomes blue and the eyes and the tongue protrude.

In the special variety of asphyxia due to the breathing of carbon monoxide gas which is contained in the fumes from coke fires, the exhaust gases of internal combustion engines, and in coal gas, the skin is pink in colour. This is due to the fact that the red corpuscles of the blood have a greater affinity for carbon monoxide than for oxygen, and the product of the gas with the hæmoglobin is brighter in colour than oxyhæmoglobin. The corpuscles having become saturated with carbon monoxide, they cannot take up oxygen and death results. As carboxyhæmoglobin is a stable compound, the pink colour persists after death.

Effects of Altered Atmospheric Pressure on Respiration. At high altitudes the atmospheric pressure is much reduced and the pressure of oxygen being so low, the blood will not take up the gas in sufficient quantity. A condition called " mountain sickness '' may result. People who habitually live in such rarefied air gradually adapt themselves to these conditions by producing more hæmoglobin in the blood, so that the total oxygen taken up is sufficient.

At very high atmospheric pressures the blood will take up nitrogen from the air in such quantity as to form minute bubbles of the gas in the blood when the person returns to normal atmospheric conditions. It is imperative that deep-sea divers and others who work at high pressures should return to the normal air pressure slowly so that this nitrogen can be eliminated from the blood *viâ* the lungs without forming bubbles in the circulation. If this precaution be neglected the condition called **caisson disease** results.

CHAPTER XII

THE FATE OF ABSORBED FOODSTUFFS
METABOLISM

It has been seen that the end-products of digestion are absorbed as glucose, fats, and amino-acids. The glucose and amino-acids enter the blood-stream directly, whilst the fat is absorbed first into the lymphatics and reaches the blood-stream *viâ* the thoracic duct. It remains to consider what purpose is served by these substances in the activity of tissues and the working of the body as a whole.

Carbohydrates and Fats. Activity of tissues occurs as a result of energy liberated by the breakdown of substances stored in the tissues. Some of the energy is liberated as heat, some is utilised in the performance of work. When a muscle contracts, for instance, some of the energy appears as heat, the remainder is appearing as the contraction of the muscle. The work done may take other forms, such, for instance, as secretion by gland tissues, but here again part of the energy appears as heat and part as work. The body maintains its temperature from this heat which is produced in the activity of its tissues, the temperature being regulated by mechanisms which will be considered later.

The substances which are broken down to provide the energy for tissue activity have only one ultimate source, namely, the products absorbed from the digested foods. These products may have been stored in the tissues themselves for some time before they are utilised for this purpose, but this does not alter the fact that they have been derived originally from food. Not all of these food materials are utilised, however, in providing energy appearing as heat and work. Some of them are used to rebuild the cell protoplasm and some are oxidised in the tissues to provide energy to restore to their original condition the substances the breakdown of which resulted in the appearance of heat and work. This may be clarified by recalling the occurrences when a muscle contracts. Contained in the muscle is the substance called **glycogen,** which is derived from the digestion of the carbohydrate part of the food. The carbohydrate is absorbed

210

from the intestine in the form of **glucose**, which finds its way into the intestinal capillaries and the portal vein and so reaches the liver. In the liver the glucose which is not necessary for the immediate needs of the body is stored as **glycogen,** whilst the remainder is carried in the blood, still in the form of glucose, to the muscles all over the body. Here it is built up into glycogen, which is stored in the muscle. It is the breakdown of this glycogen into simpler substances which provides the energy which results in the contraction of the muscle and the production of heat. The substance which is formed by the breakdown of glycogen for this purpose is **lactic acid**. During this process, then, much of the glycogen stored by the muscle has been broken down, and, in order to get the necessary energy to continue to contract, the muscle must replenish its store of glycogen. Energy is required to build the lactic acid into glycogen again, and this is provided in the following way. About one-fifth of the lactic acid which accumulates combines with oxygen brought to the tissues by the blood with the production of CO_2 and water. This combination of lactic acid with oxygen is comparable with any other oxidation or combustion process in that it results in the liberation of energy. Part of the energy produced is utilised to rebuild the remaining four-fifths of the lactic acid into glycogen, whilst the rest of the energy appears as heat and contraction. It should be understood that the process of breakdown of the glycogen to provide energy, and the process of combustion of some of the lactic acid produced, are going on both at the same time in the muscle. The energy derived from both appears partly as heat which maintains the body temperature and partly as work.

It will be obvious, from the above description, that, since some of the lactic acid is burnt in the tissues to produce energy, the amount of glycogen reformed in the process will be less than that originally present. The deficiency is made up by the mobilisation of glycogen stored in the liver. Some of this liver glycogen is passed into the blood in the form of glucose, and is carried by the blood to the muscles, where it is stored as glycogen again.

These occurrences are summarised in Scheme A overleaf.

If the amount of carbohydrate stored in the form of glycogen in the muscle tissue of the body and in the liver be insufficient to provide the energy necessary for the above processes, fat can be oxidised in the tissues in the same way as carbohydrate, and, as will be seen later, even protein can be utilised in this way. If fat be required for this purpose it is mobilised from the fat depots of the body and brought by the blood to the liver, where it is desaturated before being carried to the tissues for oxidation.

The Fate of Protein. The amino-acids absorbed from the intestine are carried in the blood-stream and are utilised partly to replace the proteins of the cell protoplasm destroyed in the

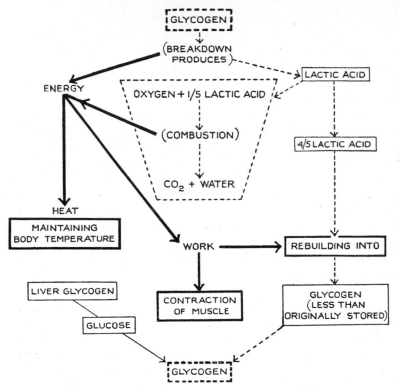

Scheme A. The Metabolism of Carbohydrate.

ordinary wear and tear of tissue activity. Amino-acids are necessary also to provide the cells with the material for growth. The tissue cells select from the amino-acids available those which are suitable for this building process, and those which remain are carried to the liver. In the liver these are broken down by the action of enzymes. As a result of this breakdown the amino component becomes separated from the remainder and is built up into the substance called **urea**. The urea is carried in the blood-stream to the kidneys, where it is excreted as one of the constituents of the urine. The **amino-free part** of the amino-acids which have undergone de-amination in this way is carried by the blood to the tissues, where it can be utilised like carbohydrate and fat to provide, by a process of oxidation, a source of energy for tissue activity.

Nucleo-proteins (proteins of nuclear protoplasm) contain nucleic acid which is necessary to replace the nuclear material in the cells of the body. The excess of this over the requirements of the body is converted by the liver into the substance called **uric acid,** which is excreted also in the urine. Apart from the nucleic acid, the remaining portions of nucleo-protein are probably dealt with in a similar manner to all other proteins, being utilised for tissue building, and, if in excess, being de-aminated so as to render them suitable for oxidation in the tissues.

The above processes, resulting in the formation of urea and uric acid, have been described as they occur in the proteins absorbed from the food. It should be remembered, however, that the proteins forming the protoplasm of the cells of the body are, in the course of ordinary wear and tear, being continually broken down and replaced. The amino-acids produced in this breakdown are treated in precisely the same way as those absorbed from the intestine. Some are utilised for tissue rebuilding, some are de-aminated with the production of urea, and are then used to provide a source of energy in the tissues. The nucleo-proteins derived from the nuclei of the tissue cells are also dealt with in the same way as nucleo-protein derived from the food, providing thus a second source of uric acid. The urea and uric acid, then, which appear in the urine are derived both from the proteins absorbed from digested foods, and from the tissues of the body itself. The nitrogenous products (urea and uric acid) derived from tissue wastage are termed **endogenous,** whilst those derived from food proteins are termed **exogenous.**

The processes described above are summarised in Schemes B and C overleaf.

Metabolism

The chemical changes occurring in living cells during their growth and in activity are referred to as metabolic changes The breakdown of substances in the protoplasm is called **katabolism,** whilst the changes involving the building up of substances by the body cells are grouped together under the term **anabolism.**

It will be obvious that the more active the tissues of the body may be, the greater will be the metabolic changes taking place. The total metabolism taking place during conditions of rest (*e.g.*, sleep) is called the **basal metabolism.** To maintain the bodily functions under such conditions requires a certain intake of food, as the materials have to be provided for maintaining muscles in a state of tone, for the heart muscle and the muscles of respiration, for the activities of glands, etc. The basal metabolic rate varies

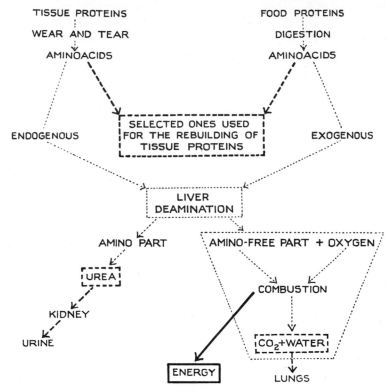

Scheme B. The Metabolism of Protein.

according to the size of the animal, small animals having a higher basal metabolism per unit of body weight than large ones. The reason for this is that small animals have a relatively greater body surface from which to lose heat (see Temperature regulation). The basal metabolism is also increased in certain diseases, notably in exophthalmic goitre.

As the activities of the body as a whole rise, for instance, in muscular exercise, the metabolic rate rises in proportion. It is necessary, therefore, to take in more food to keep up the supply for the provision of energy and for tissue replacement. A man doing heavy muscular work must take more food than one in a sedentary occupation in order to maintain the body weight at a constant level. For if a man doing heavy work is not taking sufficient carbohydrate he will have to utilise fat and excess protein for combustion in the tissues. The loss of fat from the

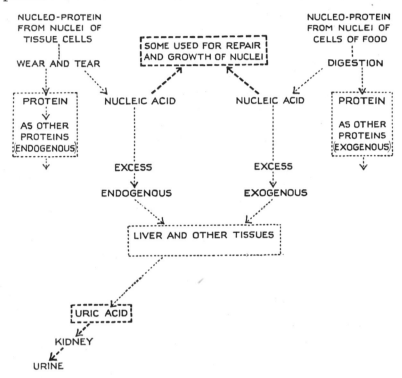

Scheme C. The Metabolism of Nucleo-protein.

fat depots leads to loss of weight. These factors have to be taken into account in the assessment of the diet suitable for the type of life any particular person is living. In actual fact, hunger and appetite generally assure that a sufficiency of food will be taken for the requirements, but scientific investigation of these problems can assure a more economic use of foodstuffs in the event of necessity. In the Great War much valuable work of this type was carried out.

In the scientific investigation of metabolism it has been found that some food substances will produce more energy for a given weight of material than others. We know that a given quantity of a substance, if burnt completely, will produce a definite amount of energy. This energy will appear in a form depending on the conditions present. Heat and mechanical work are two forms in which the energy may appear. It can be shown if a given weight of combustible material be burnt in the presence of oxygen, and the experiment repeated many times, the energy in some cases being allowed to escape as heat, and in other cases being utilised to perform work, that the amount of *work done* always bears the same definite proportion to the amount of *heat which would result from the combustion of the same quantity of material.* The amount of heat which results from the combustion in oxygen of a given weight of carbohydrate, of protein, or of fat, may be used to estimate and compare the energy which these various foods are capable of producing. The unit which is used in expressing these values is called the **calorie** (large calorie), and is the amount of heat necessary to raise the temperature of 1 kilogramme of water from freezing point to 1 degree Centigrade. The combustion in oxygen, for instance, of 1 gramme of the following substances gives these results [1] :—

        1 gramme of fat burnt in oxygen yields   .   9·3 calories
        1 gramme of protein   .   .   .   .   5·6 calories
        1 gramme of starch   .   .   .   .   4·1 calories

Since much of the protein is excreted as urea (which has itself a value in calories), the figure for protein is not its " physiological " heat value. If used in the body to provide energy it has a calorie value of more nearly 4. Carbohydrate and fat, however, have the same calorie value in the body as they have in experimental conditions, and, of the two, fat is a more economical source of stored energy than carbohydrate.

We have seen that the combustion in the tissues of carbohydrate, fat, and of excess protein which has been de-aminated, produces energy, and that, in the combustion, oxygen is used and CO_2 and water are produced. Knowing the amount of oxygen necessary to burn these substances outside the body, we can calculate from the amount of oxygen used in respiration how much of them is being burnt in the tissues.

Using these methods, the number of calories required to prevent loss of weight has been calculated in people in various states of activity. The following table gives the approximate figures :—

[1] McDowall.

Man at rest in bed (*i.e.*, basal
   metabolic rate) . . . About 1,700 calories.
Man in sedentary occupation . About 2,000 to 2,500 calories.
Man in active outdoor occupation . About 3,500 calories.

The diet for such people must therefore contain food which will give the total calorie value shown above, in order to prevent loss of weight.

In the diet of ordinary people protein is always taken in amounts in excess of what is required for rebuilding of tissue proteins. Some is therefore available for provision of energy. In designing a diet, personal taste, calorie value, and the provision of suitable quantities of vitamins (p. 112) are the factors which need consideration in the adult. In growing children, however, it is important to include certain proteins which contain substances essential for growth. It has been found, for instance, that the protein gelatin does not contain these elements, and young animals whose sole source of protein in the diet is gelatin fail to grow properly and eventually die. Fortunately most of the foods which ordinary people find appetising contain all the necessary elements in suitable amounts, and appetite is the everyday guide in the selection of a suitable diet.

The influence of the pancreas on sugar metabolism is described on p. 324.

CHAPTER XIII

THE URINARY SYSTEM

WE have seen that through the lungs the blood gets rid of the carbon dioxide which it takes up in the tissues. It is by means of the urinary excretory system that it gets rid of the protein breakdown products, of substances which are formed in maintaining the reaction of the blood at a fairly constant level, and of certain other substances if they be present in the blood in excessive amounts.

The urinary system consists of the kidneys, the ureters, the urinary bladder, and the urethra.

THE KIDNEYS

The kidneys lie one on each side of the median plain on the posterior abdominal wall behind the peritoneum (Fig. 60).

Each kidney is of characteristic shape and measures about 4 to 5 inches in length, $2\frac{1}{2}$ inches in breadth, and 1 inch in thickness. The indentation at the middle of the medial border of the kidney is called the **hilum,** and it is through this that the vessels and nerves of the kidney and the ureter pass in or out of the organ.

Position of the Kidneys. The kidney lies in front of the transverse processes of the upper three lumbar vertebræ with the hilum opposite the lower border of the body of the first lumbar. The upper pole of the organ lies in front of the twelfth rib on the right side, reaching a slightly higher level on the left side so as to overlap the last two ribs. The part overlapping the ribs is related to the diaphragm, whilst the lower part is separated from the transverse processes of the vertebræ by the psoas muscle, and lateral to this is in contact posteriorly with the quadratus lumborum and transversus abdominis muscles. The upper pole of each kidney is surmounted by the corresponding suprarenal gland (p. 321). The anterior surface of the kidney is related to other abdominal viscera and, where these are not in direct contact with it, is covered by peritoneum. In well-nourished subjects the kidneys are embedded in fat which separates them from the

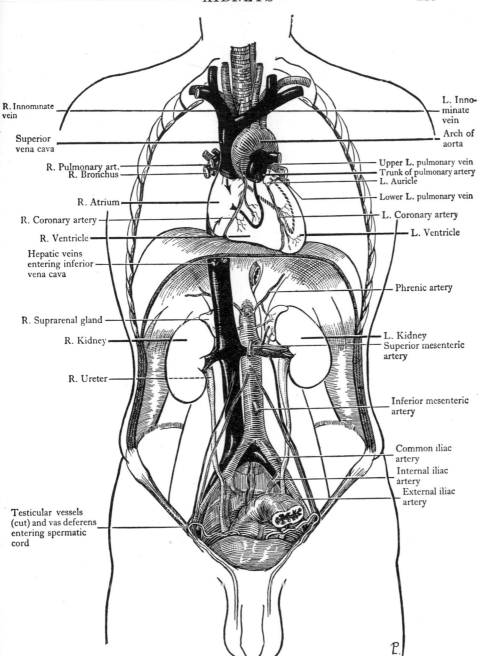

R. Innominate
vein

Superior
vena cava

R. Pulmonary art.
R. Bronchus

R. Atrium

R. Coronary artery

R. Ventricle

Hepatic veins
entering inferior
vena cava

R. Suprarenal gland

R. Kidney

R. Ureter

Testicular vessels
(cut) and vas deferens
entering spermatic
cord

L. Inno-
minate
vein

Arch of
aorta

Upper L. pulmonary vein
Trunk of pulmonary artery
L. Auricle

Lower L. pulmonary vein

L. Coronary artery

L. Ventricle

Phrenic artery

L. Kidney
Superior mesenteric
artery

Inferior mesenteric
artery

Common iliac
artery
Internal iliac
artery
External iliac
artery

Fɪɢ. 60.   The kidneys and ureters.

structures mentioned above. The kidneys are maintained in position on the posterior abdominal wall by the fat which surrounds them, by the counter-pressure against them of other viscera, and by the renal vessels which attach them to the aorta and vena cava.

Internal Structure of the Kidney. A coronal section of the kidney (Fig. 61) shows that the **hilum** opens into a space within the organ

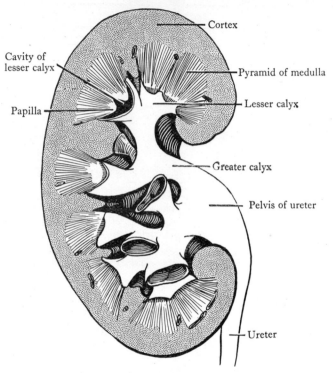

Cortex

Cavity of lesser calyx

Pyramid of medulla

Lesser calyx

Papilla

Greater calyx

Pelvis of ureter

Ureter

FIG. 61. Coronal section of kidney.

called the **renal sinus.** This is occupied by the beginning of the ureter, by the main branches of the renal blood-vessels, and by a quantity of fat. It can also be seen that the cut surface of the kidney substance has a different appearance superficially from that near the renal sinus. The superficial part of the kidney substance is called the **cortex** of the kidney and is of a uniform brownish-red colour. It is marked by a few radial extensions of the medullary substance called *medullary rays.* Enclosed within the arc formed by the cortex is the part of the kidney substance called the **medulla.** It consists of a number of conical masses which in the coronal section appear as paler triangles with the bases directed towards the cortex and the apices projecting a little into the renal sinus. These masses are termed the **renal pyramids,** and the small nipple-like projections which they form on the walls of the renal sinus are called the **renal papillæ.** The cut surface of each pyramid presents longitudinal striations converging on the renal papilla, indicating that it is composed of collecting tubules which open on the surface of the renal papilla. Adjacent pyramids are separated from one another by prolongations inwards of the cortical substance called **renal columns.**

Each renal papilla projects into a somewhat trumpet-shaped tube called a minor calyx. There are from seven to twelve **minor calyces** in all, and each has from one to three renal papillæ projecting into it. Neighbouring minor calyces unite with one another to form the **major calyces,** of which there are usually two, but occasionally three. The major calyces in turn unite to form the dilated upper extremity of the ureter called the **pelvis of the ureter.** The pelvis narrows rapidly as it approaches the hilum, through which the ureter passes to the outside of the kidney.

Minute Structure. The kidney substance consists of large numbers of **tubules** and the blood-vessels supplying them, bound together by a small amount of interstitial connective tissue. The renal tubules consist essentially of three parts : The tubule begins as a minute sac whose walls are formed of flattened cells. This is called Bowman's capsule, and is invaginated by a tuft of renal capillaries. The cavity in the interior of the capsule leads into the next part of the tubule which pursues a complicated course partly in the cortex and partly in the medulla, and is lined through most of its extent by cubical cells. This may be regarded as the **secreting** part of the tubule. The last part of the tubule may be regarded as **collecting** the urine which has been formed by the preceding portions and transferring it to the calyces. There is an enormous number of these tubules in the kidney substance, and though each, being microscopic in size, can secrete only a small amount of urine, the sum total of their secretion gives a considerable amount of urine.

THE URETERS

The ureters are the muscular tubes which convey the urine from the kidneys to the bladder. Each ureter begins in a dilated upper extremity called the **pelvis** of the ureter, which is inside the renal sinus, and is formed by the union of the major calyces. The pelvis narrows rapidly as it approaches the hilum of the kidney ; after passing through the hilum the ureter is a slender thick-walled tube. From the hilum of the kidney on each side the ureter passes downwards on the psoas muscle, behind the peritoneum, to the brim of the pelvis. Here it crosses the iliac artery to enter the pelvis, and, after running down the lateral wall of the pelvis for a short distance, turns forwards and medially to enter the bladder (Fig. 62). This pelvic part of the ureter is close to the lateral fornix of the vagina in the female, and may be injured here during the passage of the fœtal head in parturition.

The ureter does not go straight through the bladder wall, but traverses it very obliquely, so that it lies for a time between the muscle layers of the bladder. The obliquity of the ureter in the wall of the bladder makes it difficult for urine to find its way back into the ureter from the bladder as the intravesical pressure rises. As the bladder distends the two walls of the ureter tend to be pressed up against one another, forming a valve preventing retrograde flow. Much more important, however, than this valve is the muscle in the wall of the ureter itself. This muscle, which is in three layers and very thick relative to the size of the lumen of the ureter, contracts in peristaltic waves which drive the urine always towards the bladder. This peristalsis in the ureter will prevent the passage of urine in the opposite direction as the bladder fills.

THE URINARY BLADDER

The urinary bladder (Figs. 62 and 63), situated in the anterior part of the true pelvis, is the sac in which the urine is held until it is voided by the act of micturition. It is very distensible, its walls containing plain muscle, and its capacity varies greatly in different individuals.

When empty, it lies entirely within the pelvis in the adult, and is more or less pyramidal in shape, the **apex** being directed forwards towards the pubic symphysis. The **superior surface** is covered with peritoneum which, in front, passes on to the anterior abdominal wall, and behind, on to other pelvic viscera. The **base** or posterior surface of the bladder is related to the rectum in the male, but is separated from the rectum in the female by the uterus and the upper part of the vagina. The bladder has also two inferolateral surfaces in contact with the floor and lateral walls of the pelvis. At the upper and lateral angles of the base the ureters enter the bladder, whilst below, at the junction of the base with the two inferolateral surfaces, the urethra leaves the organ. The part of the bladder near the exit of the urethra is called the **neck,** and in the male the prostate gland, which contains the first part of the urethra, is attached to the bladder wall in this situation. There is no prostate gland in the female. The portion of the internal surface of the wall of the bladder between the ureteric orifices above and the urethral orifice below is called the **trigone.** The surface appearance of the trigone differs from that of the remainder of the interior of the bladder in that it is smooth. The rest of the internal surface presents infoldings of the mucous membrane which disappear as the bladder distends. Because of this the bladder mucosa does not become unduly stretched in distension of the viscus.

The relationship of the bladder to other pelvic viscera differs in the two sexes.

In the male the neck of the bladder is related to the prostate. The posterior surface is related to the rectum, the seminal vesicles and deferent ducts being interposed between the two organs. The peritoneum is reflected from the upper part of the posterior surface of the bladder on to the rectum to form the rectovesical peritoneal fossa.

In the female there is no prostate gland. The neck of the bladder is related to connective tissue in which the first part of the urethra is embedded. The posterior surface is related to the cervix of the uterus and the upper part of the vagina, which separate it from the rectum. The body of the uterus, which rests on the upper surface of the bladder, is separated from it by a pouch of peritoneum termed the uterovesical pouch.

The distended bladder is ovoid in form, and rises into the abdomen out of the pelvis. As it does so it strips the peritoneum off the anterior abdominal wall, so that the bladder can be exposed through a suprapubic incision without opening the peritoneal cavity. In the female the distended bladder raises the uterus into a vertical position, and may even tilt it backwards.

In the young child the bladder is much higher than in the adult, and a large part of it, even when empty, is in the abdomen.

THE URETHRA

The urethra is the tube along which the urine is expelled from the bladder to the surface. It differs very markedly in the two sexes.

The Male Urethra

The male urethra is a tube from 7 to 8 inches in length, and,

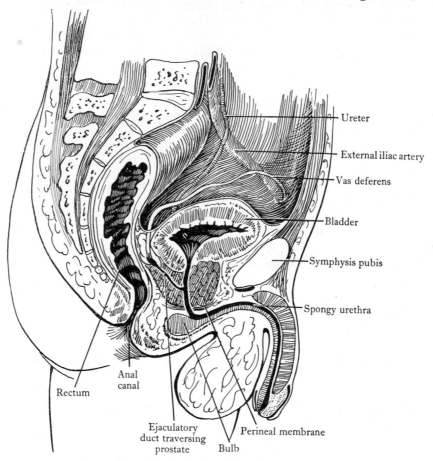

FIG. 62.   Sagittal section of male pelvis.

with the penis in the flaccid state, pursues an S-shaped curve (Fig. 62). The canal is common to the urinary and genital tracts. It is divided into parts as follows :—

The Prostatic Urethra. The first 1¼ inches of the urethra is enclosed in the prostate gland which lies at the neck of the bladder in the male. This is the widest part of the urethra and has opening into it on its posterior wall the **ducts of the prostate** itself, about twenty in number, and the **two ejaculatory ducts** which bring the seminal fluid into the urethra.

The Membranous Urethra. This short part connects the prostatic urethra with the spongy portion in the penis. It

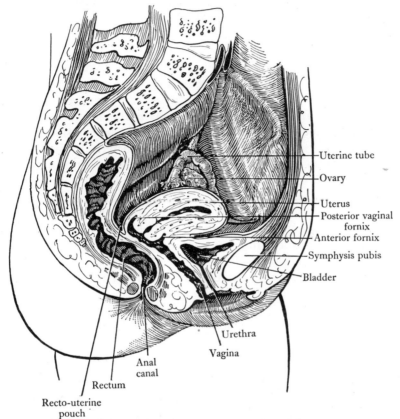

Fig. 63. Sagittal section of female pelvis.

traverses a membranous sheet which stretches from side to side across the pubic arch called the **perineal membrane** (triangular ligament). This consists of two layers with a sheet of voluntary muscle between them. This muscle can compress the urethra and is the **voluntary sphincter** which prevents the escape of urine.

The Spongy Urethra. After perforating the perineal membrane the urethra enters the bulb of the penis (p. 295) which is attached to the superficial surface of the membrane. Continuing forwards from the bulb, the urethra is contained in the corpus spongiosum of the penis, and finally opens on the surface of the glans penis at the external urethral orifice.

The bulbar portion of the penile urethra lies at a lower level than the adjacent parts, and to prevent urine accumulating here the bulb of the penis is covered by a muscle which compresses this part and ejects the accumulated urine.

The Female Urethra

The urethra in the female (Fig. 63) is much shorter than that in the male. It is about 1½ inches long, and, beginning at the internal urethral orifice at the neck of the bladder, runs downwards and forwards just anterior to the vagina. As in the male, it perforates the **perineal membrane** (triangular ligament) between the layers of which it is surrounded by the **urethral sphincter.** It ends finally at the external urethral orifice which is placed just in front of the vaginal opening. It will be noted that there is no prostate gland in the female, and that the clitoris (p. 301), which corresponds to the penis in the male, does not contain any part of the urethra, the latter opening about 1 inch behind the glans of the clitoris. The female urethra is much more easily dilated than that in the male.

Mucous Membrane of the Urinary Tract. The calyces, pelvis, ureter, bladder, and the upper part of the urethra are all lined by transitional epithelium. This has flattened cells on the surface, but in the deeper layers there is a gradual transition to cells of a more or less columnar type. In the female the lower part of the urethra is lined by stratified squamous epithelium. In the male the bulbar and spongy parts of the urethra are lined by columnar epithelium, which, close to the external orifice, gives place to stratified squamous epithelium.

PHYSIOLOGY OF THE URINARY SYSTEM

The kidneys separate from the blood the constituents of the urine. The ureters transfer the urine secreted by the kidneys to the bladder. The bladder contracts periodically to expel the urine through the urethra to the exterior. In considering these processes in more detail, it is necessary first to consider the composition of urine and see how it differs from that of the blood.

The Urine

Urine is a yellowish fluid, normally **slightly acid** in reaction, with a **specific gravity** varying from **1,015 to 1,025.**

The colour is due to pigments called urochromagen and uroerythrin.

The reaction varies in different conditions. Urine is more acid after exercise. It is less acid after meals and particularly after the taking of certain fruits and vegetables. In some circumstances the urine may be alkaline when passed, and all urine *becomes alkaline on standing* due to bacterial decomposition of the urea it contains, with the consequent production of ammonia which can be recognised by its characteristic smell. The specific gravity also varies. It is low after drinking large quantities of fluids, when the amount of urine secreted is large. The specific gravity is high after profuse sweating, when the amount of urine passed is small. Alteration in the specific gravity of the urine occurs also in pathological conditions such as diabetes, where it is raised, and in some forms of renal disease, when it is lowered.

The Amount of Urine. The usual quantity of urine secreted by an adult man in twenty-four hours is about 50 fluid ounces (1,500 cubic centimetres). The quantity varies within considerable limits in normal individuals, being less when there is loss of water from the skin in profuse sweating, and greater when the intake of fluid by drinking is increased.

Substances which increase the secretion of urine are called **diuretics,** and may act by increasing the blood pressure in the vessels of the kidney, or by increasing the activity of the kidney epithelium.

Composition of Urine. The following table gives the composition of urine with the percentages of the most important substances :—

Water	95 per cent.
Organic substances	
Urea	2 per cent.
Urates and uric acid . .	0·05 per cent.
Creatinine	
Pigments	
Inorganic salts	
Sodium chloride. . .	1·2 per cent.
Also	

Chlorides ⎫
Sulphates ⎬ of ⎰ Calcium
Phosphates ⎭ ⎱ Magnesium
Potassium
Ammonia

15—2

Secretion of Urine

The kidneys remove from the blood the urinary constituents and so keep the blood at a constant composition and prevent the accumulation in the blood of waste products. If any substances be present in the blood in too large amounts the kidney will excrete enough of those substances to reduce the quantity in the blood to the normal level. If the blood tends to become too alkaline in reaction more alkali will be excreted in the salts of the urine. If more acid substances are poured into the blood and it tends to become less alkaline than normal, more acid will be excreted. Similarly, if the amount of sugar in the blood rises beyond a certain level the excess will be removed by the kidneys. A comparison of the percentages of some of the more important substances present in the blood and in the urine gives us information on which we can base a conception of how the urine is formed. The following table shows the figures :—

	Plasma Per cent.	Urine Per cent.	
Proteins	8·0	None	
Sodium chloride	0·8	1·2	**More in urine**
Urea	0·03	2·0	**Much more in urine**
Glucose	0·15	None	

(Modified from McDowall.)

It will be noted that no protein and no sugar are excreted in normal circumstances. That the concentration of both chloride and urea is greater in the urine, but that much more urea is excreted in proportion.

The mechanism by which this is brought about is probably somewhat as follows :—

The walls of Bowman's capsules and the vessels which invaginate them (the glomerulus) allow all the constituents of the plasma except the protein to filter through them into the cavity of the capsule which communicates with the tubule (p. 221). This filtrate will contain, among other things, chloride, urea, and glucose in concentrations similar to those in the blood-plasma, the capsule having held back only the protein. A reference to the table above will show, however, that no glucose appears in the urine, so that this must be absorbed as the filtrate from the capsule passes along the tubule. This will leave a solution of urea and chloride in concentrations like those in the blood. We have seen that the concentration of these substances is greater in the urine than in the blood, so in order to accomplish this water also must be absorbed by the tubule. There is evidence that some of the chloride is absorbed too. The urea is in such great concentration in the urine that it is possible that the tubules, far from absorbing this substance from the filtrate as it passes along them, actually secrete more of it into the filtrate until it has reached the level found in the urine. The glomerulus, then, allows all the constituents of plasma except protein to filter through into the tubule. The tubule absorbs water, chloride and glucose from the filtrate, and perhaps secretes more urea into the filtrate. If chloride be absent from the diet it disappears from the urine because the tubules absorb all of it from the filtrate in order to preserve the proper level of chloride in the blood. The concentration and type of the other salts present in urine depends to a great extent on the tendency of the blood to become less or more alkaline and the urinary system is therefore of great importance in maintaining the reaction of the blood at its proper level, *i.e.*, slightly alkaline.

Effect of the Circulation on Urinary Secretion. The amount of fluid filtered through the glomeruli in the kidney is directly proportional to the pressure of blood within the capillaries which form them. When the general blood pressure rises, therefore, there is an increase in the amount of fluid filtered in a given time and an increase in the volume of urine secreted. The blood pressure rises in conditions of increased bodily activity, such as muscular exercise, and this increases the amount of fluid filtered by the glomeruli so that the waste products in the blood can be removed more quickly. At the same time, if profuse sweating occur, more fluid is lost by the skin and more fluid is reabsorbed as the glomerular filtrate passes along the tubules so as to make up for this increase in skin loss. The result is a more highly concentrated urine, but not necessarily an increase in the amount of urine. The increase in the breakdown of tissue proteins in fever also leads to a greater concentration of the urine.

Abnormal Constituents of Urine. The most important of these are albumin, sugar, pus and blood.

Albumin. Albumin in the urine is termed *albuminuria*. The normal glomerulus does not allow protein to pass through it, and the appearance of protein in the urine usually indicates an inflammation of the kidney.

Sugar. Sugar in the urine is termed *glycosuria*. In normal circumstances all the glucose is reabsorbed by the tubules from the glomerular filtrate. If, however, the amount of sugar in the blood rises to an abnormally high level the tubules will not absorb so much in an attempt to maintain the blood sugar at a more normal level. There are two main causes of a high content of sugar in the blood ; one the ingestion of very large quantities of sugar in the diet (this results in alimentary glycosuria) ; the other is the inability of the tissues to utilise sugar which is seen in the disease called *diabetes*.

Pus in the urine (pyuria) indicates some inflammatory disease of the urinary tract.

Blood in the urine (hæmaturia) may give it a bright red colour or may simply make it " smoky " in appearance. It nearly always indicates some lesion of the urinary tract.

Bile colours the urine of jaundiced patients.

Micturition

The urine secreted by the kidneys is transferred to the bladder by the peristalsis of the ureteric muscle. As it accumulates in the bladder the tension in that viscus rises and the stretching of its walls stimulates nerve endings and results in the setting up of nerve impulses which pass to the spinal cord and result in two main effects : First, impulses pass up to the brain, where they are interpreted as the feeling of a full bladder. Second, the impulses reaching the cord set up reflex impulses which pass along the motor nerves of the bladder and result in the rhythmic contraction of the bladder muscle and relaxation of the sphincter at the neck of the bladder. In the adult these rhythmic contractions are not in themselves sufficient to overcome the resistance of the external urethral sphincter. The initiation of the act of micturition is a voluntary process. The abdominal muscles are contracted and so raise still further the intravesical pressure at the same time as the external urethral sphincter is relaxed. The urine is driven along the urethra by the contraction of the bladder muscle until the viscus is completely emptied.

Disturbances of Micturition

These may be due to alterations in the inflow of urine into the bladder, or to disturbance of the mechanism of the bladder and urethra.

Disturbances of Inflow. Polyuria is the secretion of large quantities of urine. It results in increased frequency of micturition.

Anuria is the cessation of secretion of urine. It may be due to disturbance of the two kidneys together from disease or failure of the circulation, or to the blockage of both ureters by stones, or the blockage of one ureter, the other kidney being absent or destroyed by disease. It is sometimes termed **suppression of urine.** Anuria results in the condition called **uræmia,** caused by the retention in the blood of the substances normally excreted in the urine.

Disturbances of the Bladder and Urethra. Retention of urine results from inability of the bladder to expel its contents. This may be caused by obstruction of the urethra or by paralysis of the bladder muscle with a contracted sphincter. The latter may result from injuries or disease of the spinal cord. As the tension within the bladder rises the sphincters can no longer hold the urine and it dribbles out through the urethra ; this condition is termed **retention with overflow.**

Incontinence of Urine. This results from paralysis of the bladder sphincters, the urine escaping from the bladder as soon as it leaves the ureters. The condition occurs in lesions of the spinal cord.

Urinary Stones. Many of the urinary constituents are relatively insoluble substances which may in certain conditions be deposited in the urinary tract in crystalline or amorphous form. Where the urine is very concentrated, *e.g.*, in hot climates, there is a greater tendency for this to occur. In the presence of disease of some part of the urinary tract *débris* may be present which forms a nucleus round which these insoluble substances may collect to form a calculus or stone. Once formed, a calculus may produce other effects by moving, by obstructing some part of the tract, or by pressure or irritation. The stones may be passed, and the contraction of the muscle of the ureter in expelling a stone (occasionally other things like blood clots) may give rise to the pain known as **renal colic.**

CHAPTER XIV

THE NERVOUS SYSTEM

INTRODUCTION

THE nervous system is the mechanism whereby the individual is enabled to react to his environment, and whereby the various

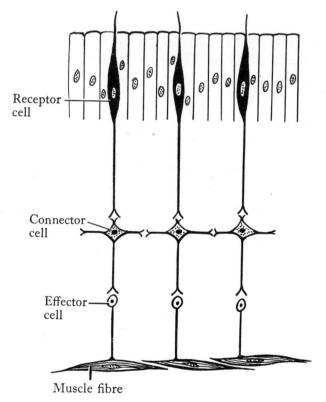

Receptor cell

Connector cell

Effector cell

Muscle fibre

FIG. 64.

activities of the body are correlated and controlled. In the higher animals the system is very complex in structure and so there is great variability in their response to changes in environment, and it may simplify the understanding of matter which is to follow if we consider briefly the means by which lower forms react to changes in external and internal conditions.

Unicellular animals (such as amœba) react to their environment because of the inherent irritability of the protoplasm of which they are composed, and we have seen how, in higher forms, the white corpuscles of the blood retain this primitive function. In such unicellular forms the functions of movement, ingestion, digestion, and reproduction are all carried out by the one cell, and its reaction to any particular stimulus is stereotyped.

A little higher in the animal scale, however, the body of the animal consists of many cells, some specialised for one function and some for another. We find, for example, that the cells on the surface become adapted for protection of the deeper cells which are set aside for the functions of movement and digestion. Such forms live in water and have a mouth leading into a central digestive cavity. It is obvious that an animal of this type must be provided with a mechanism whereby a harmful stimulus applied to a small part of its surface will result in such a generalised contraction of the muscle in its deeper layers as will enable it to move away from the danger. This is provided in a primitive type of nervous system, the elements of which are shown in Fig. 64. Certain of the surface cells are specialised for the reception of stimuli and are named **receptor or sensory** cells. These, found scattered all over the surface, have two **processes,** one of which, the **peripheral,** passes towards and may project from the surface, and the other, the **central**, passes into the deeper layers where it establishes connection with a network of cells and their processes found beneath the surface over the entire extent of the animal. This " nerve net," connected superficially in this way with the central processes of the receptor cells, has processes extending deeply from it to establish in their turn connections with isolated **motor** or **effector** nerve cells whose processes are distributed to the primitive muscles of the animal. The nervous impulse resulting from the stimulation of one of the receptor cells will, if strong enough, spread a considerable distance through the nerve net before fading out, and will therefore be brought to bear, through the motor nerve cells, on a large number of muscle fibres. There is thus brought about from a **local stimulus** a **general response**, which, conditions being identical, will always be the same response.

A nerve cell and its processes are called a **neurone,** and in the evoking of the above response there are three nerve elements involved :

(*a*) The **receptor** neurone.
(*b*) The **connector** neurones, or cells of the nerve net.
(*c*) The **motor** or **effector** neurones

At a much higher stage in the animal kingdom it is found that the connector neurones and the cells of the motor neurones are collected, for convenience, in the median plane to form the **central nervous system,** comprising the **brain and spinal cord.** The receptor cells remain outside the central nervous system and collections of them form the **ganglia on sensory nerves. Sensory** or **afferent nerves** are constituted by sensory nerve processes passing into the nervous system, and **motor** or **efferent nerves** by those passing out of the central nervous system. In most situations it is convenient for both motor and sensory fibres to be carried to any particular part of the body in the same nerve trunk, and this is called a **mixed nerve.** Mixed nerves arise from both the brain (the cranial nerves) and the spinal cord (the spinal nerves). The elements concerned in evoking a primitive response in an animal with this type of nervous system are shown in Fig. 65. The impulse carried by the receptor neurone, instead of passing by a more or less straight route to the muscle as in the more primitive forms, is, when it reaches the central nervous system, " bent back " to pass out along the motor nerve. On account of this " bending back " the phenomenon is termed a **reflex** response, and the pathways along which the impulses pass constitute a **reflex arc.**

Segmental Arrangement of the Nervous System

For some reason many animals exhibit the phenomenon of **segmentation,** that is, the body is made up of a number of similar segments superimposed. Such a condition is exemplified in a simple form in some of the worms. In such animals the central nervous system is represented by ganglia (collections of nerve cells), a pair of which are found, one on each side of the median plane, in each segment. In order that all the segments shall act in a co-ordinated manner in the activity of the animal as a whole, these segmental ganglia are linked up one with another by nerve fibres, and so the central nervous system presents the form of a chain of ganglia on each side of the median plane

The development, in the course of evolution, of special receptors for the functions of sight, smell, hearing, and balance at the head end of animals leads to an enlargement of ganglia in this region to form the **brain,** and the necessity for bringing the nerves in the segments under the influence of these new functions causes the development of great bundles of nerve fibres (**nerve tracts**) connecting the brain with the lower centres. This great growth of linking fibres has brought about a masking of the segmental arrangement of the central nervous system to such an extent that in higher forms the part below the brain is represented by a cylindrical cord made up very largely of these fibre tracts and called the **spinal cord.** In the higher animals the segmental character of the nervous system is evidenced only by the fact that pairs of nerves with a segmental distribution, the **spinal nerves,** arise from the spinal cord.

Further increase in the complexity of behaviour has led finally to great enlargement of certain parts of the brain in higher forms. It is found that the reactions to environmental changes are no longer stereotyped, but are governed and modified by all sorts of factors resulting from visual, olfactory, and auditory impressions, and from the benefit of past experience.

These impulses may augment or they may inhibit the more primitive reflex responses so as to give the required reaction. As a consequence, many of our reactions are under the **control of the will,** *i.e.,* can be governed by the activity of the brain which sorts out the impressions we receive, and, in the light of past experience of such impressions, modifies the resulting motor response.

Owing to the great complexity and specialisation of the nervous system in man, the results of stimulation of sensory neurones depend on the connections which they make with other neurones when they reach the central nervous system. In the section which follows we shall consider the various types of neurones and the main features of the nervous system as a whole, so that we can understand the physiological results of these anatomical arrangements.

GENERAL STRUCTURE OF THE NERVOUS SYSTEM

The nervous system is made up of nerve cells and their processes, and of connective tissues supporting the nervous elements.

Neurones

A **neurone** is a nerve cell and its processes. Nerve cells are of various types, differing one from another largely in the way in which their processes are arranged. There are the following main varieties :—

1. **Bipolar Nerve Cells.** These are oval or spindle-shaped cells with a process leaving each end. Some sensory neurones are of this type. This is a primitive type and is uncommon in man.

2. **Unipolar Nerve Cells.** Most sensory neurones are of this type. The cell is more or less spherical, and gives off from one side a process which after a very short course divides into two. One of these divisions passes into the central nervous system (the central process). The other division (the peripheral process) passes out to the tissue supplied by the nerve and there forms a **sensory ending.**

3. **Multipolar Nerve Cells.** Motor neurones, and the connector neurones of the central nervous system are of this type. The cell gives off a number of processes. One of these is long, and it does not give any branches until it nears its termination. This is called the **axon.** The other processes are shorter than the axon and begin to branch close to their origin. These are called **dendrites.**

Mode of Termination of the Processes of Nerve Cells

Sensory Neurones. The peripheral processes of sensory neurones form receptor endings in the skin, mucous membranes, muscles, joints, etc. The anatomical structure of these endings differs according to the function served, those for touch, taste, hearing, etc., having a very complicated form. The details are, however, of little importance. The central processes of sensory neurones pass into the central nervous system, and before they end they usually give off collateral branches. The collaterals and the central process itself all end in association with connector neurones. The processes of one neurone are not, however, in direct continuity with those of another. They are separated by undifferentiated protoplasm, which constitutes the **synapse** or junction between the two neurones. *The synapse will allow an impulse to pass across it in one direction only, and offers some resistance to its passage across from one neurone to another.*

Because of the collateral branches which the central processes of sensory neurones give off, it is possible for one receptor to affect many connector cells, each of which is a part of some reflex arc.

Connector Neurones. The processes of these neurones form synapses with the processes of other neurones. These may be sensory, motor, or connector in type. All connector neurones form a part of a reflex arc.

Motor Neurones. The **dendrites** of motor neurones form synapses with the axons of connector neurones which may in this way link them with sensory neurones, or with other connector neurones.

The **axons** of motor neurones end by forming terminal arborisations in the structures they supply. In the case of skeletal muscle these arborisations are embedded in a plate of undifferentiated protoplasm in contact with the muscle fibres, and called the **motor end plate.**

Nerve Fibres and Sheaths

The longer processes of nerve cells are known as nerve fibres. These are of two kinds, medullated and non-medullated.

Medullated Nerve Fibres. Most of the fibres of the central nervous system and of peripheral nerves are of this type.

The process of the nerve cell is surrounded by a sheath of **myelin,** a fatty substance, which is interrupted at intervals. The myelin sheath serves to insulate the nerve fibre from other nerve fibres. Outside the myelin is a very thin membranous sheath containing nuclei, which is not interrupted, and which is called the **neurilemma.** The neurilemma is absent from all fibres within the central nervous system. Motor fibres do not acquire it until they have got beyond the brain and cord, and sensory fibres lose it as they enter. Fibres without a neurilemmal sheath will not regenerate after they are divided. Complete section of fibres of the central nervous system therefore leads to permanent damage.

Non-medullated Fibres. These have no myelin sheath, but are covered by a sheath which corresponds with the neurilemma. Many of the fibres of the sympathetic nervous system (p. 274) are of this type.

Connective Tissues of the Nervous System

Peripheral Nervous System. The fibres of peripheral nerves are bound into fasciculi or bundles by ordinary connective tissue called **endoneurium.** A number of bundles are bound together to form a nerve trunk by a sheath of connective tissue called **epineurium.**

Central Nervous System. The nerve cells and fibres of the central nervous system are supported and held together by a special form of connective tissue containing branched cells and called **neuroglia.**

Grey and White Matter

Grey matter is composed mainly of **nerve cells.**

White matter is composed mainly of **nerve fibres.**

GENERAL OUTLINE OF THE SPINAL CORD, THE SPINAL NERVES AND THEIR FUNCTIONS

The Spinal Cord

The spinal cord is a soft, almost cylindrical structure, pinkish-white in colour, occupying the vertebral canal.

Above, it begins as a continuation of the medulla oblongata of the brain (p. 249) just beyond the foramen magnum. It ends below in a pointed extremity, the **conus medullaris,** at the level of the second lumbar vertebra. (The level of the elbow joints with the arms at the sides of the body.) It thus occupies the cervical, thoracic, and the upper part of the lumbar regions of the spine.

From the conus medullaris a slender fibrous cord extends downwards and connects the lower end of the cord to the back of the coccyx. This is called the **filum terminale,** and is non-nervous in structure. The cord shows two **enlargements,** the cervical opposite the origin of the large nerves supplying the arm, and the lumbar opposite the origin of the nerves to the leg.

Springing from the cord are **thirty-one pairs** of nerves, the **spinal nerves,** each arising by two roots, anterior and posterior.

Membranes of the Cord. The cord is smaller than the vertebral canal in which it lies, so that it has the necessary play to accommodate itself to the movements of the vertebral column. It is surrounded by three sheaths or membranes :—

The **pia mater** is the innermost membrane, and is intimately adherent to the cord. It carries the blood-vessels to the cord, and is invaginated into the anterior median fissure which partially divides the cord into two halves.

The **arachnoid** is a thin transparent membrane which is separated from the pia mater by the **subarachnoid space** containing **cerebrospinal fluid.** This fluid acts as lymph for the nervous system and as a water cushion, preventing the delicate cord from being damaged against the bones. The subarachnoid space is longer than the cord, extending down to the level of the second sacral vertebra. Below the level of the conus medullaris the roots of the lumbar and sacral nerves, constituting the **cauda equina** (mare's tail), and the filum terminale are suspended in the cerebrospinal fluid.

The **dura mater** is a tough fibrous sheath enclosing all the other membranes. It is pierced by the spinal nerves and the vessels to the cord.

These membranes are continuous above with the corresponding membranes of the brain, and the subarachnoid space surrounding the brain is continuous with that of the cord at the foramen magnum.

Since the subarachnoid space below the second lumbar vertebra does not contain the spinal cord itself, it is possible to draw off cerebrospinal fluid below this level without risk of damage to the cord. The procedure is called **lumbar puncture,** and is used for obtaining samples of cerebrospinal fluid and for injecting anæsthetics (spinal anæsthesia), antitoxins, and drugs round the cord and nerve roots.

The Spinal Nerves

The spinal nerves are paired nerves, thirty-one in number on each side. They are grouped according to the regions in which they arise as follows :—

        Cervical, of which there are **8.**
        Thoracic   ,,   ,,   **12.**
        Lumbar   ,,   ,,   **5.**
        Sacral   ,,   ,,   **5.**
        Coccygeal   ,,   ,,   **1.**

Each (Fig. 65) springs from the side of the spinal cord by **two roots, anterior and posterior.** The roots pass laterally, traversing the subarachnoid space, and, in the intervertebral foramen, they unite to form a single trunk. The posterior nerve root presents an oval swelling, the **posterior root ganglion,** just proximal to the point where it joins the anterior root.

All the nerve roots arise from the cord at a higher level than the point at which the spinal nerves which they form leave the vertebral canal. The obliquity of the cervical roots is slight, but the slope becomes more and more pronounced as the lower nerves are reached. The roots of the lower lumbar and sacral nerves, having to run a considerable distance from the lower part of the cord to their foramina of exit, are almost vertical in direction. They form a sheaf in the lower part of the vertebral canal which is called the **cauda equina.**

Formed in this way, the spinal nerves pierce the dura mater and leave the vertebral canal through the intervertebral foramina.

All the spinal nerves are completed by receiving a communication from the sympathetic, and some of them give branches to the sympathetic (p. 274). Each nerve divides after a short course into **anterior and posterior primary rami.**

The Posterior Primary Ramus. This branch passes through to the back to supply muscles and skin. The posterior primary rami retain a more or less segmental distribution, each supplying muscles, skin, blood-vessels, etc., almost opposite the level of the spinal nerve from which it arises.

The Anterior Primary Ramus. 1. **In the thoracic region** these form the intercostal nerves, each of which has a segmental distribution to the intercostal space in which it runs, and to the skin overlying the space. There are eleven intercostal nerves. The lower five pass beyond the intercostal spaces to supply the muscles and skin of the abdominal wall. The anterior primary ramus of the twelfth thoracic nerve is called the subcostal nerve ; it also supplies the abdominal wall.

2. In the cervical, lumbar and sacral regions the anterior primary rami form nerve plexuses.

The cervical plexus is formed by the anterior primary rami of the upper four cervical nerves, and supplies the neck and the diaphragm.

The brachial plexus is formed by the anterior primary rami of the fifth, sixth, seventh and eighth cervical, and the first thoracic nerves. It supplies the upper limb.

The lumbar and sacral plexuses are formed by the anterior primary rami of the lumbar and sacral nerves. They supply the lower limb.

The segmental distribution of these nerves is not so evident, because the segments which they supply have been rearranged in the formation of the neck and limbs, and this has resulted in a plexiform rearrangement of the nerves.

Internal Structure of the Spinal Cord and Nerve Roots

A section across the spinal cord is represented in Fig. 65. The central part is occupied by **grey matter** composed of nerve cells. Surrounding the central grey matter is the **white matter** composed of nerve fibres.

The Grey Matter. The grey matter forms a column occupying

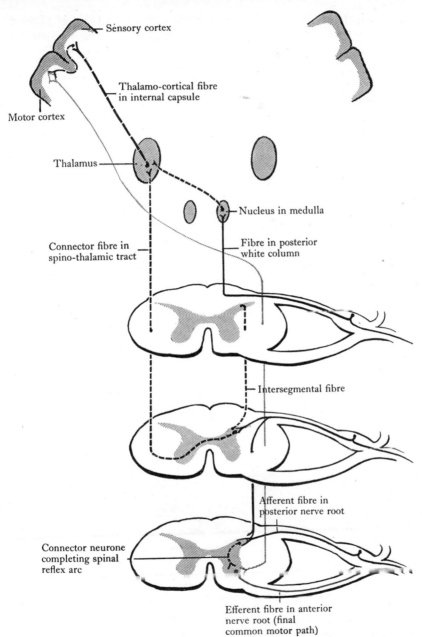

Sensory cortex

Thalamo-cortical fibre
in internal capsule

Motor cortex

Thalamus

Nucleus in medulla

Connector fibre in
spino-thalamic tract

Fibre in posterior
white column

Intersegmental fibre

Afferent fibre in
posterior nerve root

Connector neurone
completing spinal
reflex arc

Efferent fibre in anterior
nerve root (final
common motor path)

FIG. 65. Scheme of spinal reflex arc (lowest section), and of sensory
and motor pathways concerned with voluntary movement. The
upper motor neurone (cerebrospinal) is in broken red. The nerves
of the right side are omitted.

the central part of the cord. On section, it presents an H-shaped outline. The side limbs of the H are similar on the two sides ; each consists of an **anterior horn** and a **posterior horn.**

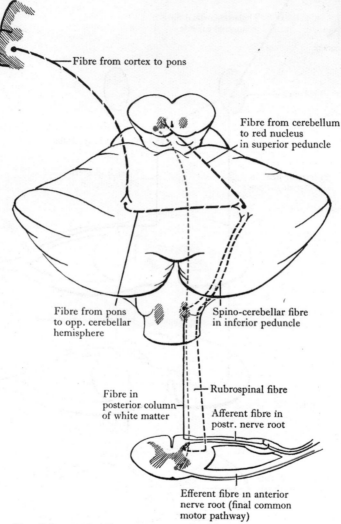

Fibre from cortex to pons

Fibre from cerebellum to red nucleus in superior peduncle

Fibre from pons to opp. cerebellar hemisphere

Spino-cerebellar fibre in inferior peduncle

Fibre in posterior column of white matter

Rubrospinal fibre

Afferent fibre in postr. nerve root

Efferent fibre in anterior nerve root (final common motor pathway)

FIG. 66.   Scheme of pathways concerned with muscular co-ordination.[1]

The Anterior Horn.   This is directed forwards and laterally towards the origin of the anterior nerve roots.   It contains large **motor nerve cells,** the axons of which are the fibres which form the anterior roots of the spinal nerves.

[1] In this diagram the cord is represented as if viewed from below.

The Posterior Horn. This is directed backwards and laterally towards the posterior nerve roots. Many of the fibres of the posterior nerve roots form synapses with the nerve cells in the posterior horn. The **neurones,** whose cell bodies are found in the posterior horn, are **of the connector type.** The fate of their axons is shown in Figs. 65 and 66.

(*a*) The axon may pass through the grey matter to form a synapse with a motor neurone in the **anterior horn of the same side** of the body, thus completing a **spinal reflex arc.**

(*b*) The axon may pass out into the white matter of the same side and so reach an anterior horn cell in **another spinal segment.**

(*c*) It may pass into the white matter of the same side of the cord and *viâ* fibre tracts to the **cerebellum** (see p. 273).

(*d*) It may cross to the white matter of the **opposite side** of the cord and join a fibre tract which runs to the **thalamus** (see p. 272).

The Grey Commissure. The transverse limb of the H of grey matter is called the grey commissure. It contains the minute central canal of the spinal cord, which is filled during life with cerebrospinal fluid.

The White Matter. The white matter of the cord consists of fibre tracts of three main types :—

1. Intersegmental. These connect the segments of the cord one with another.

2. Ascending. These form pathways linking the segments of the cord to the brain.

3. Descending. These convey impulses from the brain to the spinal cord.

The Nerve Roots. Posterior Nerve Roots. The posterior nerve roots contain receptor neurones of the unipolar type. The cells are collected in the posterior root ganglion (Fig. 65).

The **peripheral process** of the neurone passes into the spinal nerve and eventually becomes a sensory ending in the tissue supplied.

The **central process** passes *viâ* the posterior nerve root into the spinal cord and either ends in the posterior horn of grey matter or passes into the white matter.

1. Those which end in the grey matter. These central processes end in relationship with the connector neurones of the posterior horn, and these, as stated above, may link them with :—

(*a*) Anterior horn motor neurones (Fig. 65).

(*b*) Other segments of the cord (Fig. 65).

(*c*) The cerebellum (Fig. 66).

16*

(*d*) The opposite thalamus (Fig. 65).

2. Those which pass into the white matter pass either to other segments of the cord or to the medulla oblongata (Fig. 65).

Anterior Nerve Roots. The **axons of the motor cells** in the anterior horn of grey matter form the anterior nerve roots. These axons pass out in the spinal nerves to terminate in the motor end-plates of the muscles supplied. These neurones constitute the **final common motor pathways,** as they are the routes along which the motor impulses, by whatever reflex pathway they have been instigated, pass out to the effector organs.

The anterior nerve roots contain also fibres which are destined for the sympathetic system (p. 274).

Functions of the Spinal Cord

The spinal cord is the seat of primitive reflex activities. These activities can occur when the spinal cord is cut off from the influence of the higher centres of the brain, and they are termed **spinal reflexes.** For example, on touching something hot the hand is withdrawn without thinking at all, *i.e.,* without the action of the brain. It is convenient, at first, to consider spinal reflexes as occurring without influence from other centres. It should not be forgotten, however, that, when the nervous system is intact, the brain always exerts its influence on the primitive reflexes in ways to be considered later (p. 271).

We have seen (p. 234) that in a primitive reflex three nerve elements are involved :—

(*a*) The **receptor** (sensory) neurone.

(*b*) **Connector** neurones.

(*c*) The **effector** (motor) neurone.

The same elements are evident in the pathways utilised for spinal reflexes.

The Reflex Arc (Fig. 65). The **receptor neurone** has its nerve cell in the posterior root ganglion of a spinal nerve. The **peripheral process** forms a receptor ending in the tissues supplied by the nerve. The **central process** of the neurone passes, *viâ* the posterior nerve root, into the spinal cord and there gives off collateral branches. The collaterals and the fibre itself form synapses with **connector neurones** in the same and in adjacent segments of the cord. The connector neurones in their turn form synapses with **effector (motor) neurones,** the processes of which pass out, *viâ* the anterior nerve roots, to supply muscles, viscera glands, blood-vessels, etc. The impulse reaching these along the motor nerves results in reflex activity, *e.g.*, contraction of muscles or secretion by glands.

Spinal Reflexes. The following are the main varieties of spinal reflexes :—

1. **Superficial Reflexes.** These result from stimulation of receptor endings in the skin. The receptor neurones belong to the group called **exteroceptors,** *i.e.*, receptors stimulated by alterations in the external environment of the body as distinct from occurrences within the body itself. These reflexes are concerned to a great extent in the protection of the body from harmful factors in its environment.

Three examples will serve to illustrate the type of motor response evoked in this form of reflex :—

(*a*) **The Plantar Reflex.** Scratching the sole of the foot results in a contraction of the flexor muscles of the toes.

(*b*) **The Abdominal Reflex.** Scratching the skin of the abdominal wall gives rise to contraction of the abdominal muscles of the same side of body.

(*c*) **Painful Stimulation.** The application of a painful stimulus to, for example, the sole of the foot, results in a contraction of the flexor muscles of the limb which draws the leg away from the harmful stimulus. A much less severe stimulus will bring about the same result in patients who have got over the initial shock after injury to the spinal cord.

It should be noted that the stimuli producing superficial reflexes also result, when the spinal cord is intact, in the conscious appreciation of the stimuli as a **sensation.** The reason for this is that the receptors concerned in the reflex, or their collaterals, in addition to forming synapses with connectors linking them to motor nerve cells, also form synapses with connector neurones which link them to the brain (see p. 271).

2. **Deep Reflexes.** These result from stimulation of receptor endings in the deeper tissues, such as muscles, tendons, joints, etc.

The receptors belong to the group called **proprioceptors,** *i.e.*, depending for their stimulation on occurrences within the body itself. Such stimulation results from stretching of tendons, muscles or ligaments, the pressure of opposed joint surfaces, etc. The pathways involved have the general arrangement already described, viz. : receptor, connector, and motor neurones. Two important effects occur through these reflexes, viz. : the maintenance of reciprocal tone in antagonistic groups of muscles, and tendon reflexes.

16**

(a) **Reciprocal Muscle Tone.** Whatever the position of any part of the body, none of the muscles is ever " slack " or entirely relaxed. Some fibres of every muscle of the part are contracted to maintain a state of *tone*. The fibres are stimulated to contract by impulses reaching them along their motor neurones, which are themselves reflexly excited by impulses from the muscles, tendons and joints of the part itself, first along receptor and then connector neurones. The impulses are initiated by the degree of tension in the parts. If a joint be bent, even passively, the muscles on the convex side will be stretched more than those on the concave side. This stimulates the receptors in the muscles and the result is an immediate and automatic readjustment of tone (*i.e.*, the number of fibres stimulated to contract by impulses travelling *viâ* the connector and motor neurones).

We shall consider later (p. 273) how this tone can be altered according to the needs of the body as a whole in the maintenance of balance and the co-ordination of muscular activity.

(b) **Tendon Reflexes.** A sharp tap administered over the taut tendons of certain muscles results in a reflex contraction of the muscle concerned, and a coincident reciprocal relaxation of its antagonists. The example most commonly cited is the **knee-jerk,** in which tapping the patellar tendon in front of the knee elicits a contraction of the quadriceps extensor and a relaxation of the hamstrings.

As in the case of superficial reflexes, the afferent impulses producing deep reflexes may also pass to fibre tracts which reach the brain. The result is a **sensation**, such as the knowledge of the position of a limb.

3. **Visceral and Vasomotor Reflexes.** These occur through the sympathetic system (p. 274). It should be noted, however, in the present connection that they are a function of spinal segments in the same way as are superficial and deep reflexes.

Spinal " Centres "

Certain segments of the spinal cord are associated with reflex activity of certain definite parts of the body. In speaking of those segments associated with micturition, defæcation, etc., it is customary to use the term " centre " to denote the part of the grey matter concerned.

Practical Considerations. The occurrence of all forms of spinal reflexes implies the presence of intact reflex arcs in the segments of the cord concerned. Damage to any element, receptor, connector, or motor, will lead to loss of all reflexes in the parts supplied by the damaged segment.

If the damage be to the motor neurone (lower motor neurone lesion) there will, in addition, be loss of all forms of movement, both voluntary and involuntary, as all motor impulses, however instigated, reach the muscles finally along this pathway. If the damage be to the receptor (sensory) neurone, there will, in addition to loss of reflexes, be loss of sensation in the part supplied.

In injuries of the spinal cord the reflex activity of the centres below the injury is no longer influenced by impulses from the brain, as the fibre tracts are damaged. The reflexes take on a more stereotyped and primitive character. These patients need, therefore, much attention, as involuntary micturition and defæcation may occur as the bladder and rectum fill. Voluntary movement and all forms of sensation are lost below the lesion. Great care must be taken not to damage the skin with hot-water bottles, etc., as the patient cannot tell when he is being burned, and troublesome bedsores may develop from burns or pressure.

THE BRAIN

INTRODUCTION

The brain is the part of the central nervous system contained within the skull. From it arise twelve pairs of cranial (cerebral) nerves. Some of these, like spinal nerves, serve both motor and sensory functions; others are either purely motor or purely sensory.

The Sensory Components of Cranial Nerves

Those nerves which are sensory may serve for the conduction of impulses of common sensation, like the posterior roots of the spinal nerves. Some, however, are set aside for the " special senses " of smell, sight, hearing, and taste.

The cells of the sensory neurones of most of the cranial nerves are in ganglia found on the nerve trunks. The central processes (like the posterior root fibres of spinal nerves) enter the central nervous system and form synapses with connector neurones. The cells of the connector neurones form masses of grey matter in the brain called **sensory nuclei** or **nuclei of termination**. The axons of the connector neurones may terminate as follows :—

(*a*) They may form synapses with the **motor neurones of the cranial nerve** which contained the receptor neurones. This occurs in the mixed cranial nerves, and is comparable with the reflex arcs seen in the spinal segments.

(*b*) They may form synapses with the **motor neurones of some other cranial nerve.** This is comparable with the fibres passing to other segments in the case of the spinal cord.

(*c*) They may pass into fibre tracts linking them to **some other part of the brain.** (*Cf.* the connector neurones of the posterior horn in the cord linking with thalamus of opposite side, and cerebellum of the same side, p. 243.)

(*d*) They may pass down the **spinal cord** to form synapses with motor neurones, giving rise to anterior roots of spinal nerves. (This occurs in the case of the vestibular nerve. See p. 291.)

Through connections (*a*) and (*b*) it is possible, therefore, to get reflex motor responses through reflex arcs comparable with those of the spinal segments. These reflexes, like the spinal reflexes, can be grouped as :—

1. Superficial.
2. Deep.
3. Visceral.

An example of this is the reflex control of the rate of the heart. When the aorta is stretched by the output of a large amount of blood from the heart receptors in its wall are stimulated, and impulses travel along the vagus nerve to the brain ; along connector neurones and the efferent fibres of the vagus impulses return to the heart and reduce its rate.

As in the case of the spinal nerves, the afferent impulses conducted by cranial nerves may travel by connector neurones to the fore-brain and so result in **sensations**, as well as producing local reflexes.

The Motor Components of Cranial Nerves

Of those nerves which have a motor function some supply striped muscle, others (through the parasympathetic system, see p. 278) supply unstriped muscle and glands. The fibres constituting the motor cranial nerves are the axons of cells which, collected together, form masses of grey matter in the brain stem called **motor nuclei** or **nuclei of origin.** These cells correspond more or less to those in the anterior horn of grey matter in the spinal cord.

PARTS OF THE BRAIN

The brain comprises the following parts :—

The **cerebrum** and the **cerebellum,** both large expanded parts ; and a narrower portion, which appears to be the upward continuation of the spinal cord, termed the **brain-stem.**

The brain-stem is divided into :—

(*a*) The **medulla oblongata.**

(*b*) The **pons.**

(*c*) The **mid-brain.**

The cerebrum is sometimes termed the **fore-brain,** and the medulla oblongata, pons and cerebellum the **hind-brain.**

The Brain-stem (Figs. 67, 68 and 69)

The Medulla Oblongata. The medulla oblongata is the part of the brain-stem which is the direct upward continuation of the spinal cord. In its upper part it is overlapped posteriorly by the cerebellum. Anteriorly it presents the eminence called the **pyramid** at each side of the median plane. The fibres constituting the pyramids can be seen crossing the median plane in the lower part of the medulla at the **decussation of the pyramids.**

Arising from the medulla are four pairs of cranial nerves, viz. :—

The **ninth** or **glossopharyngeal.**

The **tenth** or **vagus.**

The **eleventh** or **accessory.**

The **twelfth** or **hypoglossal.**

The Pons. The pons is the part of the brain-stem which appears when viewed from in front to be a broad thick strand of fibres crossing the surface of the brain just above the medulla oblongata. It is so named because it appears to be a bridge between the two sides of the cerebellum, but this is not really true (see p. 273).

Arising from the pons are four pairs of cranial nerves, viz. :—

The **fifth** or **trigeminal,** arising from the lateral part of the anterior surface on each side.

The **sixth** or **abducent** } All arising in the groove at the lower
The **seventh** or **facial** } border between the pons and the
The **eighth** or **auditory** } medulla oblongata.

The Mid-brain. The mid-brain is a short, constricted part forming the connection between the cerebrum and other parts of the brain.

Anteriorly, it has the form of two thick bundles called the

cerebral peduncles, these being separated from one another by a deep depression. Posteriorly, the mid-brain consists of four eminences called **quadrigeminal bodies.** The superior pair of quadrigeminal bodies are the lower centres for sight, the inferior pair are the lower centres for hearing.

In the centre of the mid-brain is the narrow **aqueduct of the**

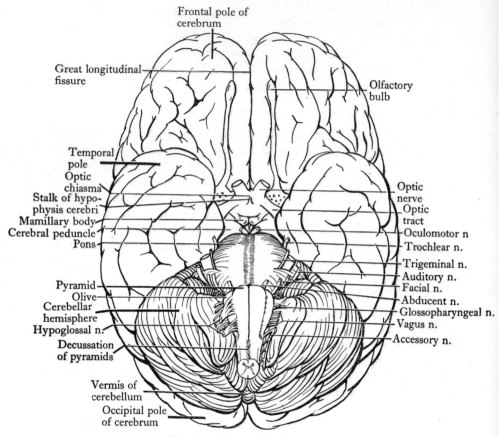

Frontal pole of cerebrum

Great longitudinal fissure

Olfactory bulb

Temporal pole
Optic chiasma
Stalk of hypophysis cerebri
Mamillary body
Cerebral peduncle
Pons

Optic nerve
Optic tract
Oculomotor n
Trochlear n.
Trigeminal n.
Auditory n.
Facial n.
Abducent n.
Glossopharyngeal n.
Vagus n.
Accessory n.

Pyramid
Olive
Cerebellar hemisphere
Hypoglossal n.
Decussation of pyramids

Vermis of cerebellum
Occipital pole of cerebrum

Fig. 67. The base of the brain.

mid-brain (Sylvius), a canal through which the cavity of the fourth ventricle in the hind-brain communicates with that of the third ventricle in the cerebrum.

Two pairs of cranial nerves arise from the mid-brain, viz. :—

The **third** or **oculomotor** nerves, which arise medial to the cerebral peduncle on each side.

The **fourth** or **trochlear** nerves, which arise posteriorly, just below the quadrigeminal bodies.

The Cerebellum. The cerebellum is the part of the hind-brain lying behind the pons and medulla oblongata. It occupies the posterior cranial fossa and consists of two expanded lateral parts called **hemispheres** joined to one another across the median plane by the median portion termed the **vermis** (Figs. 67 and 68).

Unlike the parts of the brain we have already considered, the cerebellum has grey matter on its surface, with white matter containing

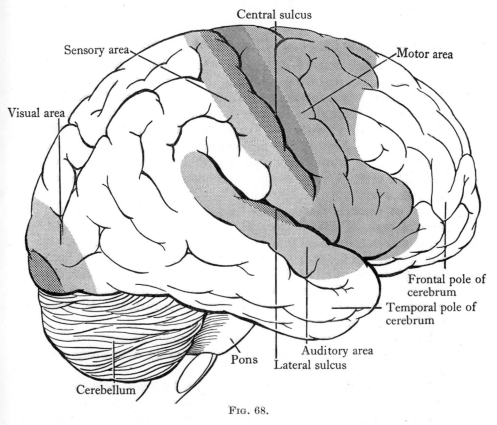

FIG. 68.

the small **dentate nucleus** in its interior. The surface grey matter is termed the cerebellar cortex, and it is thrown into numerous leaf-like folds termed **folia,** separated from each other by deep furrows. The interior of the cerebellum consists mainly of white matter. Most of the fibres constituting this white matter are those connecting the cerebellum with other parts of the brain. As they enter and leave the cerebellum they are collected into strands or bundles, called the **peduncles,** of which there are three pairs, viz. :—

The **superior cerebellar peduncles** connecting the cerebellum with the mid-brain. This is the efferent pathway from the cerebellum.

When the superior peduncles enter the mid-brain they cross one another, and each goes to the red nucleus (p. 273) of the opposite side.

The **middle cerebellar peduncles** connect the cerebellum with the pons, and the **inferior cerebellar peduncles** connect the cerebellum with the medulla oblongata. These are the afferent pathways to the cerebellum.

Between the cerebellum behind, and the pons and medulla oblongata in front, is the cavity of the hind-brain termed the **fourth ventricle.**

The Cerebrum or Fore-brain (Figs. 67, 68 and 69)

The fore-brain consists of a part in the median plane containing the cavity of the **third ventricle** and of the two **cerebral hemispheres,** each containing a cavity called the **lateral ventricle.** The cerebral hemispheres are, in most of their extent, separated from one another by the deep **longitudinal fissure.** In the depths of this fissure, however, they are connected with one another by a thick band of white fibres called the **corpus callosum.** Each hemisphere has frontal, parietal, occipital, and temporal parts, or lobes, underlying the bones of the same name.

1. **The Cerebral Hemispheres** (Figs. 67 and 68). When the human brain is viewed from above, the cerebral hemispheres, separated one from another by the longitudinal fissure, conceal the rest of the brain from view. The surface of each cerebral hemisphere is composed of grey matter which, as in the cerebellum, is called the **cortex.** It is thrown into many folds, or **gyri,** separated from one another by **sulci** or **fissures.** Of these sulci, two are of special importance, viz. :—

The **central sulcus** (fissure of Rolando) which, beginning at the upper border of the hemisphere, runs obliquely downwards and forwards across the lateral surface.

The **lateral sulcus** (fissure of Sylvius) is a deep cleft between the temporal lobe and the rest of the hemisphere.

Cortical Areas. It is definitely known that certain areas of the cortex are concerned with special functions (Fig. 68) :—

(*a*) Just anterior to the central sulcus is a strip of cortex concerned with voluntary movement of *the opposite side of the body.* This is called the **motor area** (precentral gyrus).

Just posterior to the central sulcus is the similar strip concerned with sensation on the opposite side of the body, and called the **sensory area** (post-central gyrus).

The parts of the body are represented upside down in these

areas, the order from above downwards being : lower limb, trunk, upper limb, neck, and head.

The cortex of the temporal lobe in the vicinity of the lateral fissure is concerned with **hearing.** The cortex of the occipital pole is concerned with **vision.**

The cortex in the frontal region just above the anterior end of

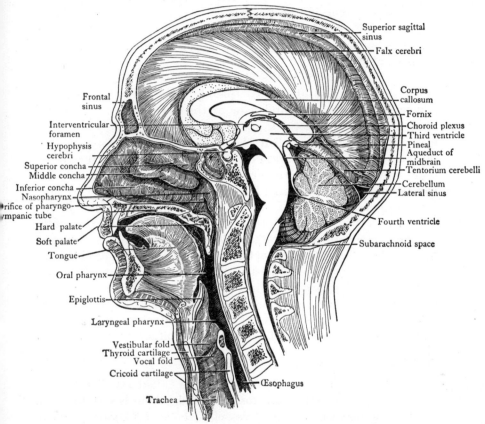

FIG. 69. A sagittal section of the head and neck a little to the left of the median plane. The nasal septum has been removed to expose the lateral wall of the nose.

the lateral sulcus (on the left side in right-handed people, on the right side in left-handed people) is concerned with **speech** ; it is called Broca's area.

The interior of each cerebral hemisphere is composed mainly of white matter, or nerve fibres. Some of these connect various parts of the cerebral cortex one with another and are called

association fibres ; others connect the cerebral hemisphere of one side with that of the other side and constitute the **corpus callosum** at the bottom of the great longitudinal fissure. These, because they connect one side of the brain with the other, are called **commissural fibres** ; others again connect the cortex of the cerebral hemisphere with other parts of the central nervous system and are termed **projection fibres.** These latter are collected together in the lower part of the cerebrum to form, on each side, the **internal capsule,** but as they approach the cortex they spread out in a fan-shaped manner to form the **corona radiata.**

2. **The Part containing the Third Ventricle** (Fig. 69). This part of the fore-brain is almost completely hidden by the cerebral hemispheres. The roof and floor of this part are thin, but the lateral walls are very thick and formed on each side by a large mass of grey matter called the **thalamus.** The floor of this central part of the fore-brain can be seen on the basal surface of the brain (Fig. 67). It presents here the **stalk** which attaches the **hypophysis cerebri** (pituitary body) to the brain (see p. 315), and behind this a pair of rounded eminences called the **mamillary bodies.** In front of the stalk of the pituitary is the **optic chiasma,** joined anteriorly by the **two optic nerves** and continuous posteriorly with the **two optic tracts,** the whole having the appearance of a cross on the base of the brain. Running forwards on to the inferior surface of the hemisphere from the region close to the chiasma on each side is the **olfactory tract.** Each olfactory tract ends in a bulbous extremity, the **olfactory bulb,** which receives from the nose the filaments of the **olfactory nerve.**

Ventricles of the Brain

The brain contains a system of cavities called **ventricles** in its interior. These contain **cerebrospinal fluid,** which is secreted into them from plexuses of blood-vessels (chorioid plexuses) which project into the cavities. After circulating through the ventricular system, the cerebrospinal fluid finds its way down the central canal of the spinal cord, and also, through three openings in the roof of the fourth ventricle, out to the surface of the brain, where it circulates in the subarachnoid space round the brain and spinal cord. The cerebrospinal fluid, which forms a water cushion round the brain and cord, is finally reabsorbed into the bloodstream through projections of the arachnoid (arachnoid granulations) into the walls of the venous sinuses of the skull, and through small villi covering the surface of the arachnoid. The cerebro-spinal fluid serves the same function for the brain as lymph for other tissues.

The Lateral Ventricle

There is a lateral ventricle in each cerebral hemisphere. Both communicate with the third ventricle through the interventricular foramen (Munro).

The Third Ventricle

The third ventricle is between the thalami of the two sides. It communicates with both lateral ventricles through the interventricular foramen, and posteriorly is joined to the fourth ventricle by the aqueduct of the mid-brain.

The Aqueduct of the Mid-brain (Sylvius)

This is a narrow canal traversing the mid-brain. It joins the third ventricle of the fore-brain to the fourth ventricle of the hind-brain.

The Fourth Ventricle

The fourth ventricle is a cavity in the pons and medulla. Below, it is continuous with the central canal of the cord, and above, it communicates with the third ventricle through the aqueduct of the mid-brain.

Three holes in the roof of the fourth ventricle allow the cerebrospinal fluid to pass out into the subarachnoid space on the surface of the brain.

Membranes of the Brain

The brain, like the spinal cord, is surrounded by three membranes, or *meninges* : the pia mater, the arachnoid, and the dura mater from within outwards. Between the pia and arachnoid is the cerebrospinal fluid, which acts as a water cushion for the brain.

The Pia Mater

The pia covers the surface of the brain intimately, and dips into all the fissures. It carries the smaller branches of blood-vessels to and from the brain.

The Arachnoid

The arachnoid is separated from the pia by the cerebrospinal fluid in the subarachnoid space. It does not dip into the fissures, and in some places there are wide spaces, the **subarachnoid cisterns,** between it and the underlying brain. One of the biggest of these is found in the angle between the cerebellum and the medulla.

The Dura Mater

The cranial dura mater differs from the spinal dura mater in that one layer of it actually forms the periosteum on the inner surface of the skull bones. The other layer is, in places, deeply infolded to form septa partially dividing the cranial cavity. The most important of these septa (Fig. 69) are :—

The **falx cerebri**, which dips between the two cerebral hemispheres as far as the corpus callosum.

The **tentorium cerebelli**, which is between the cerebellum and the occipital lobes of the cerebral hemispheres.

The venous sinuses draining the brain (p. 171) are between the periosteal and internal layers of the dura. Between the dura and the skull bones are the meningeal vessels.

THE CRANIAL NERVES

There are twelve pairs of cranial (cerebral) nerves attached to the brain. They are :—

1. The olfactory.
2. The optic.
3. The oculomotor.
4. The trochlear.
5. The trigeminal.
6. The abducent.
7. The facial.
8. The auditory.
9. The glossopharyngeal.
10. The vagus.
11. The accessory.
12. The hypoglossal.

The first, second and eighth nerves will be considered with the nose, eye and ear respectively.

The third, fourth and sixth nerves are purely motor, are concerned with the eye movements, and may be considered together.

The Oculomotor Nerve

This arises from the mid-brain (p. 250). It supplies **muscles which move the eyeball** and the **muscle which raises the upper eyelid.** It also supplies the **constrictor** muscle **of the pupil,** and the **ciliary muscle** which accommodates the eye for near vision.

After a short course through the subarachnoid space the nerve runs for a time in the lateral wall of the cavernous blood sinus. It enters the orbit through the superior orbital fissure.

The Trochlear Nerve

This also arises from the mid-brain. Its course is similar to that of the third nerve and it supplies the **superior oblique muscle** of the eyeball.

The Abducent Nerve

The sixth cranial nerve arises from the lower part of the pons (p. 249). Its course is similar to that of the third and fourth nerves, and it supplies the **lateral rectus muscle** of the eyeball.

The Trigeminal Nerve

The fifth nerve is the great **sensory nerve of the face and head.** Incorporated in one of its divisions is the nerve supply to the **muscles of mastication.** The nerve arises from the front of the pons by two roots, of which the sensory is much the larger. Both motor and sensory roots pass forwards into the middle cranial fossa, where the sensory root has on it the large **trigeminal** (semilunar, or Gasserian) **ganglion.** This ganglion serves the same purpose on the sensory part of the fifth nerve as the ganglia on the posterior roots do on the spinal nerves. It contains nerve cells, the central processes from which pass, *viâ* the sensory root, into the pons, whilst the peripheral processes pass, *viâ* one of the divisions of the nerve, to the structures supplied. From the front of the ganglion spring the three **divisions** of the nerve—ophthalmic, maxillary and mandibular. The motor root, which has hitherto been separate from the sensory part, becomes incorporated in the mandibular division.

It may be stated as a general rule that each division supplies the mucous membrane lining cavities which are underlying the area of skin supplied by the division.

The **Ophthalmic (First) Division of the Trigeminal.** The ophthalmic division of the trigeminal passes into the orbit through the superior orbital fissure. It is purely sensory, and supplies :—

(*a*) **The eyeball.**

(*b*) **The upper part of the interior of the nose.**

(*c*) The area of **skin** shown in Fig. 70.

The **Maxillary (Second) Division of the Trigeminal.** The maxillary division leaves the middle cranial fossa through the foramen rotundum, and, after traversing the maxilla in the floor of the orbit, it emerges finally on to the face through the infra-orbital foramen as the **infra-orbital nerve.** It supplies :—

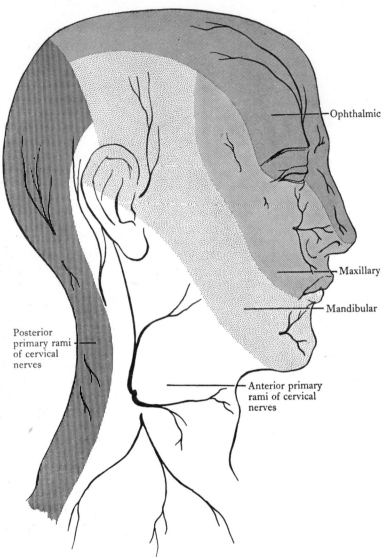

Ophthalmic

Maxillary

Mandibular

Posterior
primary rami
of cervical
nerves

Anterior primary
rami of cervical
nerves

Fig. 70. The nerve supply of the skin areas in the head and neck.

(*a*) **Mucous membrane** of most of the **interior of the nose,** the **maxillary sinus,** and the **roof of the mouth** and **upper lip.**

(*b*) The **teeth in the upper jaw.**

(*c*) **Skin** shown in Fig. 70.

The Mandibular (Third) Division of the Trigeminal. The mandibular division of the trigeminal nerve passes into the

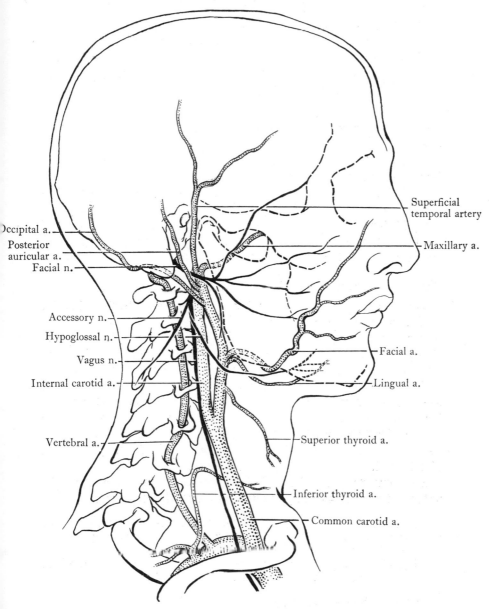

FIG. 71. Nerves and vessels of right side of head and neck.

region deep to the jaw through the foramen ovale. It is distributed as follows :—

(*a*) **Sensory.** (1) **Lingual Nerve.** This supplies the mucous membrane of the **anterior two-thirds of the tongue** and the **floor of the mouth.**

(Incorporated with the lingual nerve is the chorda tympani branch of the facial nerve which carries taste fibres from the anterior two-thirds of the tongue.)

(2) **Buccal Nerve.** This supplies the mucous membrane of the **cheek.**

(3) **Inferior Dental Nerve.** This supplies the **teeth in the lower jaw** and some of the gum.

(4) **Skin.** The area shown in Fig. 70 is supplied by branches of the mandibular division.

(*b*) **Motor.** The nerve gives the motor supply to the **muscles of mastication** and the **muscles of the floor of the mouth** (mylohyoid and anterior belly of the digastric).

The Facial Nerve (Fig. 71)

The seventh nerve is the **motor** nerve to the **muscles of facial expression** and a **sensory** nerve for **taste.**

It arises from the lower part of the pons, and, running with the eighth nerve, it enters the temporal bone through the internal auditory meatus. After a complicated course in the bone, during which it comes into close relationship with the middle ear cavity, the nerve emerges on to the surface through the stylomastoid foramen. It here gives branches to muscles behind the ear and to the **digastric and stylohyoid** muscles. It then passes through the substance of the parotid gland on to the face, where it is distributed.

The **sensory** part of the facial receives **taste** fibres from the **anterior two-thirds of the tongue** and parts of the palate.

The nerve from the tongue is called the chorda tympani, and runs for a time with the lingual nerve, joining the facial by crossing the deep surface of the ear drum.

The facial nerve also gives secreto-motor (parasympathetic) fibres to the submaxillary sublingual and lacrimal glands.

The Glossopharyngeal Nerve

The ninth nerve is the **sensory** nerve of the **pharynx, tonsil** and the **posterior one-third of the tongue** (both taste and common sensation).

It arises from the medulla oblongata, leaves the skull through the jugular foramen, and reaches the pharynx by passing forwards, among the great vessels in the upper part of the neck. With the vagus (the motor nerve of the pharynx) it forms the pharyngeal plexus of nerves.

The Vagus Nerve (Figs. 54 and 71)

The tenth nerve supplies most of the viscera of the body. It consists of both motor and sensory fibres.

The vagus arises from the medulla oblongata and leaves the skull through the jugular foramen.[1] After running down the neck posteromedial to the internal jugular vein, the nerve passes into the thorax, where, behind the root of the lung, it breaks up into a plexus. From the plexuses on the two lung roots there is formed a plexus round the œsophagus. At the lower part of the œsophagus this plexus ends in two nerve trunks which pass through the œsophageal opening in the diaphragm to be distributed in the abdomen.

Distribution of the Vagus

The Larynx. The vagus nerve is sensory to the mucous membrane of the larynx and motor to its muscles.

The Pharynx. Through the pharyngeal plexus the vagus gives the motor supply to the muscles of the pharynx and most of the muscles of the palate.

The Heart. The vagus carries afferent impulses from the heart and aorta and also efferent impulses which slow the heart.

The Lungs. The vagus carries afferent impulses from the lungs and also supplies the muscle in the walls of the bronchi and bronchioles.

The Œsophagus. Through the œsophageal plexus the vagus is both motor and sensory to the œsophagus.

The Distribution in the Abdomen. In the abdomen the vagus supplies all the gut except the lower part of the colon. It also supplies secreto-motor fibres to the digestive glands.

The Accessory Nerve

The eleventh nerve arises from the medulla oblongata and leaves the skull through the jugular foramen. It pierces the **sternomastoid,** and supplies it, and then passes across the posterior triangle to supply the **trapezius.**

The Hypoglossal Nerve (Fig. 71)

The twelfth nerve arises from the medulla oblongata and leaves

[1] Two sensory ganglia are present on the nerve here, and are similar to those on the posterior roots of spinal nerves.

the skull through its own canal in the condylar part of the occipital
bone. After crossing the carotid vessels it passes on to the **tongue**
and supplies the **muscles** of that organ.

THE NERVE PLEXUSES FORMED BY THE ANTERIOR PRIMARY RAMI OF SPINAL NERVES

We have seen that, except in the thoracic region, where they
form the eleven intercostal and the subcostal nerves, the anterior
primary rami of the spinal nerves form plexuses for the supply
of the neck, the arm and the leg. We must now consider in a
little more detail the constitution and distribution of these
plexuses.

The Cervical Plexus

The cervical plexus is formed by the anterior primary rami
of the upper four cervical nerves. Its branches are concerned
mainly with the supply of the **skin** over the anterior and posterior
triangles of the neck (Fig. 70) and the **muscles of the neck.**

One very important branch, the **phrenic nerve,** arises from the
third, fourth and also from the fifth cervical nerves. The phrenic
nerve, after running through the thorax under the pleura which
covers the mediastinum, supplies the **diaphragm** (Fig. 45).

The Brachial Plexus

The brachial plexus is formed in the root of the neck by the
anterior primary rami of the fifth, sixth, seventh and eighth
cervical nerves and the larger part of the anterior primary ramus
of the first thoracic nerve.

Trunks of the Plexus. The **fifth and sixth** nerves unite to form
the **upper trunk** of the plexus.

The **seventh** nerve by itself is continued to form the **middle
trunk.**

The **eighth cervical and first thoracic** nerves unite to form the
lower trunk of the plexus.

The trunks are very short, as each divides almost as soon as it is
formed into **anterior and posterior divisions** which unite behind
the clavicle to form the cords of the plexus.

Cords of the Plexus. The cords are formed behind the clavicle
by the union of divisions of the trunks. In their further course
they are grouped round the axillary artery until they divide, in the
lower part of the axilla, into their branches.

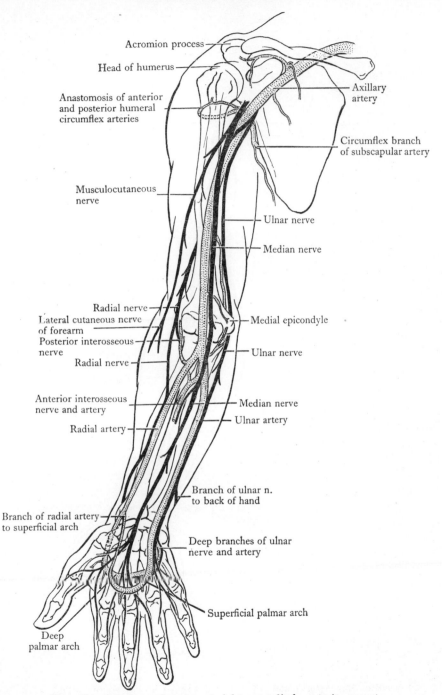

Acromion process

Head of humerus

Anastomosis of anterior
and posterior humeral
circumflex arteries

Axillary
artery

Circumflex branch
of subscapular artery

Musculocutaneous
nerve

Ulnar nerve

Median nerve

Radial nerve

Lateral cutaneous nerve
of forearm

Posterior interosseous
nerve

Radial nerve

Medial epicondyle

Ulnar nerve

Anterior interosseous
nerve and artery

Median nerve

Ulnar artery

Radial artery

Branch of ulnar n.
to back of hand

Branch of radial artery
to superficial arch

Deep branches of ulnar
nerve and artery

Superficial palmar arch

Deep
palmar arch

FIG. 72. Arteries and nerves of right upper limb, anterior aspect.

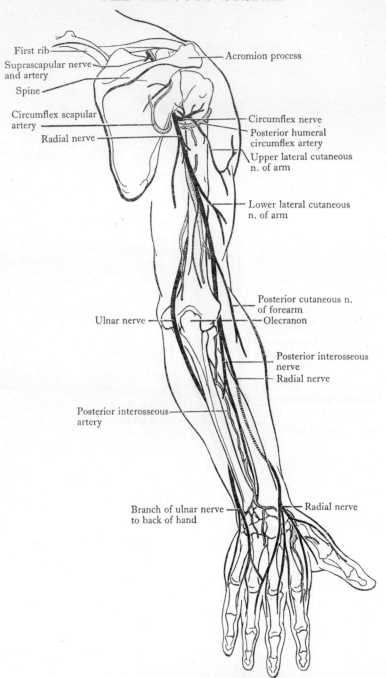

First rib

Suprascapular nerve
and artery

Spine

Circumflex scapular
artery

Radial nerve

Acromion process

Circumflex nerve

Posterior humeral
circumflex artery

Upper lateral cutaneous
n. of arm

Lower lateral cutaneous
n. of arm

Posterior cutaneous n.
of forearm

Olecranon

Ulnar nerve

Posterior interosseous
nerve

Radial nerve

Posterior interosseous
artery

Branch of ulnar nerve
to back of hand

Radial nerve

Fig. 73.   Arteries and nerves of right upper limb, posterior aspect.

The **posterior cord** of the plexus is formed by the union of the posterior divisions of the three trunks.

The **lateral cord** is formed by the union of the anterior divisions of the upper and middle trunks.

The **medial cord** is formed by the anterior division of the lowest trunk.

Branches of the Brachial Plexus. Branches are given off from the plexus in the neck and in the axilla.

In the Neck. The **nerve to the serratus anterior** muscle (nerve of Bell) arises from C5, 6 and 7.

The **suprascapular nerve** from the upper trunk supplies the posterior scapular muscles.

The **nerve to the rhomboid muscles** arises from C5.

In the Axilla. Small branches arise in the upper part to supply the muscles of the anterior and posterior walls of the axilla. The larger branches arise in the lower part of the axilla (Figs. 72 and 73).

1. From the Posterior Cord

The **Radial Nerve** (musculo-spiral). The radial nerve leaves the axilla behind the brachial artery, but soon leaves this and passes spirally round the back of the humerus between the heads of the triceps and in close contact with the bone. On the lateral side it gives off its posterior interosseous branch and passes into the forearm, where it runs between the deep and superficial muscles over the front of the radius. In the lower third of the forearm it passes to the back and breaks up into branches which spread out on the back of the hand.

Distribution. Muscles. The **extensor muscles** of the arm and forearm (branches are also given to the brachialis and brachioradialis) and the **supinator.**

Skin. The **extensor aspect** of the arm and forearm and the posterior surface of the hand and of the thumb, the index and half of the middle finger.

The elbow joint receives a branch from the nerve.

The **Circumflex Nerve** (axillary). This nerve passes below the shoulder joint to the back of the limb, where it breaks up into branches beneath the deltoid muscle.

Distribution. Muscles. The **deltoid** and the **teres minor.**

Skin. The skin of the lateral side of the arm.

The shoulder joint is also supplied by the nerve.

2. The Lateral Cord

The Lateral Root of the Median Nerve. The **median nerve** is formed by two roots, one from the lateral and one from the medial cord. It runs through the upper arm, crossing the brachial artery from the lateral to the medial side. Running down the middle of the forearm (hence its name), it finally enters the lateral part of the palm of the hand, where it breaks into its terminal branches.

Distribution. Muscles. The **flexor and pronator** muscles of the forearm (except the flexor carpi ulnaris and part of the digitorum profundus) and the **short muscles of the thumb** (except the adductor) and the first and second lumbrical muscles.

Skin. The **flexor aspect of the** palm of the **hand** and of the **thumb** and the **index, middle and half the ring fingers.**

The elbow and wrist and digital joints are also supplied.

The Musculo-cutaneous Nerve. This nerve pierces the coracobrachialis muscle and then, running between the biceps and brachialis muscles, it emerges to the surface on the lateral side.

Distribution. Muscles. The **coracobrachialis, brachialis** and **biceps.**

Skin. The lateral half of the flexor aspect and the lateral border of the forearm.

3. The Medial Cord

The Medial Head of the Median Nerve. This joins the lateral head to form the trunk of the nerve which has been described above.

The Ulnar Nerve. The ulnar nerve enters the arm medial to the brachial artery, but soon leaves the latter to pass behind the medial epicondyle of the humerus. It then passes down the ulnar side of the front of the forearm into the hand, where it breaks up into its terminal branches.

Distribution. Muscles. The **flexor carpi ulnaris,** part of the **flexor digitorum profundus** and the **hypothenar, interosseous** and medial two **lumbrical** muscles and the **adductor pollicis.**

Skin. Small parts of the palm and back of the hand ; the **ulnar border of the hand** ; the palmar surfaces of the ulnar one and a half digits and the dorsal surfaces of the ulnar two and a half digits.

The Medial Cutaneous Nerves of the Arm and Forearm. These nerves supply the areas of skin which their names indicate.

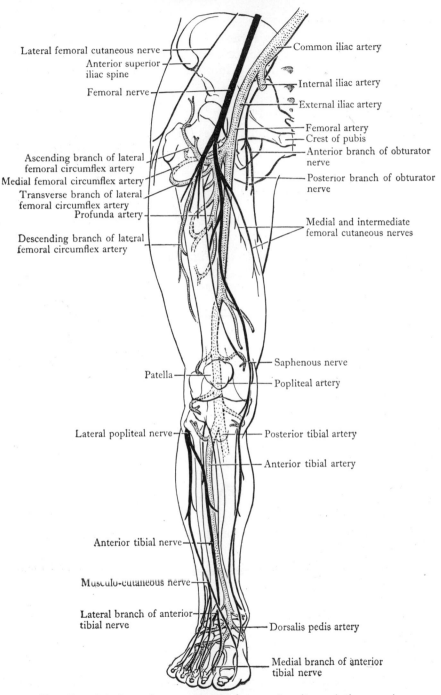

Lateral femoral cutaneous nerve

Anterior superior iliac spine

Femoral nerve

Common iliac artery

Internal iliac artery

External iliac artery

Femoral artery
Crest of pubis

Anterior branch of obturator nerve

Ascending branch of lateral femoral circumflex artery

Medial femoral circumflex artery

Transverse branch of lateral femoral circumflex artery

Profunda artery

Descending branch of lateral femoral circumflex artery

Posterior branch of obturator nerve

Medial and intermediate femoral cutaneous nerves

Patella

Saphenous nerve

Popliteal artery

Lateral popliteal nerve

Posterior tibial artery

Anterior tibial artery

Anterior tibial nerve

Musculo-cutaneous nerve

Lateral branch of anterior tibial nerve

Dorsalis pedis artery

Medial branch of anterior tibial nerve

FIG. 74. Arteries and nerves of right lower extremity, anterior aspect.

The Lumbar Plexus

The lumbar plexus is formed in the substance of the psoas major muscle by the anterior primary rami of the upper four lumbar nerves. (The fourth lumbar nerve also gives a branch to the sacral plexus.)

Branches of the Lumbar Plexus

Iliohypogastric and Ilioinguinal Nerves (Fig. 20)

These both arise from the first lumbar nerve, and they are distributed mainly to the muscles and skin of the abdominal wall.

Genito-femoral Nerve (Fig. 20)

This arises from the first and second lumbar nerves, and is distributed to the cremaster muscle (p. 294) and to the skin just below the inguinal ligament.

Lateral Femoral Cutaneous Nerve (Fig. 20)

This crosses the iliac fossa and passes under the inguinal ligament to supply the skin over the lateral part of the thigh.

Femoral Nerve (Fig. 74). This is the biggest branch from the lumbar plexus, and it arises from the second, third and fourth lumbar nerves. It passes into the thigh under the inguinal ligament just lateral to the psoas tendon, and, in the upper part of the femoral triangle, divides into a sheaf of branches.

Distribution. Muscular. To the **quadriceps extensor** of the thigh, to the **sartorius,** to the **pectineus and iliacus** muscles.

Cutaneous. By the intermediate and medial femoral cutaneous nerves, to the skin of the **front and the medial side of the thigh.**

By the saphenous nerve to the skin over the **medial side of the leg** and the posterior half of the medial border of the foot.

Articular. To the hip and knee joints.

The Obturator Nerve (Fig. 74). This nerve passes out into the thigh through the obturator foramen in the hip bone. It arises from the second, third and fourth lumbar nerves.

Distribution. Muscular. To the obturator externus and to the **adductors** of the thigh.

Cutaneous. To the **medial side of the thigh.**

Articular. To the hip and knee joints.

The Sacral and Coccygeal Plexuses

Part of the **fourth lumbar** anterior primary ramus and the **fifth lumbar** anterior primary ramus form the **lumbo-sacral**

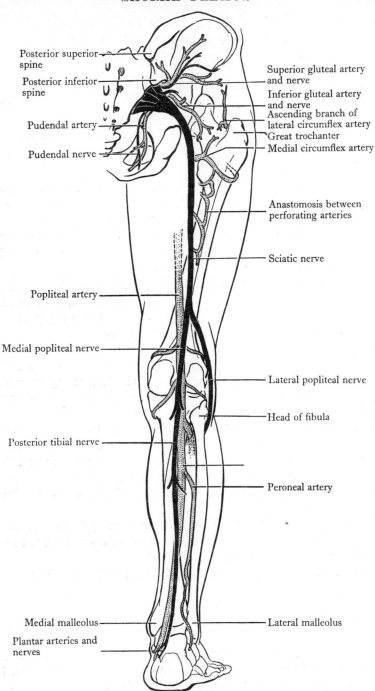

Posterior superior spine

Posterior inferior spine

Pudendal artery

Pudendal nerve

Superior gluteal artery and nerve

Inferior gluteal artery and nerve

Ascending branch of lateral circumflex artery

Great trochanter

Medial circumflex artery

Anastomosis between perforating arteries

Sciatic nerve

Popliteal artery

Medial popliteal nerve

Lateral popliteal nerve

Head of fibula

Posterior tibial nerve

Peroneal artery

Medial malleolus

Plantar arteries and nerves

Lateral malleolus

Fig. 75. Arteries and nerves of right lower limb, posterior aspect.

trunk. This passes into the pelvis and forms, with the anterior primary rami of the **upper four sacral** nerves, the sacral plexus. This is situated on the posterior wall of the pelvis.

A twig from the fourth sacral and the anterior primary ramus of the fifth sacral nerve and the coccygeal nerve form the coccygeal plexus.

Branches of the Sacral Plexus. In addition to a number of smaller branches, the sacral plexus gives off the following important nerves :—

The Gluteal Nerves (superior and inferior) (Fig. 75). These emerge from the pelvis through the great sciatic notch and are distributed to the **gluteal muscles.**

The Posterior Femoral Cutaneous Nerve. This leaves the pelvis through the great sciatic notch and runs down to supply the **skin of the back of the thigh** and in the perineum.

The Pudendal Nerve (Fig. 75). This, after emerging through the great sciatic notch, passes into the perineal region through the lesser sciatic notch and is concerned with the supply of the **skin and muscles of the external genital organs.**

The Sciatic Nerve (Fig. 75). This very large nerve emerges from the pelvis through the great sciatic notch and passes down the thigh between the **adductor magnus** and the **hamstring muscles,** supplying both. On reaching the popliteal fossa it divides into medial and lateral popliteal nerves.

1. The Medial Popliteal Nerve. This runs, with the popliteal vessels, down the middle of the popliteal space. It is continued into the posterior compartment of the leg as the **posterior tibial nerve** which runs between the superficial and deep plantar flexors to the medial side of the ankle, where it divides into medial and lateral plantar nerves.

Distribution. Muscular. The **calf muscles** (plantar flexors) through the posterior tibial, and the muscles of the **sole of the foot** through the plantar nerves.

Cutaneous. Posterior surface of the leg ; sole of foot (plantar nerves).

Articular. Knee and ankle joints.

2. The Lateral Popliteal Nerve. This runs along the lateral side of the popliteal fossa to the neck of the fibula, where it divides into the anterior tibial nerve and the musculo-cutaneous.

The **anterior tibial** nerve enters the extensor compartment, in which it passes down to the dorsum of the foot.

The **musculo-cutaneous** enters the lateral compartment of the leg and ends by giving cutaneous branches on the dorsum of the foot.

Distribution. Muscular. Short head of biceps (lateral popliteal). **Extensors** (dorsiflexors) of leg and foot (anterior tibial). **Peronei** (musculo-cutaneous).

Cutaneous. Posterior surface and lateral side of **calf** and lateral border of foot (lateral popliteal). **Extensor surface of leg and foot** (anterior tibial and musculo-cutaneous).

Articular. Knee (lateral popliteal). Ankle and foot (anterior tibial).

FUNCTIONS OF THE BRAIN

Apart from the motor and sensory functions of the cranial nerve nuclei which have been seen to resemble the similar activities of spinal nerves, the brain acts as the great co-ordinating and controlling element in the nervous system. The brain is also the seat of the appreciation and analysis of the various sensations of which we are conscious, and is the part of the nervous system concerned with the storage of past impressions (memory). Many of these past impressions need some train of circumstances (often similar to those which produced the original sensation) to recall them to consciousness, and they are said therefore to be stored in " the subconscious " mind. These subconscious impressions may, however, produce effects without ever coming into consciousness at all, and many are, because of some unpleasant association, actively " repressed " by the conscious mind. These processes of the " mind " are very difficult to understand, and in the ensuing account of the physiology of the brain only the relatively simpler mechanisms of the co-ordinating and controlling activities of the brain will be considered. The matter can be discussed under two heads—the initiation of voluntary movements and the balancing and co-ordination of the muscles of the whole body.

(1) The Initiation of Voluntary Movements

(*a*) **The Sensory Pathways** (Fig. 65). Voluntary movement of necessity implies conscious appreciation of our environment, so that in the pathways concerned with voluntary movement we must first consider the pathways whereby impulses coming from the parts of the body reach the brain and there result in conscious sensation. We have seen (p. 243) that sensory neurones may end in the grey matter of the spinal cord, or pass into the white matter. Some of those ending in the grey matter form synapses with connector neurones which cross the median plane in the cord and then pass up through the cord, medulla, pons, and mid-brain to reach the **thalamus.** Those which enter the white matter pass up the posterior part of the spinal cord to the medulla oblongata, where they form synapses with connector neurones. The axons of these also cross the median plane (in this case in the medulla oblongata) and pass then through the pons and mid-brain to the **thalamus.** In the thalamus very crude sensations are appreciated. The connector neurones we have considered form, in the thalamus, synapses with other connector neurones, the axons of which pass *viâ* the internal capsule and corona radiata to the **sensory area of the cortex of the cerebral hemisphere,** where analysis and finer appreciation of the sensation are carried out. It should be noted that, because of the crossing of the fibres of the first connector neurones, the left side of the cortex is concerned with the right side of the body and *vice versâ*.

By impulses passing along these pathways we become conscious of circumstances in our environment which make us want to perform some voluntary movement. For instance, we may feel uncomfortable and wish to change our position ; we may have a stone in our shoe and wish to perform the complicated series of movements which we have learnt will remove it.

(*b*) **The Motor Pathways.** By short connector neurones the sensory cortex is linked to the motor cortex, and from the cells of the motor cortex arise fibres which pass down to the spinal cord. These neurones are called the **upper motor neurones** to distinguish them from the motor neurones of the spinal reflex arcs, which are called the **lower motor neurones.**

The upper motor neurone fibres pass from the cerebral cortex through the corona radiata, internal capsule, mid-brain and pons to the medulla oblongata, where they occupy the pyramid (p. 249). In the decussation of the pyramids they cross to the opposite side and then run down in the white matter in the lateral region of the spinal cord as the **crossed cerebrospinal (pyramidal) tract.** The fibres end finally by forming synapses with the motor neurones in the anterior horn of grey matter, *i.e.*, the **final common motor pathway.** There is evidence that the impulses coming along the pyramidal pathway can control or " damp down " the activity of spinal reflexes, as well as produce impulses which result in voluntary movement. In disease of these upper motor neurones there is loss of voluntary movement and the reflexes are increased, the tone of the muscles of the paralysed parts being augmented. Irritation of the motor cortex produces the spasmodic movements which constitute " fits."

(2) **Balance and Muscle Co-ordination** (Fig. 66)

We have seen (p. 245) that sensory impulses coming from muscles, tendons, joints, etc. (proprioceptive), travel along fibres which, when they reach the cord, may enter either the white or the grey matter.

Those which enter the white matter pursue a course like those described on p. 272, ultimately establishing connections with the thalamus and cerebral cortex of the opposite side. The impulses travelling along this pathway produce conscious sensations of joint position, etc.

Those which enter the grey matter may form the spinal reflex arcs responsible for reciprocal muscle tone (p. 246). Others, however, form synapses with connector neurones which go to the **cerebellum** of the same side of the body. The cerebellum is in turn linked to the **red nucleus** of the mid-brain from which arises a tract which passes down the lateral region of the spinal cord. The fibres of this tract end by forming synapses with the motor cells in the anterior horn of the grey matter of the cord, and so can influence the impulses passing out along the final common motor pathway. In the cerebellum proprioceptive impulses from all over the body are, as it were, " sorted out " in such a way that the various groups of muscles of the body as a whole act in a co-ordinated manner.

A consideration of the events occurring when a baby learns to walk may help in understanding this system. The first voluntary efforts the child makes are jerky and uncontrolled, and, because muscles in other parts of the body are not acting in a co-ordinate manner with those of the legs, he often loses his balance and falls down. As the cerebellar pathways become opened up by continued use, however, the muscles in other parts act reflexly in harmony with those of the limbs and walking becomes almost an automatic procedure. Other examples of a similar sort are learning to ride a bicycle, to skate, or to swim.

Each side of the cerebellum is also under the influence of the cerebral cortex of the opposite side through fibres which pass to the pons, where they form synapses with neurones whose fibres pass in the transverse fibres of the pons into the opposite middle cerebellar peduncle. It is possible that this pathway forms a " short cut " for the impulses responsible for co-ordination of voluntary movements.

The cerebellum is also responsible to some extent for muscle tone, for when it is damaged by disease flaccidity of muscles is noted in addition to inco-ordination of muscles.

Practical Considerations. Concussion. Concussion is a condition which occurs in head injuries. The patient is unconscious and paralysed, the breathing is shallow and the pupils dilated. The condition is probably due to the force of the blow driving the blood out of the capillaries in the brain and so producing a cerebral anæmia.

Fainting. This is also due to cerebral anæmia and recovery usually follows the placing of the head in a dependant position.

Cerebral Irritation. This is usually due to congestion or œdema of the brain, but may be the result of direct pressure from bone driven in in depressed fractures or of cerebral tumours, etc. If affecting the cortex, fits may occur. Vomiting is a common feature.

Hydrocephalus. Hydrocephalus or " water on the brain " is due to some obstruction in the outflow or circulation of the cerebrospinal fluid. The head becomes large and the bones thinned and separated.

THE AUTONOMIC NERVOUS SYSTEM

This is the part of the nervous system concerned with the supply of plain muscle, glands, etc. The system is quite involuntary, *i.e.*, it is not under the control of the will, and it normally produces its results without our being conscious of its activity at all.

There are two main subdivisions of the autonomic system, viz. : the sympathetic nervous system and the parasympathetic nervous system (Fig. 76).

1. The Sympathetic Nervous System

Fibres which arise from cells in the grey matter of the thoracic and upper lumbar segments of the spinal cord are given off as branches called **white rami communicantes,** from all the thoracic and the upper two or three lumbar spinal nerves. The white rami enter almost at once two gangliated chains called the **sympathetic trunks,** which lie one on each side of the whole length of the

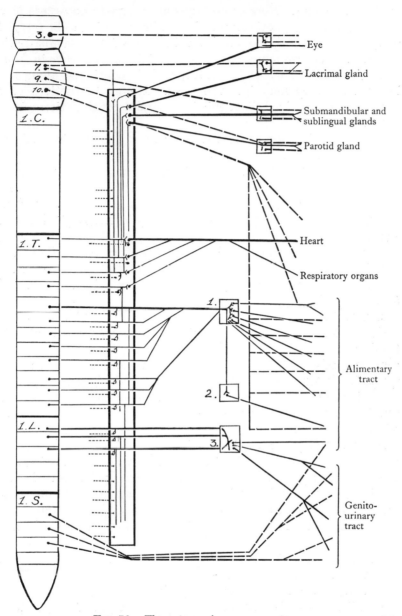

Fig. 76. The autonomic nervous system.

The spinal cord and brain-stem on the left; the sympathetic trunk immediately on its right. The parasympathetic fibres are in heavy dotted lines.

1, 2 and 3, Cœliac, superior mesenteric and inferior mesenteric ganglia.

vertebral column.   Here some fibres are relayed and others pass
through the sympathetic trunk without interruption to be relayed
in some more outlying ganglion in one of the sympathetic
plexuses.   The two sympathetic trunks join one another in front
of the coccyx below, whilst above, each is continued along the
internal carotid artery into the skull.   The sympathetic nerves
to the eye are derived from this intracranial continuation of the
trunk.

Branches arise from both the lateral and medial sides of the
sympathetic trunk.

(*a*) **Lateral Branches.**   The lateral branches are composed
of fibres which have been relayed (formed synapses) in the
ganglia of the sympathetic trunk.   They are called **grey rami
communicantes,** and one is given off to join *every* spinal nerve.
Through the spinal nerves these fibres supply the following
structures in the area to which the spinal nerve is distributed.

1 **Muscle.**   Plain muscle in the walls of the blood-vessels.

Plain muscle in the skin which makes the hair stand on end
(arrectores pilorum).

2. **Glands.**   Sweat and sebaceous glands in the skin.

(*b*) **Medial Branches.**   The medial branches of the sympathetic
trunk are distributed mainly to viscera.   Most of them are
composed of fibres which have passed, *viâ* the white rami, to the
sympathetic trunk and, without being relayed, right through the
trunk into one of its medial branches.   They pass generally to
ganglia in one of the more outlying sympathetic plexuses in
relation to the blood-vessels which supply the viscera.

In the cervical region medial branches are given off to
accompany some of the blood-vessels of the head and neck, and
others pass down into the thorax to reach the **heart** *viâ* the
cardiac plexuses.   Stimulation of these cardiac branches increases
the rate of the heart and dilates the coronary vessels (an effect
opposite to that of the sympathetic on all other blood-vessels).

The trunk also gives off, from the highest of the cervical
ganglia, branches which join some of the cranial nerves and others
which accompany the internal carotid artery.   Some of these
fibres, which are relayed in the superior cervical ganglion, reach
the orbit and are distributed to the **dilator muscle of the pupil.**

In the thoracic region medial branches are given to the heart
and lungs.   Stimulation of the latter branches dilates the
bronchial muscle and makes it easier for air to enter the alveoli.
The three **splanchnic nerves** which arise from this portion of

the trunk enter the abdomen and end in the ganglia in the **cœliac or solar plexus.** The fibres arising from these ganglia form plexuses which accompany the aorta and its branches. Scattered ganglia are found in the plexuses which accompany the **renal** and the **superior and inferior mesenteric** arteries, and these plexuses are further reinforced by branches which arise from the lumbar part of the trunk.

In the intestine these fibres are motor to the sphincter muscles and to the muscle of the blood-vessels and inhibitory to the ordinary gut muscle. They supply also the suprarenal glands, the kidneys, ureters and the genital glands.

In the lumbar region medial branches reinforce the aortic, superior mesenteric, and inferior mesenteric plexuses.

In the pelvis the pelvic plexuses are formed by the continuation of the plexus on the aorta reinforced by branches from the pelvic and lumbar parts of the sympathetic trunks. They supply the pelvic viscera. The supply to the bladder makes the internal sphincter of the urethra contract and relaxes the muscle of the bladder wall.

Function of the Sympathetic System. The sympathetic nervous system is concerned with the preparation of the body for conditions of stress. It is specially active, for instance, when an animal is frightened. In fright the skin becomes pale (because of constriction of its arterioles), sweating occurs (from stimulation of the sweat glands) and the hair stands on end (stimulation of the arrectores pilorum); the heart-rate is at the same time increased, and the pupils are dilated. These effects are still further increased by the liberation of the secretion called adrenalin (p. 321) from the suprarenal glands in response to sympathetic stimulation. The adrenalin circulating in the blood stimulates the endings of sympathetic nerves throughout the body. As the effect of sympathetic stimulation is to constrict the arterioles of the whole body except in the heart, the peripheral resistance of the circulation is increased and the blood-pressure tends to rise. The effect is greatest on the vessels of the skin and the gut, so that blood is redistributed from those parts where it is not needed to the heart (where the vessels are *dilated*) and to the muscles (where vascular channels which are usually small are opened up). More blood being available for these parts because of this redistribution and because of the increased rate of the heart, the animal is in a better state for flight or fighting, both of which involve severe muscular activity. The adrenalin circulating in the blood causes also the mobilisation in the form of glucose of some of the glycogen stored in the liver, the glucose being utilised in the processes of muscular contraction.

The Parasympathetic Nervous System

The parasympathetic system comprises fibres which pass out in some of the cranial nerves and in the second and third sacral nerves. These fibres end in ganglia which are placed very near or actually in the structures supplied. From the ganglia arise fibres which pass directly to the plain muscle or gland tissue. Where structures receive a supply from both the sympathetic and the parasympathetic the effects of the two systems are antagonistic. For example, in the heart the sympathetic quickens and the parasympathetic (vagus) slows the rate ; in the eye the sympathetic dilates and the parasympathetic (oculomotor) constricts the pupil ; in the intestine the sympathetic is motor to the sphincters which prevent the passage of contents along the lumen, and inhibits the rest of the muscle which propels the contents, whilst the parasympathetic (vagus and sacral 2 and 3) has the reverse effect.

The following table gives a summary of the origin and distribution of the fibres of the parasympathetic system :—

Nerve containing parasympathetic fibres	Ganglion for relay	Structures supplied	Function
Oculomotor.	Ciliary ganglion (near eyeball).	Plain muscle of iris and ciliary muscle.	Accommodation and constriction of pupil.
Facial (1) (Great superficial petrosal branch). (2) (Chorda tympani branch).	(1) (Sphenopalatine ganglion). (2) (Submandibular ganglion).	(1) Lacrimal gland. (2) Submandibular and sublingual salivary glands.	(1) Secretion of tears. (2) Secretion of saliva.
Glossopharyngeal.	(Otic ganglion).	Parotid gland.	Secretion of saliva.
Vagus (1) Cardiac branches (through cardiac plexus). (2) Pulmonary branches (through pulmonary plexus). (3) Abdominal branches (through cœliac plexus).	(1) Ganglia in heart muscle. (2) Ganglia in lung root. (3) Ganglia in wall of intestine and in digestive glands.	(1) Sinuatrial node ; heart muscle ; bundle of His. (2) Bronchial muscle and mucous glands (3) Muscle of intestine ; glands producing digestive juices.	(1) Slowing of heart. (2) Constriction of bronchioles and secretion of mucus. (3) Motor to intestinal muscle ; inhibitory to sphincters; secretion of digestive juices.
Second and third sacral spinal nerves.	Ganglia in walls of viscera.	Descending colon, pelvic colon and rectum ; bladder.	Motor to bowel and bladder muscle ; inhibitory to internal sphincters of rectum and bladder.

Practical Considerations

Certain drugs paralyse the endings of the parasympathetic nerves. Atropine is one of these, and is used to dilate the pupil (by removing the effect of the parasympathetic which constricts it) when an especially clear view of the interior of the eye is required. Atropine is also used to diminish the secretion of mucus from the respiratory tract in anæsthesia and to relieve the spasm of plain muscle in such conditions as colic or impaction of a calculus in the ureter.

Adrenalin, which stimulates sympathetic endings, is used in asthma to relieve the bronchial spasm.

CHAPTER XV

THE SPECIAL SENSES

THE sensations of smell, sight, taste and hearing are rather different from the sensations considered already in the general account of the nervous system. Special end-organs are associated with each of these senses and must now be considered.

THE SENSE OF SMELL

The nose (Fig. 69), which is the organ of smell, has been described already (p. 187). The part of the nose which contains the receptor nerve cells for smell is that portion near the roof of the nose and including the upper parts of the lateral wall and the septum in each nasal cavity. The receptor cells (olfactory cells) are supported between columnar cells of the mucous membrane, and each has two processes, peripheral and central. The peripheral processes project beyond the surface of the mucous membrane and are termed **olfactory hairs** ; they are stimulated by the various aromatic substances, and thus an impulse is set up which travels *viâ* the central processes to the brain. The central processes of the olfactory cells are collected into bundles which are the filaments of the **olfactory nerves.** These nerves pass through the foramina in the cribriform plate of the ethmoid bone (Fig. 11 B) which forms the roof of the nose ; they reach in this way the **olfactory bulb** (Fig. 67) of the fore-brain. From the olfactory bulb impulses are conducted by the **olfactory tract** to the higher centres, special regions of the cortex of the **temporal lobe** of the cerebral hemisphere being the most important.

THE SENSE OF SIGHT

The sense of sight is dependent on a system which includes the eyeballs, the muscles which move the eyeballs, and the nervous structures which conduct the impulses originating in the eyeball to the parts of the brain concerned with their reception and interpretation.

The Eyeball (Fig. 77)

The eyeball is the structure in which the rays of light coming from an object are converted into an image which, impinging on the nervous tissue of the eye (the retina) results in the initiation of nerve impulses in the fibres of the optic nerve.

The orbit, in which each eyeball is placed, is much larger than the

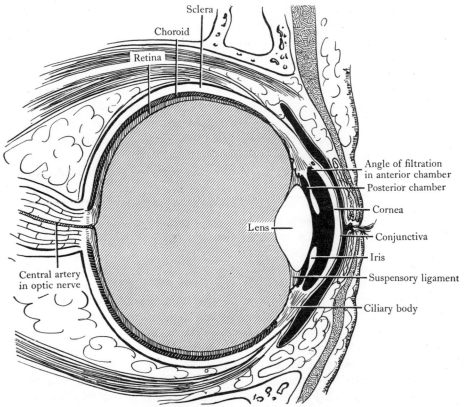

FIG. 77.   Sagittal section of eyeball.   (The shaded part in the interior is occupied by vitreous humour.)

eyeball itself.   The space is filled by a quantity of fat, and this is lined by a fascia called the **fascia bulbi** (capsule of Tenon). This forms a smooth socket adapted to the shape of the eyeball so that the latter may move freely.   The optic nerve and the ocular muscles traverse the orbital fat to reach the eyeball.

The eyeball itself has a form like sectors of two spheres placed together, a large part of a big sphere posteriorly and a part of a smaller sphere forming a prominence anteriorly.   The eyeball is bounded by three layers or coats, and its interior contains the refracting media which bend the rays of light entering the eye so as to focus them and produce a sharp image on the innermost nervous coat or retina.

Coats of the Eye. There are three coats constituting the walls of the eyeball.

1. **The Outer Coat.** The outer coat is protective in function, and is tough and elastic so that the eyeball retains its shape. In the posterior part of the eye, which is constituted by the section of the larger sphere, this coat is opaque and called the **sclera.** The anterior part of the sclera is the " white of the eye " as it is seen in life. The most anterior portion of the outer coat (the part corresponding to the section of the smaller sphere) is transparent during life and is called the **cornea.** It forms a window which admits the rays of light into the eye and also plays a part in focussing the rays on the retina. After death the cornea becomes " glazed " or opalescent.

2. **The Middle Coat.** The middle coat is called the **choroid,** and carries most of the blood-vessels of the eyeball. It contains much pigment and has an iridescent appearance. The black pigment in the choroid serves the same purpose as the matt black paint inside a camera, preventing " scattering " of the light.

In the neighbourhood of the junction of the sclera and cornea of the outer coat, the choroid is much thicker and forms here the **ciliary body.** In front of the ciliary body the choroid is prolonged as a sort of circular curtain, the **iris,** behind the cornea. This constitutes the " coloured part " of the eye. The aperture in the centre of the iris is called the **pupil.** Both the ciliary body and the iris contain muscle ; in the iris some fibres run radially and can by their contraction increase the size of the pupil, others run circularly and form a sphincter or constrictor which can reduce the size of the pupil. (See Accommodation and the Light Reflex.) The ciliary muscle and the constrictor pupillæ are supplied by the oculomotor nerve, the dilator pupillæ by the sympathetic.

3. **The Inner Coat.** The innermost coat of the eye is nervous, and is called the **retina.** It is faintly purple in colour, due to the presence of a pigment called visual purple. The nervous elements of the retina are present only in the posterior two-thirds ; they would be useless anterior to this, as rays of light could not reach the retina here owing to the position of the pupil and lens.

Anteriorly the retina is devoid of nervous elements and forms a thin lining for the anterior part of the choroid.

There are several layers of nerve cells in the retina and the light traverses its whole thickness to affect the outermost layer, the cells in which are termed **rods and cones**. The nerve impulse set up passes from without inwards through the various layers. The fibres arising from the nerve cells of the innermost layer stream over the surface of the retina to reach the **optic disc,** the point where the optic nerve leaves the eye, and where the central artery for the supply of the retina enters. The nerve fibres pierce the sclera at the optic disc and then pass backwards in the optic nerve. At the **macula** just lateral to the optic disc the retina is thinner and the visual sense most acute.

The Contents of the Eyeball. The eyeball contains in its interior the other refractive media which assist the cornea in bending the rays of light so as to produce, on the retina, an inverted image of the objects looked at. The most important is the crystalline lens.

The Lens. The lens is placed just behind the iris and pupil, and is attached to the ciliary region of the choroid all round its margin by the **suspensory ligament.** The pull of the suspensory ligament on the margin of the lens causes it to flatten. If the suspensory ligament be slackened, the lens, by its own elasticity, becomes thicker and more convex. The slackening of the suspensory ligament is brought about by contraction of the **ciliary muscle** in the ciliary body. This muscle drags the attachment of the suspensory ligament to the choroid further forwards and therefore into a part of the eye with a smaller circumference ; the ring for attachment of the suspensory ligament being smaller, the ligament becomes slackened all round the circumference of the lens and the latter then bulges.

The Aqueous Humour. The space within the eye in front of the lens and behind the cornea is divided by the iris into two parts, the **anterior and posterior chambers**, which communicate one with another through the aperture of the pupil. Both chambers are filled with fluid called the **aqueous humour**, which is secreted by the blood-vessels of the iris and ciliary body and is reabsorbed in the angle between the cornea and the iris (angle of filtration) into a small vein (canal of Schlemm) running circumferentially near the corneo-scleral junction.

The Vitreous Body. The vitreous is a jelly-like mass which occupies the interior of the eyeball behind the lens. The latter rests in a depression on its anterior surface, whilst behind, the vitreous keeps the eye from collapsing and retains the retina in contact with the other coats.

Practical Considerations

Normally the cornea, the aqueous, the lens and the vitreous are quite transparent. Opacity in any of them interferes with vision. **Cataract** is an opacity of the lens and, if progressive, ultimately leads to blindness. Interference with the absorption of the aqueous humour leads to the condition called **glaucoma**. The increased tension inside the eye results in destruction of the nervous elements, and blindness.

The **Muscles of the Eyeball.** The muscles which move the eyeball are described on p. 64.

The **Eyelids and Lacrimal Apparatus.** The eyelids and the lacrimal apparatus form a protection for the eye against injury, dust, etc.

Each eyelid contains a fibrous plate, the **tarsus**, attached to the margin of the orbit by fascia. Superficial to the tarsus is the orbicularis oculi muscle which closes the eye. The superficial surface of each lid is covered with skin which bears the eyelashes at the margin. The deep surfaces of the lids are covered with the membrane called the **conjunctiva**, which is reflected from them so as to cover the anterior part of the eyeball. Underneath the conjunctiva which covers the deep surface of the lid are found the tarsal glands. When the eyelids are brought together the conjunctiva is a closed sac, the conjunctival sac. Above and laterally the conjunctival sac receives the ducts of the **lacrimal gland,** which secretes the tears, situated in the lateral part of the roof of the orbit. By movements of the eyelids (blinking) the tears are milked across the surface of the eye and keep it moist. Normally evaporation is sufficient to get rid of the tears which are produced, but, if in excess, the fluid passes across the eye to the medial side of the palpebral fissure (the gap between the eyelids). Here they are collected by the **lacrimal ducts,** each of which begins at a tiny aperture called the **punctum**, situated on a small eminence at the inner end of each eyelid, and ends in the lacrimal sac. The **lacrimal sac** lies in a bony groove on the medial side of the orbit. From the sac the tears pass *viâ* the **naso-lacrimal duct** into the inferior meatus of the nose. The secretion of tears is greatly increased by the presence of irritants in the conjunctival sac, and by emotion.

The eyelids are approximated by the action of the orbicularis oculi muscle. The upper lid is raised by a special muscle called the levator of the upper eyelid.

Nervous Structures concerned with the Conduction and Appreciation of Visual Impulses

Owing to the fact that the eye contains a lens, the image on the retina is inverted and reversed. The nasal half of each retina receives light from objects to the temporal side of the head, whilst the temporal half of each retina receives light from objects in the central part of the field of vision. The fibres leaving the retina are collected together at the optic disc to form the optic nerve.

The **optic nerve** on each side leaves the eyeball a little medial to the posterior pole, and thence runs backwards and medially through the orbital fat to the optic foramen, where it enters the cranial cavity. Inside the skull the two optic nerves meet one another and some of their fibres cross in the **optic chiasma,** behind which the fibres are continued into the two **optic tracts.**

The fibres from the nasal parts of the retinæ decussate in the chiasma and are so carried into the optic tract of the opposite side of the body ; those from the temporal parts of the retinæ do not cross, but continue into the optic tract of the same side.

The optic tract ends on each side in the **lower visual centres** (masses of grey matter in the lateral geniculate and superior quadrigeminal bodies). From the lower visual centres the **optic radiation** of fibres passes to the occipital pole of the corresponding cerebral hemisphere to end in the **visual cortex** (p. 253).

Physiology of Vision

In binocular vision the two eyes are working harmoniously, and the result is we are able to direct the eyes towards objects looked at, and at the same time to focus the two eyes so that the images on the retinæ will be sharp. In most optical instruments focussing is accomplished by moving the lens nearer to or further away from the surface which takes the image. In the eye, however, the same object is achieved by altering the convexity of the lens itself. The process is called **accommodation** and entails quite a number of different actions, which together bring about the desired result.

Accommodation. The least effort is expended in viewing distant objects, and it is when close work, such as reading, is performed that effort is needed to bring the objects viewed into sharp focus.   The ocular muscles act together so as to direct both eyes towards the object.   In looking at something near at hand the eyes converge slightly.

This phenomenon can be observed at its extreme if an attempt be made to view something which is brought so close as to be beyond the capacity of the eyes to focus (*i.e.*, closer than 9 inches).   If this be done the convergence becomes so marked that we call it a squint.

At the same time as the eyes converge, the pupil contracts ; this increases the depth of focus of the eye.   The focussing of the image on the retina is brought about by contraction of the ciliary muscle and consequent slackening of the suspensory ligament of the lens.   This reduces the traction on the edge of the lens and the latter, by its own elasticity, becomes more convex and thicker.

On looking at a distant object the eyes become more nearly parallel, the pupil dilates, and the ciliary muscle relaxes so that the consequent pull of the suspensory ligament on the lens flattens it again.   It should be noted that more muscular effort is required to view near objects and that the muscles concerned may become fatigued so that more and more concentration and effort are required to keep near objects in focus.   The consequence of too much close work with the eyes may be actual " eye strain," and this is especially liable to occur in general bodily fatigue or poor health.

The Light Reflex.   In a bright light the pupils of the eyes contract so as to prevent the entrance of too much light, which might damage the retina.   In a dim light the pupils dilate so as to allow the maximum amount of light into the eyes and so produce the maximum effect on the retina.

The pupil is also altered in other conditions, for example :—

It dilates in emotion and severe pain, after injuries of the oculomotor nerve, and under the effect of drugs, such as atropine, adrenalin, cocaine, and, in poisonous doses, alcohol and chloroform.

It contracts in sleep, mental excitement and injuries of the cervical part of the sympathetic ; also under the influence of drugs, such as morphia or opium, pilocarpine and physostigmine, and, in their smaller doses, alcohol and anæsthetics.

The Conjunctival Reflex.   Stimulation of the conjunctiva produces blinking.   By this means the surface of the eyeball is protected from injury.   Under continued irritation the secretion of tears is increased and the irritant may in this way be washed out of the conjunctival sac.

THE SENSE OF HEARING

The ear (Fig. 78) is the organ of hearing and is a mechanism for converting sound waves, caused by agitation of the air, into nervous impulses which, on reaching the brain, result in the sensation of hearing. The ear consists of three parts, the external ear, the middle ear, and the internal ear. The latter, in addition to being concerned with hearing, has to do with balance, the

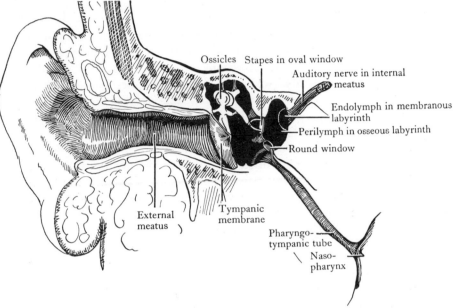

FIG. 78. Section through the ear.

appreciation of the position of the head in space, and muscular co-ordination.

The External Ear

The external ear is the part which collects sound waves and transmits them to the eardrum. It comprises the auricle and the external auditory meatus. The **auricle** projects from the side of the head so as to collect the sound waves. Except for the soft lower part called the lobule of the ear, it is composed of cartilage covered with skin. The lobule consists of skin covering fibrous and fatty tissue.

The **external auditory meatus** is a narrow tube, slightly curved in an S-shaped manner, which leads from the deepest part of the auricle to the eardrum. It is about one inch long, and lined with skin. The lateral part is formed of cartilage continuous with that of the auricle ; the medial part has walls of bone. By pulling the auricle upwards and backwards the curves in the meatus can be straightened out sufficiently to see the eardrum at the bottom.

The skin lining the meatus contains glands which secrete wax (cerumen) which, if it collect in the meatus, may obstruct hearing.

The Middle Ear

The middle ear is called the tympanum, from its resemblance to that musical instrument. It serves to convert sound waves in the air into mechanical vibrations.

The **tympanic cavity,** which is filled with air, is inside the temporal bone. It is narrower from side to side than in its other dimensions. Its lateral wall is formed by the **tympanic membrane** or eardrum, which is composed of fibrous tissue, covered on the outside by modified skin and on the inside by the mucous membrane which lines the whole of the tympanic cavity. The medial wall is a thin plate of bone which separates the tympanic cavity from the internal ear ; in this bone are two foramina or windows : the fenestra vestibuli (oval window) which lodges the footpiece of the stapes (p. 289), and the fenestra cochleæ (round window), which is closed by a fibrous membrane. The roof of the tympanum is a thin plate of bone, on the upper surface of which rests the temporal pole of the brain.

Anteriorly the middle ear communicates with the nasopharynx through the **pharyngo-tympanic (Eustachian) tube.** Posteriorly a narrow channel, the **aditus,** leads backwards into a cavity called the **mastoid antrum,** in the mastoid part of the temporal bone.

Infections may spread from the nasopharynx along the Eustachian tube to the middle ear, producing acute or chronic inflammation in that cavity (otitis media). Obstruction of the pharyngeal orifice of the tube by adenoids is a predisposing cause of this condition. Fluid accumulates in the cavity and produces intense earache, relieved when the fluid is allowed egress by rupture or incision of the tympanic membrane ; discharge from the ear may follow, and, if the infection become chronic, may persist for years. Sometimes middle ear infection spreads to the mastoid antrum and even beyond this, through the bone to the lateral sinus (p. 171) giving rise to septic thrombosis and pyæmia. Spread may occur through the roof of the tympanum to the membranes and the brain, or through the medial wall to the internal ear.

The Auditory Ossicles. The cavity of the middle ear is crossed by a chain of small bones, termed the **auditory ossicles.** These are the malleus, the incus and the stapes.

The **malleus** (hammer) is attached to the deep surface of the tympanic membrane by a long slender process called the handle. The head of the malleus forms a joint with the incus.

The **incus** (anvil) is intermediate between the malleus and the stapes, forming joints with both bones. The joint between it and the malleus occupies a small recess called the epitympanic recess (attic) in the upper part of the tympanum.

The **stapes** (stirrup) articulates with the incus laterally, whilst its footplate occupies the fenestra vestibuli in the medial wall of the tympanum.

These bones transmit the vibrations of the tympanic membrane in response to sound waves across the cavity to the fenestra vestibuli. When the tympanic membrane moves inwards the footplate of the stapes is pushed in also ; when the membrane returns, so does the stapes. The bones thus serve as a mechanical link between the cardrum and the internal ear.

The Pharyngotympanic (Eustachian) Tube. This tube connects the middle ear with the nasopharynx, and serves to equalise the pressure on the two surfaces of the tympanic membrane. If it were not present the air in the tympanum would be absorbed and the eardrum drawn inwards and immobilised.

The tube is lined by mucous membrane continuous, on the one hand, with that of the tympanum, and, on the other, with that of the pharynx. At its tympanic end it has bony walls, but nearer the pharynx its wall is composed of cartilage which bulges the mucous membrane of the pharynx inwards to produce the tubal elevation (Eustachian cushion) surrounding its pharyngeal orifice.

Occasionally the lumen of the tube becomes blocked because of catarrhal infection and the air in the tympanum is absorbed. Deafness results until the lumen of the tube is cleared.

The Internal Ear

The internal ear is the part where the mechanical vibrations which result from the sound waves impinging on the tympanic membrane are converted into nervous impulses which pass along the auditory nerve to the brain, the result being the sensation of hearing. It comprises a complicated series of cavities in the temporal bone called the **bony labyrinth,** within which is contained a system of delicate tubes, similar in shape to but smaller than the bony labyrinth, and called the **membranous labyrinth.** The membranous labyrinth being smaller than the bony labyrinth a space is present round about it which is filled everywhere with the

fluid called **perilymph**. The membranous labyrinth contains
fluid called **endolymph,** and in parts of its wall are found the
endings of the nerves of hearing and balance.

The Bony Labyrinth

The bony labyrinth consists of three main parts which communicate
with one another. The most anterior part is like a snail's shell, and
is called the **cochlea.** The cochlea contains the part of the membranous
labyrinth called the duct of the cochlea. The cochlea communicates
at its base with the middle part of the bony labyrinth called the
vestibule. This contains the parts of the membranous labyrinth called
the utricle and saccule. The vestibule is separated from the middle
ear, which lies lateral to it, by a thin plate of bone in which is the oval
window receiving the footplate of the stapes. The most posterior part
of the bony labyrinth comprises the **semicircular canals**. These canals
are placed at right angles one to another. The lateral semicircular
canal is horizontal ; the superior semicircular and posterior semicircular
canals are both in the vertical plane and therefore at right angles to the
lateral canal, but in addition they make a right angle with each other.
The canals contain the semicircular ducts of the membranous labyrinth,
and they communicate anteriorly with the vestibule.

The Membranous Labyrinth

The membranous labyrinth occupies part of the space within the
bony labyrinth and is of approximately the same shape. All its parts
are in free communication with one another. Occupying the cochlea
is the part called the **duct of the cochlea,** which contains the special
spiral organ (organ of Corti) in which the branches of the cochlear part
of the auditory nerve end. Occupying the vestible are the **utricle** and
saccule, whilst in the semicircular canals are the **semicircular ducts** ;
these parts contain specialised end-organs in which end the branches
of the vestibular division of the auditory nerve.

Physiology of the Ear
A. Hearing

Sound waves are disturbances in the air. These waves are
collected by the external ear and impinge on the tympanic membrane, causing it to vibrate at a speed which depends on the
pitch and character of the sound. The vibrations of the
tympanic membrane are transmitted across the middle ear by
the auditory ossicles in such a way that the footplate of the stapes
follows the movements of the tympanic membrane. Since the
footplate of the stapes occupies the fenestra vestibuli in the
lateral wall of the vestibule, vibrations of the stapes will produce
movement of the perilymph filling all parts of the bony labyrinth.[1]

---

[1] When the stapes is pushed inwards the membrane closing the fenestra
cochleæ (round window) bulges outwards so as to allow the displacement of
fluid.

These disturbances of the perilymph affect the walls of the membranous labyrinth and produce corresponding vibrations in the endolymph which fills it. The result is stimulation of the endings of the **auditory nerve** in the cochlea, and impulses pass along that nerve to the brain, producing there the sensations of hearing and vibration.

B. Balance

When the head is moved the endolymph inside the membranous labyrinth tends, because of its inertia, to remain still. (In much the same way as when a glass is tilted the upper level of the fluid it contains remains horizontal.) This means that there is movement of the fluid relative to the walls of the labyrinth and consequent stimulation of its nerve endings. The result is the passage of nerve impulses along the vestibular division of the **auditory nerve** to the brain. The effect of these impulses is to produce sensations whereby we are conscious of the position of the head in space and also, through connections made by the vestibular nerve with tracts which pass to the spinal cord and to other parts of the brain, so to influence the tone of muscles all over the body that when we tilt the head we do not lose our balance.

Disease of the internal ear may produce deafness because of involvement of the cochlea, or giddiness and loss of balance from damage to the vestibule or semicircular canals.

THE SENSE OF TASTE

The end-organs and the nerves of taste are considered on pp. 91 and 260.

CHAPTER XVI

THE GENITAL SYSTEM

THE MALE GENITAL SYSTEM

THE male genital organs comprise the testes (testicles), the deferent ducts, seminal vesicles and ejaculatory ducts, and the penis and scrotum. Associated with the system is the prostate gland.

The Testes

The testes are the reproductive glands in the male, and produce the spermatozoa or male germ cells. The testes hang in the scrotum, the left a little lower than the right, and they are suspended by the spermatic cords which pass from the testes through the inguinal canals into the abdomen.

Each testis has a **body**, ovoid in shape, and a somewhat crescentic part called the **epididymis,** placed along the postero-lateral aspect of the body. The body of the testis contains tubules lined with cells which, by their division, form the mature **spermatozoa**.

An enormous number of spermatozoa are discharged in one ejaculation of semen, but only one of these is required to fertilise the female germ cell or ovum. Each spermatozoön has a head and neck, which contain the nuclear material of the cell, and a tail which, being actively motile, enables it to propel itself along the female genital tract from the vagina.

Between the tubules which produce the spermatozoa are the masses of **interstitial cells** of the testis.

From the body of the testis the spermatozoa pass to the upper part or head of the epididymis. The middle part, or body, of the epididymis contains a very slender and much coiled tube, which at the lower end or tail of the epididymis is continuous with the vas deferens.

The Scrotum. The scrotum is the bag-like structure which contains the testes. It is composed of skin lined by a thin layer of muscle (the dartos) and fascia. The dartos muscle contracts on the application of cold and the skin then becomes very rugose.

Each testis is enclosed in an invaginated sac, derived originally from the peritoneum, and called the **tunica vaginalis**. This

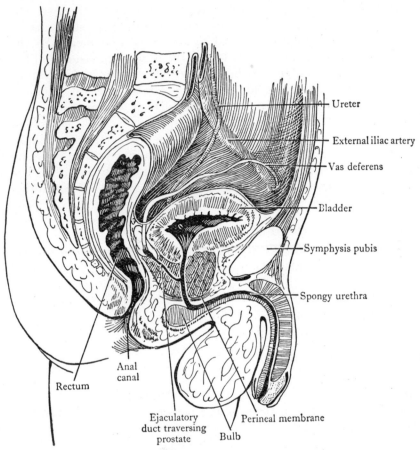

Ureter

External iliac artery

Vas deferens

Bladder

Symphysis pubis

Spongy urethra

Anal
canal

Rectum

Ejaculatory
duct traversing
prostate

Perineal membrane

Bulb

Fig. 79. Sagittal section of male pelvis.

allows the skin to move freely over the testis and so prevents injury of the gland.

A persistence of the communication which exists during intrauterine life between the peritoneal cavity and the tunica vaginalis constitutes one variety of congenital inguinal **hernia.**

Occasionally the testes, which are developed inside the abdomen, fail to descend properly into the scrotum. This condition is termed **undescended testicle.**

The Vasa Deferentia (Deferent ducts) (Figs. 55 and 79)

The vasa deferentia are the ducts by which the spermatozoa are carried away from the testis.

Each **vas deferens** begins at the tail of the epididymis and runs first upwards behind the testis. At the upper pole of the testis the vas enters the spermatic cord, and within this structure it traverses the inguinal canal and so enters the abdomen. At the abdominal end of the canal it leaves the other constituents of the spermatic cord and passes into the pelvis, where it finally runs behind the base of the bladder to the prostate, where it joins the duct of the seminal vesicle to form the ejaculatory duct.

The **Spermatic Cord** (Fig. 22). The spermatic cord is composed of the vas deferens and the blood-vessels, nerves and lymphatics of the testis on each side. These are wrapped in a covering of fascia derived from the muscles of the abdominal wall. The **cremaster muscle** in these coverings is capable of retracting the testis towards the inguinal canal.

The Seminal Vesicles (Fig. 79)

Each seminal vesicle lies alongside the terminal part of the vas deferens of the same side, between the bladder in front and the rectum behind. It is about an inch and a half in length and is drained at its lower end by a duct which joins the vas deferens to form the ejaculatory duct. The secretion of the seminal vesicles forms a vehicle for the spermatozoa.

The Ejaculatory Ducts (Fig. 79)

The ejaculatory duct on each side is formed by the union of the vas deferens with the duct of the seminal vesicle. The ejaculatory ducts run through the posterior part of the prostate and end by opening into the prostate urethra.

The Prostate (Fig. 79)

The prostate is placed at the neck of the bladder in the male. It is traversed by the first part of the urethra and by the two ejaculatory ducts. It consists of gland tissue enclosed by trabeculæ of plain muscle. The secretion is squeezed by this muscle into the urethra just before ejaculation ; it there mixes with the suspension of spermatozoa in the secretion of the seminal vesicles, which has reached the urethra along the ejaculatory ducts. The **seminal fluid** (semen) formed in this way is ejaculated through the urethra during coitus.

In old men the prostate frequently undergoes enlargement, and, as it contains the first portion of the urethra, this results in obstruction to micturition, which may need removal of the prostate for its cure.

The Penis (Fig. 79)

The penis contains the terminal part of the urethra. It is composed of two main parts : the **corpus cavernosum** and the **corpus spongiosum.** The corpus cavernosum is the larger part and is formed by the union of two crura, or roots, which are attached in the perineum to the rami of the pubis and ischium. The corpus spongiosum contains the urethra, and in the perineum is expanded to form the median **bulb of the urethra**. After running in a groove on the surface of the corpus cavernosum to the extremity of the penis, the corpus spongiosum is there continuous with the expanded part called the **glans penis,** on which the urethra opens. All these parts of the penis are composed of spongy tissue which becomes distended with blood during erection of the organ. The penis is covered with a sleeve of skin, called the **prepuce** or **foreskin**. The open end of the prepuce is lined by mucous membrane which is reflected from its deep surface on to the glans penis.

Occasionally in children the opening of the prepuce is so small as to interfere with proper cleanliness of the glans, or even to obstruct micturition. This condition is termed **phimosis** and may need **circumcision** for its cure.

THE FEMALE GENITAL SYSTEM

The female genital system comprises the ovaries, the uterine (Fallopian) tubes, the uterus, the vagina, the external genitalia, and the mammary glands.

The Ovaries (Figs. 80 and 81)

The ovaries are the female genital glands and they produce the ova or female germ cells.

The ovary on each side lies against the lateral wall of the pelvis, and is attached by a short mesentery to the posterior surface of the broad ligament of the uterus (p. 299). It is about one and a quarter inches long and three-quarters of an inch wide, and is flattened somewhat like an almond. One pole is attached to the fimbriated end of the uterine tube which overlaps the upper part of the ovary.

The ovaries contain the female germ cells. Most of these are in an immature state, and are called oöcytes. Some are, however, in a state of active development or maturation to form **ova**. Fluid accumulates round the maturing ovum to form a vesicle called the **Graafian follicle.** As more and more fluid distends the follicle the tension within it becomes so great that it bursts, setting free its contained ovum. This is termed **ovulation.** The

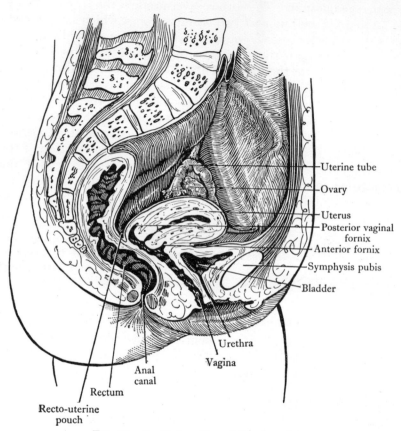

Fig. 80. Sagittal section of female pelvis.

liberated ovum enters the uterine tube and is passed along this to the uterus by the movements of the cilia which cover the epithelium lining the tube. If the ovum be fertilised by a spermatozoön during its passage along the tube, it remains in the uterus and develops into a new individual. Ova which are not fertilised die, and are discharged with the succeeding menstrual flow. Several oöcytes mature at about the same time, but usually

only one reaches the stage of a mature follicle ; the remainder
retrogress and degenerate.

The cells lining the ruptured follicle begin to multiply after the
ovum is discharged and eventually they fill up the follicle to form

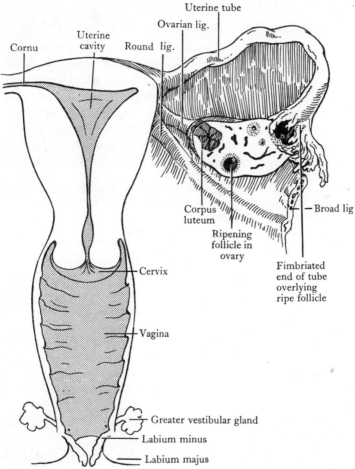

FIG. 81.   Scheme of female genital organs in coronal section.

a yellowish mass, called a **corpus luteum**.   Unless fertilisation of
the ovum occurs the corpus luteum lasts for several days and
then atrophies ; if pregnancy supervene, however, the corpus
luteum develops still further and persists until the later months
of gestation.

The cells lining the maturing follicles as well as other cells
scattered between the follicles and called interstitial cells,

produce an internal secretion (p. 315) called **œstrin**. The corpus luteum produces a secretion called **progestin**. There is evidence that the maturing of the Graafian follicles, the development of the corpus luteum, and the production of œstrin are all under the control of the pituitary gland (see p. 317).

The Uterine Tubes (Figs. 80 and 81)

The uterine (Fallopian) tubes convey the ova from the two ovaries to the uterus. The tubes extend laterally from the uterus in the upper free edges of the broad ligaments. At the lateral end, each tube is dilated and communicates with the peritoneal cavity. This opening of the tube is surrounded by a fringe of irregular processes called **fimbria**, one of which is attached to the ovary, and so retains the opening near that gland. The tubes communicate medially with the cavity of the uterus.

The wall of the uterine tube is composed of plain muscle, and the tube is lined with mucous membrane with cells of the ciliated columnar type ; the cilia work towards the uterus.

The Uterus (Figs. 80 and 81)

The uterus, or womb, is a hollow organ with very thick muscular walls, situated in the pelvic cavity between the bladder in front and the rectum behind. It is somewhat pear-shaped and measures $2\frac{1}{2}$ to 3 inches in length, and about 2 inches across its widest part.

The uterus consists of three parts : the fundus, the body, and the cervix. The **fundus** is the rounded extremity above the entry of the uterine tubes. The parts where the tubes enter are called the **cornua** or horns. In the normal position of the organ the fundus is directed forwards.

The **body** is the central part of the uterus. Its lateral margins give attachment to the broad ligaments.

The **cervix**, or neck, of the uterus is the narrowest part and is normally directed downwards and backwards. The extremity projects into the vagina, so that the cervix has supravaginal and intravaginal parts.

The uterus is slung from the lateral wall of the pelvis on each side by the peritoneal fold called the broad ligament ; its position varies according to the degree of distension of the bladder. When the bladder is empty the uterus lies on its upper surface at a slight angle with the horizontal (Fig. 80), but as the bladder fills the uterus becomes more and more vertical, and if the bladder be distended it may even be turned backwards (retroversion of the uterus).

The Uterine Cavity. The cavity of the uterus is small relative to the size of the whole organ, because of the great thickness of the muscular walls. When viewed in sagittal section (Fig. 80) it is a mere cleft, as the anterior and posterior walls are almost in apposition. In coronal section (Fig. 81) the cavity is triangular, the superior angles being at the cornua, where the uterine tubes enter, whilst the inferior angle is at the entrance to the cervical canal.

The cavity of the cervix or **cervical canal,** communicates internally with the cavity of the body of the uterus at the opening called the **internal os.** Externally the cervical canal opens into the vagina at the **external os** on the summit of the cervix.

Supports of the Uterus. The uterus is maintained in position by several means. First, its weight is carried on the upper surface of the bladder, which tends to some extent to prevent its displacement. Second, the cervix is attached to the wall of the vagina where it enters, and the vagina is, in turn, attached to the muscular floor of the pelvis (levator ani) where it passes through it. Thirdly, the uterus has certain ligaments supporting it. Of the above factors the support given by the muscular floor of the pelvis is probably the most important ; if the pelvic floor be damaged in parturition **prolapse** or displacement of the uterus may occur.

The Broad Ligament

The broad ligament is a double layer of peritoneum extending on each side from the uterus to the pelvic wall. The two ligaments and the uterus divide the pelvic cavity in the female into two parts. Between the layers of the broad ligament are carried the vessels, nerves and lymphatics of the uterus, and, in its upper free edge, the uterine tube. The **ovarian ligament,** connecting the ovary with the cornu of the uterus, and the **round ligament** are also between the layers.

The Round Ligament

The round ligament of the uterus is a cord-like structure composed of plain muscle and fibrous tissue. It runs first from the cornu of the uterus, between the layers of the broad ligament, to the lateral wall of the pelvis. Turning upwards here it crosses the iliac vessels at the brim of the pelvis and then runs through the inguinal canal, like the spermatic cord in the male ; it ends in the labium majus.

The Vagina (Figs. 80, 81 and 82)

The vagina is the canal which leads from the uterus to the exterior. It is at an angle of about 45 degrees with the horizontal and is placed between the rectum and anal canal posteriorly, and the bladder and urethra anteriorly. The cervix of the uterus projects through its anterior wall, which is about 3 inches long, the posterior wall measuring about 4 inches. The groove which surrounds the projecting cervix is called the **fornix** of the vagina.

The vagina pierces the muscular floor of the pelvis (levator ani) and the perineal membrane (p. 226), the former exerting a sphincteric action on the canal. In the virgin, a membrane,

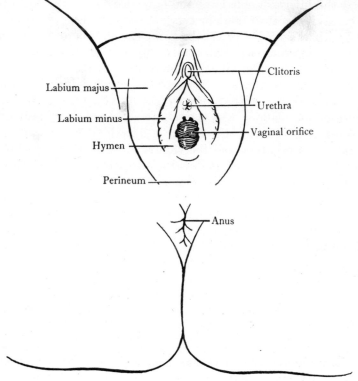

FIG. 82.   Scheme of female external genital organs.

called the **hymen,** partly closes the lower part of the vagina.

Opening into the lowest part, or **vestibule,** of the vagina are the ducts of the **greater vestibular (Bartholinian) glands,** which are placed one on each side, just lateral to the vaginal wall in this situation.

The External Genitalia (Fig. 82)

The external genital organs in the female comprise the labia majora, the labia minora, the clitoris and the mons pubis.

The opening of the vagina is guarded by two lips of erectile tissue covered with skin, called the **labia minora**. Each labium minus is partially hidden by the corresponding labium majus. In the cleft between the labia minora, just in front of the vaginal opening, is the **aperture of the urethra,** and in front of this is the **clitoris**. The latter is the homologue of the penis, but is very much smaller and does not contain any part of the urethra. The **labia majora** are homologous with the scrotum in the male. They are placed lateral to the labia minora and are composed of fatty connective tissue covered with skin. Posteriorly, they meet one another just in front of the anus, whilst anteriorly they are continuous with the eminence covered with the pubic hair termed the **mons pubis**. The parts round the vaginal orifice are often grouped under the term *vulva* and the tissue between the vulva and the anus is termed the *perineum*.

Relation of Peritoneum to the Female Genital Organs. The two uterine tubes open into the peritoneal cavity, so that in the female there is direct continuity of the peritoneum with the external air. Infection may reach the peritoneum from the genital tract by this route.

In a sagittal section of the pelvis (Fig. 80) it can be seen that the peritoneum is reflected on to the uterus from the bladder forming the **uterovesical pouch**. After covering the uterus the peritoneum passes on to the posterior fornix of the vagina and then on to the rectum so forming the **recto-uterine pouch** (pouch of Douglas). It is possible by vaginal examination therefore to detect some abnormal conditions of the pelvic peritoneum.

The Mammary Glands

The mammary glands or breasts are accessory organs of the reproductive system in the female.

Each is situated in the subcutaneous tissue on the front of the chest and covers an area from the level of the second rib above, to that of the sixth rib below. The gland is covered with skin and is surmounted by the **nipple**. The skin round the nipple is pigmented, forming the **areola**, the pigmentation being darkest in dark-haired women.

Structure of the Breast. The true gland tissue of the breast is composed of tiny tubes called **acini**, which are lined by epithelial cells which form the milk. The acini are grouped together to form **lobules**, and these in turn are grouped to form **lobes**, separated one from another by septa of connective tissue. There are about eighteen to twenty lobes in the breast, and each is drained by its own duct. The **ducts** from the lobes converge on the nipple on which they open. Entangled among the other elements of the gland is a considerable amount of fat, which gives the breast its rounded contour.

The above account refers to the adult female breast. The male breast throughout life and the female breast before puberty are rudimentary and consist of solid cords of epithelium radiating for a short distance into the fat near the nipple. At puberty the female breast develops, and it reaches its full activity when lactation occurs.

PHYSIOLOGY OF REPRODUCTION

Cyclical Changes in the Female Genital Organs. Menstruation. Ovulation

From the age of puberty until the menopause or climacteric the genital organs in the female undergo every twenty-eight days a series of cyclical changes which are concerned with ovulation. For a period of from five to seven days out of the twenty-eight there occurs a discharge of blood and epithelial *débris* from the uterus through the vagina. This is known as **menstruation** or the menstrual flow. Beginning from the end of this period the *rest* of the twenty-eight day cycle can be divided as follows :—

1. During the seven days following each menstrual flow the muscle and mucous membrane of the uterus are undergoing hypertrophy or enlargement due to the presence in the blood of the substance called **œstrin,** produced by the ovary (p. 298). These changes really constitute a repair of the mucous membrane which broke down in the previous menstrual period.

2. On or about the fourteenth day a Graafian follicle in the ovary ruptures, an ovum is set free, and a corpus luteum begins to develop in the ruptured follicle. The corpus luteum produces an internal secretion called **progestin,** which is absorbed into the blood. The œstrin and progestin circulating in the blood together produce further changes in the mucous lining of the uterus ; the glands in the mucosa become elongated and tortuous and the blood-vessels more numerous and dilated. These latter changes prepare the mucous membrane for the reception of a fertilised ovum.

3. If fertilisation of the ovum does not occur, the corpus luteum, formed in the ovary when the ovum was discharged from the follicle, degenerates and this means that progestin is no

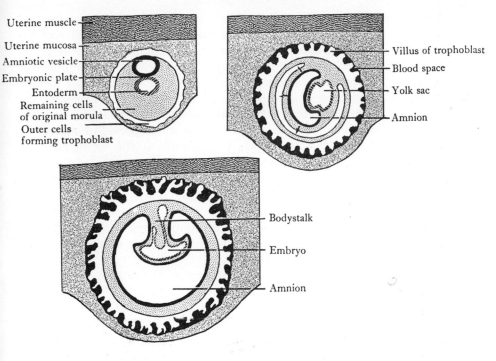

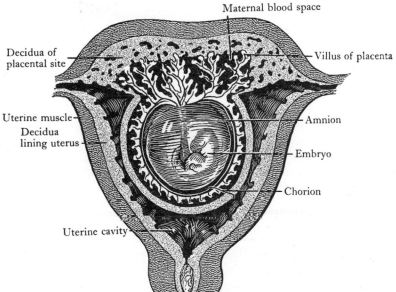

Fig. 83. Progressive stages in the formation of the embryo, the lowest at about two and a half months.

The upper three figures are greatly enlarged.

longer produced to be absorbed into the blood. At the same time the amount of œstrin in the blood decreases. The effect of withdrawal of the progestin while the œstrin in the blood is decreased is that the highly developed uterine mucosa becomes unstable; the surface layers are shed, and, in the process, the enlarged blood-vessels are opened and on the twenty-first day bleeding occurs and a new menstrual flow begins.

These cyclical changes go on during the whole period of active sexual life. Menstruation ceases in later life at the **menopause or climacteric.** As age advances fewer and fewer oöcytes are left to mature, until eventually the ovary becomes inactive. As no œstrin or progestin are produced by the inactive ovary the cyclical changes no longer occur.

Menstruation is suppressed during pregnancy, because the corpus luteum formed in the ovary persists and goes on producing progestin.

Pregnancy (Fig. 83)

A new individual is developed by a series of changes which occur after the fertilisation of a female germ cell, or **ovum,** by a male germ cell or **spermatozoön.** The latter is provided with an actively motile " tail," which enables it to propel itself from the vagina through the uterus into the uterine tube where conjugation of the two cells takes place.

Once fertilised, the ovum divides and subdivides until a mass of cells like a tiny mulberry is produced. The outermost cells of this mass constitute a layer on the surface called the **trophoblast.**

When the fertilised ovum reaches the uterus the trophoblast erodes the mucous membrane which has already become thickened under the influence of œstrin and progestin. This burrowing into the substance of the mucosa usually takes place near the fundus and is termed **implantation** of the ovum. Meanwhile, the cells in the interior of the developing ovum undergo a complicated series of changes by which the new individual or **embryo** is formed. In the course of these changes fluid collects among some of the cells in the interior of the mass so that a vesicle called the **amnion** is formed. The fluid in the amnion increases in amount until it surrounds the embryo and presses the amnion out into contact with the trophoblast and against the stalk by which the embryo is attached to the trophoblast. This stalk subsequently forms the **umbilical cord** which carries blood-vessels from the embryo to the trophoblast and back from the trophoblast to the embryo. The amniotic fluid in which the embryo floats serves as an additional protection against injury. The mucous membrane lining the uterine cavity during pregnancy is called the **decidua**. As the ovum develops it distends the decidua in which it is embedded, and at about the third month the decidua covering the ovum is pressed against the decidua lining the rest of the uterus and the uterine cavity is obliterated. Meanwhile the trophoblast gives off processes or **villi,** which erode the maternal blood-vessels in the decidua and so become bathed in the maternal blood. These villi are invaded by blood-vessels from the embryo through the umbilical cord, and in this way the embryo derives nourishment from the maternal blood. The villi ultimately disappear except over a limited area surrounding the attachment of the umbilical cord, in which they develop further and form the **placenta.** The part of the trophoblast over which the villi have disappeared, together with the thinned decidua which covers it, forms the **chorion** ; the chorion and the embryonic surface of the placenta are lined by the **amnion.** The amnion and chorion together constitute the fœtal **membranes**.

Occasionally the ovum becomes embedded near the cervix instead of at the fundus ; the placenta then lies over the internal os, and severe hæmorrhage may occur during delivery. This is termed *placenta prævia.* Sometimes the fertilised ovum embeds itself in the mucosa lining the uterine tube. This is called **ectopic gestation** or **tubal pregnancy**, and the muscular wall of the tube ruptures early in such cases ; the embryo dies and severe hæmorrhage occurs into the peritoneal cavity.

Parturition

The usual duration of pregnancy is ten lunar months or 280 days. During the later months of this period movements of the embryo, which is now called the **fœtus,** can be detected and its heart-beats can be heard through the abdominal wall of the mother. The usual position occupied by the fœtus in utero is with the head downwards towards the maternal pelvis, and in the last month of pregnancy the fœtal head enters the pelvic cavity.

At the onset of labour, contractions of the uterine muscle become more pronounced and also painful (the characteristic " labour pains "). The cervical canal dilates, and this leaves the lower part of the membranes without support, so that the force of the uterine contractions causes the amniotic fluid to burst them and some of the fluid escapes. The events up to this point constitute the **first stage** of labour.

During the second stage of labour the fœtus is expelled through the genital canal by the contraction of the uterine muscle, aided by voluntary contraction of the abdominal muscles. The child is usually born head first, but may present by the breech. On exposure to the air the child cries and respiration begins. At this point the umbilical cord is tied and cut by the obstetrician. This ends the **second stage** of labour.

In the **third stage** the placenta and membranes (the " afterbirth ") are expelled by further contraction of the uterine muscle. This process leaves the ends of the blood-vessels in the uterus open, but if the uterine muscle contract properly it squeezes the vessels and so prevents the severe post-partum hæmorrhage which would otherwise occur.

The fact that large maternal veins in the placental site are opened when the placenta is expelled makes it imperative that all the operations in a confinement should be conducted with the greatest care to ensure surgical cleanliness. Infection transmitted to the mother at this time may result in the serious blood poisoning termed **puerperal septicæmia.** Expulsion of the uterine contents during the first three months of pregnancy is termed **abortion** ; during the second three months it is usually called **miscarriage.** After the sixth or seventh month premature birth of the child may occur ; the child is capable of leading an independent life, but extra care is needed in nursing it. The weight of a child born at **full term** is about 7–7½ lb.

Lactation

During pregnancy the breasts enlarge and the glandular epithelium increases in amount. Towards the end of pregnancy secretion called **colostrum** may escape from the nipple. When suckling begins the breasts become fully active and secrete milk.

The composition of human milk is compared with that of cow's milk in the following table [1] :—

	Human	Cow	Comparison
Protein	1·5	3·5	More in cow.
Fats	3·5	4·0	Almost equal.
Milk sugar (lactose)	6·5	4·5	Less in cow
Salts	0·2	0·7	More in cow
Water	88·3	87·3	

[1] Modified from Bainbridge and Menzies.

It will be seen that if the mother's milk fail and the child must be fed artificially it is necessary to modify cow's milk to make it a suitable food. The milk must be diluted with water to reduce relatively the amount of protein and salts. After dilution, fats (cream) and milk sugar (lactose) must be added in appropriate amounts. Vitamins may be added in the form of grape juice and cod-liver oil. A baby should be breast-fed for the first eight months if the milk be in sufficient amount and the health of the mother good. The preparation and enlargement of the breasts during pregnancy is due to **œstrin** and **progestin** (p. 298) circulating in the maternal blood. These substances come chiefly from the placenta. There is evidence that the *initial* secretion of milk is due to a hormone called **prolactin,** produced by the pituitary. The continuance of the secretion of milk depends on the stimulus provided by the infant suckling.

If the nipples are not kept clean they may become infected. In addition to harming the child this may cause fissures of the nipple and acute abscess in the breast. If this occur the infant must be weaned and the abscess opened.

It should be remembered that certain drugs taken by the mother may be excreted in the milk. Alcohol is an example, and should on this account be avoided by nursing mothers.

CHAPTER XVII

THE SKIN

THE skin is the outer covering of the body. In addition to serving as a protection for the underlying tissues, the skin has other important functions, and its structure is adapted for the performance of these.

Structure of the Skin

Examination of a section of the skin (Fig. 84) shows that it

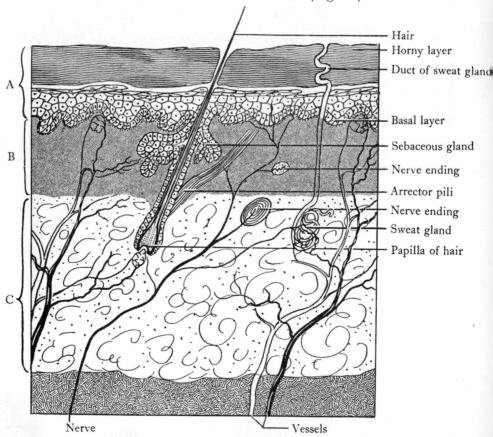

FIG. 84. Scheme of section of the skin and subcutaneous tissues.
A. Epidermis. B. Corium. C. Subcutaneous fat.

consists of two main layers, viz., the **corium,** or true skin, and the **epidermis,** or cuticle.

The Corium. The corium constitutes the greater part of the thickness of the skin. It is formed of a feltwork of connective tissue and contains numerous blood-vessels, the hair follicles, and the sebaceous and sweat glands.

The corium presents, superficially, numerous projections called **papillæ,** which fit into corresponding depressions on the deep surface of the epidermis. This interlocking prevents the epidermis being pushed off the corium by shearing forces applied to the skin. The blood-vessels are especially numerous in the papillæ.

The variation in papillary pattern in different individuals is the basis of the fingerprint method of identification.

The **hair follicles** are tubes of the surface epithelium (epidermis) containing the hairs. The root of the hair is invaginated by a papillary projection of the corium. Attached to the hair follicles are strands of plain muscle (arrectores pilorum) which, when they contract, cause the hair to stand on end.

The **sebaceous glands** form an oily substance called sebum, which makes the surface layers of the skin slightly greasy. The sebaceous glands open mostly into hair follicles, but some open directly on to the surface of the skin.

The **sweat glands** have the form of long coiled tubes. The sweat which they produce passes along their ducts on to the skin surface, and there evaporates or is absorbed by clothing.

The Epidermis. The epidermis is the epithelial layer of the skin. It forms a covering for the whole body, and is continuous at the lips, anus and nostrils with the mucous lining of the alimentary and respiratory tracts.

The epithelium is of the **stratified squamous** variety. The deepest cells (basal layer) are cubical and are in contact with the papillæ of the corium. The succeeding cells are polygonal, are called " prickle cells," and contain most of the pigment of the skin. The most superficial layers consist of flattened cells which die and become cornified or horny. The horny scales formed in this way are rubbed off by the continuous wear to which the skin surface is subjected. The deeper cells of the epithelium multiply to replace the surface layers which die and are shed.

Nerves and Blood-vessels. The sensory nerves form several types of receptor endings in the skin. The details of their structure are not of great importance. It is probable that the endings concerned with pain are in close relationship to the papillæ of the corium, as the superficial layers of the skin can be shaved off without producing pain. The endings concerned with touch are found both in the corium and among the cells of the epidermis.

The blood-vessels of the skin are in the corium. There are none in the epithelium.

The Subcutaneous Tissues. The subcutaneous tissue allows the skin in most parts of the body to move freely over the underlying structures. It is one of the fat depots of the body.

Functions of the Skin

1. **Protection.** Because of the dense horny layer of the epithelium the skin is hard enough to withstand the ordinary wear and tear to which it is subjected. The presence of a number of layers in the epithelium makes it possible, by multiplication of the cells of the deepest layer, to renew superficial cells which are shed.

The secretion of the sebaceous glands keeps the skin smooth, prevents too rapid scaling off of the surface layers, and makes the skin waterproof. This waterproof character of the surface, to which the density of the horny layer contributes, prevents the loss of body fluids, as well as the entrance of water from outside.

2. **Reception.** The sensory nerve-endings in the skin are concerned with the reception of the stimuli for touch and pressure, pain, and temperature sensations. The skin is thus one of the most important structures concerned in the reaction of the body to its surroundings.

3. **Absorption and Excretion.** The skin excretes, through the sweat, water and salts. It also absorbs and excretes certain other substances to a very limited degree.

As the skin is greasy, it is necessary to exhibit drugs for absorption in an oily base (ointments).

4. **Vitamin Formation.** On exposure to ultraviolet light substances called sterols in the skin are converted into vitamin D (p. 113). The process is accompanied by an increase in pigmentation (sunburn).

5. **Regulation of Body Temperature.** The regulation of the body temperature is one of the most important functions of the skin.

The **normal temperature** in man is 98·4° F. (37° C.) even in widely differing circumstances. Normal slight variations occur, especially in severe muscular exercise, when, because of excessive heat production in the body, the temperature may be raised temporarily a few degrees.

Excessive rise in the temperature causes "heat stroke," and excessive fall causes unconsciousness ; both of these conditions may be fatal.

The body temperature is the result of two factors, viz., heat production or gain and heat loss. The temperature remains constant because, when heat production is increased, the heat loss is proportionately increased, and *vice versâ*.

Heat Production. The metabolic changes in the body result in heat production. All the tissues are concerned in this, but the most important factor of all is the activity of the muscles of the body. In conditions of rest, heat is still being produced by the muscles, as some of their fibres are contracting to maintain the muscle tone.

The activity of glands (especially the liver, as it is so large) also produces heat. Heat production is greatly increased in muscular exercise (p. 87), and it is common knowledge that the best way to keep warm in cold weather is by vigorous exercise. **Shivering** is produced by spasmodic contractions of some of the muscles and is an automatic attempt to produce more heat in conditions of extreme cold.

The heat produced in metabolism is due partly to tissue breakdown, but still more to the oxidation (combustion) of foodstuffs to provide energy for tissue rebuilding (p. 211). For a given weight the combustion of fat produces the most, and of protein the least heat.

Increased activity of the thyroid gland, by raising the general metabolic rate, increases this heat production.

Exposure to temperatures above that of the body also leads to a gain in body heat.

Heat Loss. Heat is lost from the body in three ways, viz., by the **skin**, by the **expired air,** and by the **excreta** (urine and fæces), all of these being warmer than the surrounding air.

The heat lost in expiration is much more important in certain animals than in man. In the dog, for instance, in which the distribution of sweat glands in the skin is limited to certain regions, it is the most important method of the regulation of heat loss, and this is why the dog pants when hot.

The skin provides the most important mechanism for heat loss in man. Moreover, the amount of heat lost by the skin can be controlled.

The skin is warm partly because of the blood circulating in the vessels in the corium, but also because of conduction to it, through the subcutaneous tissue, of heat from the underlying muscles. As, however, the subcutaneous tissues contain fat, which is a poor conductor, the amount of heat reaching the surface in this way is small relative to the warming effect of the blood in the skin vessels, and too rapid a loss from the deeper parts is thus prevented. The horny layer of the skin is also a poor conductor, and this prevents too rapid a loss from the skin itself.

Heat is lost from the skin by **radiation** and by the **evaporation** of sweat from the surface.

Radiation. When the air on the surface of the skin is cooler than the skin itself, as is the case in equable climates, the skin loses heat by **radiation.**

So long as the layer of air next to the skin remains still, it will ultimately become as hot as the skin itself. Unless the layer of air is confined as, for example, by clothing, it does not remain still ; the hot air tends to rise and colder air is drawn in to replace it. In this way **convection** currents are set up which carry the hot air away and so increase the loss of heat. Convection is prevented by **clothing,** and it is really the layers of air which the clothes enclose which keep us warm, rather than the clothes themselves. Convection is increased by **blowing** on the skin, and this is the rationale of the use of a fan.

In furry animals the hair lies flat in hot weather so as to reduce the air which it entangles to the thinnest layer possible. In cold weather the hair is raised by the arrectores pilorum so as to make the layer of still air as deep as possible. This factor is of less importance in man on account of the sparsity of hair, but the effect of raising the hair follicles is to produce the appearance called " goose-flesh." The greater the surface of the skin which is exposed, the greater will be the heat loss by radiation. In small animals the surface is greater relative to the body weight, and such animals have a high metabolic rate to make up for this greater loss by increased production of heat.

Evaporation. Heat is required to convert water into water vapour. In the evaporation of the sweat this heat is derived from the skin itself, which becomes cooler in the process.

If the humidity of the air be great, evaporation of the sweat is retarded. This is why a hot dry climate is easier to stand than a hot damp climate.

Regulation of Temperature

We can now summarise the means by which the body responds to heat and cold so as to keep the temperature constant.

On Exposure to Heat. (*a*) **Heat production** is lessened because muscle tone decreases. Lassitude results and there is no inclination to perform muscular exercise.

(*b*) **Heat loss** is greater because of :—

1. Increased radiation. The blood-vessels in the corium become dilated so that the skin is flushed. More warm blood passes through the dilated vessels in a given time and more heat is lost by radiation.

2. Increased convection. Less clothing is worn and greater areas of the skin surface are exposed. This leads to increase in convection currents carrying heated air away from the skin.

3. Increased evaporation. The skin vessels being dilated, sweating is profuse and more evaporation occurs unless the humidity of the atmosphere be very high.

On Exposure to Cold. (*a*) Heat production is increased because the tone of the muscles is augmented. A feeling of vigour results, and there is an inclination to perform muscular exercise. In conditions of enforced inactivity, shivering provides an increase in muscular activity.

(*b*) **Heat loss** is lessened because of :—

1. Decreased radiation. The cutaneous vessels constrict so that less warm blood is passing through the corium. The hairs are erected, producing the appearance of " goose flesh." (Both these results are due to increased activity of the sympathetic system and increase of the amount of adrenalin in the blood.)

2. Decreased convection. More clothing is worn so as to decrease convection by interposing layers of confined air round the body surface.

3. Decreased evaporation. Sweating is markedly decreased. Fluid being retained in the body, the amount excreted in the urine rises.

Nervous Control of Temperature. There is evidence that all the changes described above are under the control of the " heat regulating centre " situated in the cerebrum.

Fever, or rise of body temperature, generally occurs as a reaction of the body to infection with micro-organisms. It is a part of the attempt by the body to cure the infection and should not, therefore, be hindered, but aided. During the early stages, when the body is trying to conserve its heat, production is increased by rise in muscle tone, restlessness, and often shivering ; loss is prevented by the skin, which is dry. The heart rate is increased (see p. 145). During this stage conservation of heat should be aided by keeping the patient warm with hot bottles, blankets, etc.

When the body has overcome the infection the temperature falls, production of heat being diminished by decrease in muscle tone, and loss being increased by profuse sweating.

Appendages of the Skin. The **hairs** and **nails** are included under this head. They are formed by modification of the horny layer of the epithelium.

CHAPTER XVIII

THE DUCTLESS GLANDS

THE glands so far considered in the digestive, respiratory and genital systems and in the skin all transfer their secretion by a duct or ducts on to some surface where the secretion is utilised.

The **ductless glands,** or **endocrine organs,** produce substances called **internal secretions,** which are absorbed into the bloodstream through the walls of the capillaries which traverse the glands. The secretions are carried in the blood to all parts of the body so that they can produce effects on structures at a distance from the glands which secrete them.

Internal secretions belong to a group of chemical substances called **hormones** which all produce their action through the bloodstream. Other examples of hormone activity are the action of CO_2 on the respiratory centre (p. 206) and the action of gastrin in the secretion of gastric juice (p. 118).

As the secretions of *all* the ductless glands are being absorbed into the blood the healthy working of the body is dependent on their *concerted* action. The effect of depriving the body of one of these secretions may be due not so much to actual lack of that particular secretion as to a disturbance of the balanced action of all of them.

THE HYPOPHYSIS CEREBRI (PITUITARY GLAND)

The hypophysis cerebri, or pituitary gland (Fig. 85), is situated on the inferior surface of the cerebrum. It is lodged in the hypophyseal fossa of the skull (p. 23), is closely related above to the optic chiasma and optic tracts, and is attached by a stalk to the floor of the third ventricle of the brain. It consists of two main parts, viz., the **anterior lobe** which is glandular, and the **posterior lobe** which is partly glandular (pars intermedia) and partly nervous tissue (pars nervosa). The anterior and posterior lobes have different functions.

Functions of the Anterior Lobe

The functions of the secretion of the anterior lobe are control of skeletal growth and control of the activity of the sex glands and the thyroid gland.

1. Growth of the Skeleton

Increase in the secretion of the anterior lobe augments the growth of the skeleton. If this occur before the epiphyses have

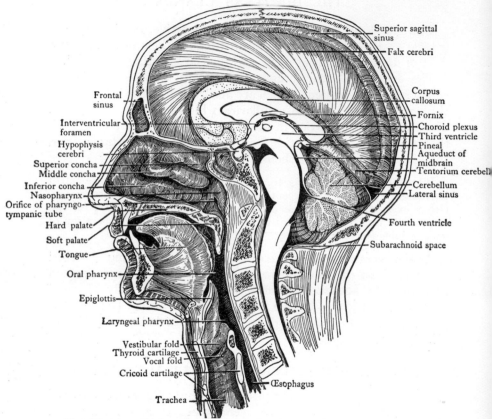

Fig. 85. A sagittal section of the head and neck a little to the left of the median plane. The nasal septum has been removed to expose the lateral wall of the nose.

united, all the bones are affected and **gigantism** results, a height of 7 or 8 ft. often being attained. If the oversecretion occur later, the enlargement affects especially the bones of the face, hands and feet, causing the condition called **acromegaly**. Undersecretion by the anterior lobe results in impaired skeletal development and **dwarfism**. Occasionally this is accompanied by impairment of mentality.

2. Activity of the Sex Glands

(*a*) Female. **Prolan.** The secretion of the anterior lobe of the hypophysis contains substances called prolan A and prolan B. These increase the activity of the ovary so that more œstrin and progestin are produced by that gland. Secondary effects on the uterus are due to these substances and not to the prolan, as they do not occur after removal of the ovaries.

Prolactin. The *initial* secretion of milk is due to stimulation of the fully developed breast by the substance called prolactin produced by the anterior lobe of the hypophysis.

(*b*) Male. The secretion of the anterior lobe increases the development of both the sperm-producing and interstitial cells of the testis. Secondary effects are, in turn, produced by the secretion of the interstitial cells (p. 325).

3. Activity of the Thyroid Gland

Anterior lobe secretion increases the rate of metabolism, probably by stimulating the thyroid gland.

Functions of the Posterior Lobe

The posterior lobe produces a substance called **pituitrin.** The actions of pituitrin can be dealt with under three heads :—

1. Contraction of Plain Muscle

Pituitrin causes contraction of the muscle of the intestine, bladder and the pregnant uterus. It causes also constriction of arterioles (by stimulation of their plain muscle) and of capillaries. As this increases the peripheral resistance in the circulatory system, pituitrin raises the blood pressure.

2. Control of Urinary Secretion

Injection of pituitrin in man causes diminution in the amount of water excreted in the urine.

3. Control of Carbohydrate Metabolism

The posterior lobe of the hypophysis exercises some control over the metabolism of sugar, but this activity is as yet incompletely understood.

Practical Considerations

Disease of the hypophysis may be accompanied by signs of over-secretion (hyperpituitarism) or undersecretion (hypopituitarism). If

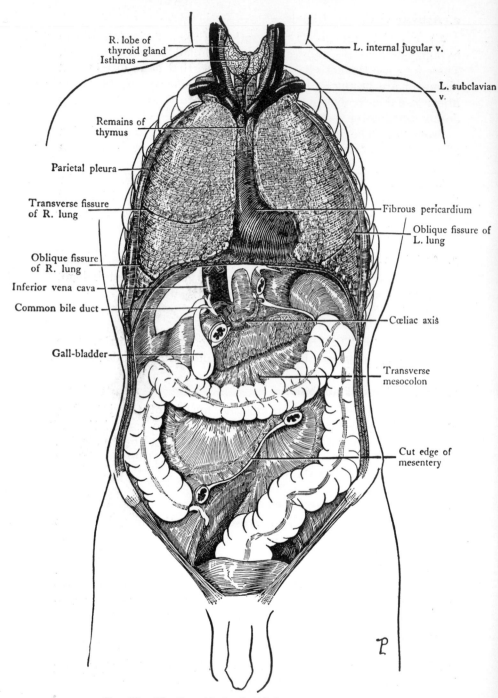

R. lobe of
thyroid gland

Isthmus

Remains of
thymus

Parietal pleura

Transverse fissure
of R. lung

Oblique fissure
of R. lung

Inferior vena cava

Common bile duct

Gall-bladder

L. internal jugular v.

L. subclavian
v.

Fibrous pericardium

Oblique fissure of
L. lung

Cœliac axis

Transverse
mesocolon

Cut edge of
mesentery

Fɪɢ. 86.   The thyroid gland and the remains of the thymus.

there be enlargement of the gland the signs of disturbed function are usually accompanied by disturbances of vision because of the close relationship of the optic chiasma and tracts to the gland.

Pituitrin is sometimes used to assist parturition (because of its action on the uterus), to overcome some forms of intestinal obstruction (because of its action on the gut muscle), and to raise the blood pressure in surgical shock.

THE THYROID GLAND

The thyroid gland (Fig. 86) is placed in the lower part of the neck. It consists of two more or less symmetrical **lobes** joined one to another by a bridge of gland tissue called the **isthmus.** Each lobe lies at the side of the trachea and the lower part of the larynx, whilst the isthmus lies in front of the trachea at the level of its second and third cartilaginous rings.

Structure of the Thyroid Gland. The gland tissue is composed of spherical vesicles lined with cubical epithelium and containing a semi-fluid substance called **colloid.** The colloid stores the excess secretion of the thyroid until it is needed by the body.

Function of the Thyroid Gland

The active principle of the thyroid secretion is called **thyroxin,** and is a substance containing **iodine.** The thyroxin is contained in the colloid stored in the thyroid vesicles ; the colloid is absorbed from the vesicles into the rich plexus of blood-vessels throughout the gland.

The amount of thyroxin circulating in the blood influences the level of general **metabolism** and keeps it at a rate in accord with the activities of the body as a whole. Too little or too much thyroxin in circulation results in a metabolic rate which is incorrectly balanced to the needs of the body.

Thyroxin is necessary for healthy growth, both physical and mental.

Hypothyroidism. Deficiency of thyroxin is termed hypothyroidism. Hypothyroidism in adults results in the condition called **myxœdema,** and in children the condition called cretinism. Administration of thyroxin or thyroid extract cures these conditions, but the treatment must be begun early and continued throughout life.

Myxœdema. Reduction in the thyroid secretion in adults may result from disease or surgical removal of the thyroid gland.

The signs are those of reduced metabolism. Obesity occurs

the skin becomes thick and coarse, and the hair drops out. A peculiar myxomatous deposit occurs beneath the skin. Pulse and respiration rates are retarded and the mental processes very slow, the person often answering a simple question some moments after it is asked. Sexual function is depressed and amenorrhœa often results in females.

Cretinism. This is usually due to congenital absence of the thyroid gland.

Usually nothing is noticed during the first six months of life, but after this both physical and mental development are retarded. A cretin shows also all the signs of delayed metabolism cited above. The expression is stupid, partly because of delayed mental development, but also because the tongue is enlarged and too big to allow the mouth to be closed.

Hyperthyroidism. Increase of thyroxin in the blood is termed hyperthyroidism. It occurs in some diseases of the thyroid gland, and normally to a slight extent at puberty in both sexes, and at the menstrual periods and at the menopause in women.

The signs are those of increased general metabolism, but the effects are disproportionately large on the heart and the nervous system. The appetite is large, but, because of the greater utilisation of foodstuffs in the increased metabolism, the subject of hyperthyroidism is usually very thin. The heart-rate is rapid, and the body temperature raised. Extreme nervous irritability accompanied by rapidity of the mental processes, and gastro-intestinal disturbances are common features.

Practical Considerations

Goitre is the name given to an enlargement of the thyroid gland. Goitre is due in some cases to increased demands on the thyroid or to lack of iodine in the diet, whilst in others it is due to actual disease of the gland. It is sometimes accompanied by signs of hyperthyroidism and sometimes by those of hypothyroidism.

Exophthalmic goitre (Graves' disease) is a disease of the thyroid in which signs of hyperthyroidism are associated with great prominence of the eyes. Its treatment is removal of a part of the thyroid gland to attempt to restore the amount of thyroxin in the blood to normal.

THE PARATHYROID GLANDS

The parathyroid glands are four in number, being situated, two on each side, behind or imbedded in the substance of the lobes of the thyroid gland.

Function of the Parathyroid Glands

The parathyroid glands are concerned with the regulation of the amounts of calcium and phosphorus in the blood, and with the deposition of calcium in bones.

Oversecretion by the glands leads to decalcification of the bones and an increase of the amount of calcium in the blood.

Undersecretion produces the symptom called **tetany,** in which the fingers are held in a characteristic position by spasm of the muscles, and there is laryngeal spasm. The amount of calcium in the blood is decreased.

THE SUPRARENAL GLANDS

The two suprarenal glands (Fig. 87) are situated on the posterior abdominal wall surmounting the upper poles of the kidneys. The right is somewhat pyramidal in shape, the left is semilunar, and each consists of an outer part or **cortex** surrounding an internal part called the **medulla.** The gland has a very rich supply of sympathetic nerves derived from the cœliac plexus, and the medulla is extremely vascular.

Functions of the Suprarenal Glands

1. **The Cortex.** Removal of the cortex of the suprarenals results in the death of the animal. Its functions are not completely understood, but it is probably concerned (possibly in association with the hypophysis cerebri) in the regulation of metabolism, and it may also have an influence on the development of the sex glands and the secondary sexual characters.

2. **The Medulla.** The medulla of the suprarenal secretes a substance called **adrenalin.** Injection of this substance produces effects very like those occurring on stimulation of the sympathetic nervous system (see p. 277) except on the sweat glands, whose secretion is diminished (see also functions of skin, p. 313). Adrenalin is concerned, therefore, in the reaction of the body to conditions of stress, redistributing the blood especially to the voluntary muscles, heart and brain, facilitating the entry of air into the lungs (see p. 276), diminishing heat loss, and causing the liver to form glucose from its stored glycogen. These results are caused by the stimulating action of the adrenalin on the sympathetic nerve endings.

Practical Considerations

Because of its constricting effect on blood-vessels adrenalin is used

ANATOMY. 21

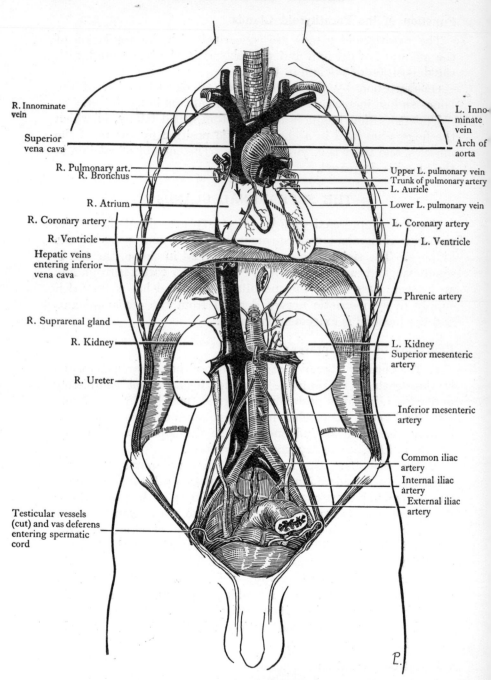

R. Innominate
vein

L. Inno-
minate
vein

Superior
vena cava

Arch of
aorta

R. Pulmonary art.
R. Bronchus

Upper L. pulmonary vein
Trunk of pulmonary artery
L. Auricle

R. Atrium

Lower L. pulmonary vein

R. Coronary artery

L. Coronary artery

R. Ventricle

L. Ventricle

Hepatic veins
entering inferior
vena cava

Phrenic artery

R. Suprarenal gland

R. Kidney

L. Kidney
Superior mesenteric
artery

R. Ureter

Inferior mesenteric
artery

Common iliac
artery
Internal iliac
artery
External iliac
artery

Testicular vessels
(cut) and vas deferens
entering spermatic
cord

Fig. 87. The suprarenal glands.

as a local application to stop hæmorrhage, and is mixed with local
anæsthetics to prevent their dispersal by absorption into the blood.

Relief is obtained in asthma by administration of adrenalin because
it prevents the spasm of the muscle of the bronchioles.

Adrenalin is destroyed by the gastric juice so that it must be
administered by injection.

Addison's disease is associated with pathological changes in the
suprarenal glands and is characterised by pigmentation of the skin,
low blood pressure, decrease in muscle tone and gastro-intestinal
disturbances.

THE THYMUS GLAND

The thymus gland is present up to the age of puberty and then
rapidly undergoes atrophy, being replaced by a mass of fibro-fatty
tissue. It is at its maximum size between the ages of seven and
fourteen years.

The gland is situated in the thorax in front of the great vessels
in the superior mediastinum and behind the upper part of the
sternum (Fig. 86).

Function of the Thymus Gland

The internal secretion of the thymus, if administered to young
animals, causes increase of growth, but delays the development
of sexual function. The atrophy of the gland at puberty seems
to indicate that it is concerned, with other glands, in the normal
regulation of general and sexual development. The thymus
contains large numbers of lymphocytes, and is probably concerned
with the lymph glands and spleen in the formation of these cells.

Status lymphaticus is the name given to a condition in which the
thymus is enlarged. Subjects of this condition may die suddenly after
some slight shock.

THE PINEAL GLAND

The pineal gland is situated in the median plane, just behind
the upper part of the posterior wall of the third ventricle of the
forebrain (Fig. 85). Its functions are unknown.

DUCTLESS GLANDS WHICH ARE PARTS OF
OTHER GLANDS

The glands so far considered are complete entities. There are
also, however, masses of cells which function as ductless glands
in the pancreas and in the sex glands.

THE PANCREAS

Among the alveoli which produce the pancreatic juice are found groups of cells constituting the **islets of Langerhans.** These cells produce an internal secretion which is called **insulin,** and which is concerned with the regulation of the metabolism of carbohydrate.

Action of Insulin

Insulin enables the tissues to utilise glucose, *i.e.*, to oxidise it to produce energy. It also causes increased storage of glucose in the form of glycogen by the muscles and liver, and prevents the liver forming sugar from proteins and fats.

If, under the influence of insulin, more glucose is stored and utilised by the tissues, less will be free to circulate in the blood and so insulin tends to lower the blood-sugar level. The secretions of the suprarenal, pituitary and thyroid glands all antagonise insulin and tend to raise the level of the blood-sugar.

Carbohydrate taken in the diet is absorbed from the bowel as glucose (and other simple sugars which are converted into glucose by the liver), and glucose is always being filtered from the blood into the renal tubules (see p. 228). When the level of the sugar in the blood is normal, all the glucose is reabsorbed from the filtrate as it passes along the kidney tubules, and none appears in the urine. The function of the pancreas is to secrete just so much insulin as will produce the correct utilisation and storage of glucose by the tissues so that the blood-sugar is kept at the proper level. If this function is not carried out properly and the level of the blood-sugar rises, the kidney attempts to reduce it to normal ; less glucose is reabsorbed from the glomerular filtrate as it passes through the tubules and sugar appears in the urine (glycosuria).

It is probable that many of these factors concerned in the maintenance of the blood-sugar at the correct level are controlled by a " sugar regulating centre " in the forebrain.

Hyperglycæmia. Rise in the blood-sugar level is termed hyperglycæmia. The condition results from **lack of insulin** in the blood and accompanies the condition called **diabetes mellitus.**

Owing to lack of insulin the tissues can neither utilise nor store glucose. The glycogen stores are depleted and the liver, in an attempt to rectify this, converts fat and amino-acids into glucose. The utilisation of fat and amino-acids for this purpose leads to wasting. The glomerular filtrate contains more glucose than normally, and this is not reabsorbed by the tubules so that sugar appears in the urine. Because of incomplete sugar metabolism, there is defective oxidation of fats by the tissues and intermediate oxidation products appear in the urine and make it and the breath smell of acetone.

Diabetes can be controlled by giving injections of insulin so that the tissues can again utilise and store sugar.

Hypoglycæmia. Fall in the level of the blood-sugar is termed hypoglycæmia. It is the result of **too much insulin** circulating in the blood and causing increased utilisation and storage of glucose. Hunger, coma, and convulsions may result. If occurring after the therapeutic administration of insulin, the condition is relieved by giving glucose either by the mouth or intravenously.

THE SEX GLANDS

The Testis

Among the seminiferous tubules of the testis are found masses of **interstitial cells** which produce an internal secretion. Removal of both testes before puberty, in addition to producing sterility, prevents the development of the secondary sexual characters. The voice does not break, and the facial and pubic hair is absent. Boys treated in this way are termed eunuchs.

The Ovary

The ovary produces the internal secretions called œstrin and progestin. These are considered on p. 302.

CHAPTER XIX

THE SPLEEN AND LIVER

THE SPLEEN

THE spleen is a soft red organ situated on the left side of the abdomen just below the diaphragm in front of the upper part of the left kidney and behind and to the left of the stomach (Figs. 31 and 33).

It is covered with peritoneum and, inside this, has a tough capsule containing much elastic tissue and some plain muscle. Radiating through the spleen from the capsule are trabeculæ, which form in its interior a network somewhat like a sponge. The surfaces of the trabeculæ are covered with endothelial cells, and the spaces which they enclose are filled by a delicate reticulum with blood entangled in its meshes and termed the **splenic pulp.** The terminal arterioles in the spleen are surrounded by masses of lymphoid tissue constituting the **lymphatic nodules.** The terminal subdivisions of the vessels in the spleen have openings in their walls so that blood can escape from them into the splenic pulp. As the blood accumulates in the spleen the elastic capsule stretches and its recoil from time to time squeezes extra blood into the veins leaving the spleen. The splenic vein takes part in the formation of the portal vein so that the blood from the spleen passes through the liver.

Functions of the Spleen

The spleen is not essential to life. Its functions are as follows :—

1. **Storage of Blood.** Because of its distensibility, the spleen forms a reservoir for blood, and when extra blood is needed it can be restored to other parts of the circulatory system by contraction of the splenic capsule, the muscle of which is supplied by the sympathetic.

2. **Formation of Blood Corpuscles.** During intra-uterine life the spleen forms both red and white blood corpuscles. In post-natal life, however, it is concerned with the formation of white corpuscles only, the majority of these being lymphocytes formed in the lymphatic nodules.

3. Destruction of Red Corpuscles. The reticulo-endothelial cells in the spleen (see p. 129) destroy worn-out red blood corpuscles and split the hæmoglobin into its constituent parts. The iron is retained and used for the manufacture of new hæmoglobin ; the iron-free part of the pigment is converted into bile pigment which is excreted by the liver in the bile.

THE LIVER

The anatomy of the liver has been considered in the section on the alimentary system (see p. 100). The consideration of its function has been deferred because it involves so many other activities that without knowledge of these it is impossible to understand those of the liver.

1. The Formation of Bile. Bile has two main constituents, namely, the bile pigments, which give it its yellow or green colour, and the bile salts.

The **bile pigments** are produced from the hæmoglobin of effete red blood corpuscles. The corpuscles are broken up by the reticulo-endothelial cells in the bone-marrow, spleen, lymphatic glands and the liver. The reticulo-endothelial cells retain the iron of the hæmoglobin so that it can be used again, and they liberate the iron-free part of the pigment into the blood. Some of this is excreted in the urine and the rest is altered by the liver cells and excreted by them into the bile.

The **bile salts** are manufactured by the liver cells. On reaching the intestine they reduce surface tension and so render easier the emulsification of fats. The bile salts also assist the action of the pancreatic and intestinal ferments, and increase the peristaltic movements of the intestine. Having fulfilled their function in digestion, they are eventually reabsorbed from the intestine and carried in the portal bloodstream back to the liver.

2. Rôle of the Liver in Carbohydrate Metabolism. The liver cells have the power, in the presence of insulin from the pancreas (p. 324), of converting glucose into glycogen. The liver stores this glycogen and so the blood-sugar is kept at a constant level. As the tissues use glucose and the blood-sugar level falls, the liver liberates some of the glycogen (reforming it into glucose) so as to replenish the sugar in the blood.

If the supply of carbohydrate in the diet be greatly in excess of the needs of the body, the glycogen storage capacity of the liver and other tissues is exceeded. In these circumstances the liver will convert some of the glucose into fat which is then carried by the blood to the fat depôts, where it is stored. This is the main method of laying down fat in herbivorous animals.

The liver cells also convert other simple sugars such as lactose and fructose into glucose.

3. Rôle of the Liver in Protein Metabolism. Amino-acids cannot be stored and held in reserve by the body. Such of the amino-acids as are necessary for rebuilding the cell proteins are selected and extracted by the tissues from the blood as it circulates through them. Because of the amount of protein taken in the diet, the amino-acids circulating in the blood are always in excess of the requirements for this rebuilding. The excess amino-acids are carried to the liver, where they are de-aminated, the amino part being converted into urea, which enters the blood and is excreted by the kidneys. The amino-free part is carried by the blood to the tissues, where, like fat or glucose, it is oxidised to provide energy for tissue rebuilding. Fibrinogen (p. 133), the protein of the blood which is concerned with clotting, is manufactured by the liver from amino-acids.

4. Rôle of the Liver in Fat Metabolism. Fat stored in the fat depôts of the body is in a form called saturated fat. Before this can be utilised for oxidation in the tissues it must be changed into an unsaturated form. This process of desaturation is carried out by the liver cells.

5. Heat Production. Because of its size and the amount of work it performs, the liver produces quite a considerable amount of the total body heat.

INDEX

329

22

PRINTED IN GREAT BRITAIN BY THE WHITEFRIARS PRESS LTD
LONDON AND TONBRIDGE